THE THERAPY OF THE
NEUROSES AND PSYCHOSES

A SOCIO–PSYCHO–BIOLOGIC ANALYSIS
AND RESYNTHESIS

BY

SAMUEL HENRY KRAINES, M.D.

ASSOCIATE IN PSYCHIATRY, UNIVERSITY OF ILLINOIS, COLLEGE OF MEDICINE; ASSISTANT
STATE ALIENIST, STATE OF ILLINOIS; DIPLOMATE OF AMERICAN BOARD OF
PSYCHIATRY AND NEUROLOGY

LEA & FEBIGER
PHILADELPHIA
1941

PRINTED IN U. S. A.

PREFACE

THE treatment of nervous and mental conditions is very frequently reserved for the specialist; but from one-third to three-quarters of the cases of the general practitioner or the non-psychiatric specialist are in need of psychotherapeutic as well as medical attention. This volume is intended to state as clearly and pragmatically as possible the factors underlying the formation of nervous and mental diseases and their treatment. It is believed that physicians other than psychiatrists will be able to make practical and valuable application of the principles of therapy herein discussed.

Contrary to the often held belief that psychiatry deals only with bizarre ideas and definitely "peculiar" persons, in reality, psychiatry takes as its province the entire realm of human thinking, feeling, and acting. The reader of this book will realize anew how indefinite is the line of demarcation between the normal and the neurotic, and will be impressed that psychoneurotic symptoms are to a large degree but an intensification of attitudes and reaction patterns common to us all. The earliest psychiatrists in everything but name were the writers, poets, and philosophers who analyzed and commented upon human actions in poems, plays, and stories. Every person who understands human actions and who attempts to correct or modify them is to a greater or less degree a psychiatrist.

However, science connotes an orderly and systematic body of knowledge; and psychiatry as a science had its first formalized statement when Emil Kraeplin culled out of the "general insanities" (vesania, moral insanity, etc.) the classifications which are still used in modern times. However, such a classification is relatively rigid, and cannot adequately interpret man who is consistently individualistic and variable. The second step in the science of psychiatry was made when Sigmund Freud brought forth in

(3)

organized fashion the unconscious and the dynamic activity of human thought and emotions. All psychiatry today has been influenced by his dynamic concept. Freud, however, elaborated upon this basic concept a vast super-structure which many psychiatrists, including the author, regard as extremely fanciful. In this volume the author has made an attempt to separate the chaff from the wheat, and to give as much of the school of psychoanalysis (limited by common consent to the school of Freud) as is of logical and practical value. The third step in the advancement of psychiatry came with the advent of the shock therapies. These shock therapies have given impetus to the general understanding of the physiologic nature of the body-mind, and to the specific nature of insanity. Much needs as yet to be learned about the nature of these therapies and their site of action; but the fact of their existence has proved a tremendous stimulus to the advance of our knowledge of man.

This book has been written to state not only some of the facts about man and the malady of his actions but to offer an interpretation of and a practical technique for meeting some of his problems. This book is an attempt at an orientation: an orientation which studies man as he is, in the social, psychologic, and biologic setting in which he is conceived and matured. The cases cited are taken from actual practice, and specific suggestions are made for the understanding of the illness and for the therapy thereof. The techniques cited offer specific and practical suggestions which can be used in most instances by most physicians.

S. H. KRAINES, M.D.

CHICAGO, ILLINOIS.

FOREWORD

SOME years ago an earnest and eager and self confident young physician started his contacts with psychiatric patients with obvious talent and devotion. Eminently sincere and anxious to learn, he never forgot to give himself as he was and as he felt and as he saw his opportunities in a true therapy of service—a pleonasm for therapy—and devotion to his cases. He reached and remained true to himself and his thought and he reached his students. And here he presents what he would like physicians to share with him. He has written a compend, personal but shareable, ringing true and helpful to both fellow worker and patient— a book which has arisen out of real life, and adaptable enough to encourage others to make their own working equally true to their and their patients' nature and needs. Its sincere and practical spirit puts critical theory into the background without sacrificing the search for the realities and the opportunities for service. May the spirit of the reader join that of the writer.

Adolf Meyer

TABLE OF CONTENTS

CHAPTER I

CHAPTER II

CHAPTER III

CHAPTER IV

CHAPTER V

CHAPTER VI

CHAPTER VII

CHAPTER VIII

I. *Nature of stress.* Relative term. Complexity of social demands and desires. Stress, tension producing in terms of attitude toward it.

II. *Therapy of Stress by removal.* Financial assistance the best therapy in case of actual want; medical aid, in case of physical illness. Removal from stress. Children's behavior problems cured when parents are cured. Excessive demands on retarded children. Reducing requirements made on patients suffering from senility or brain injury.

III. *Therapy of matrimonal stress.* Causes of marital difficulties. Value of discussion with mate. Giving specific information and advice on technique of intercourse, use of contraceptives, etc.

IV. *Alleviation of Stress.* Removal of or from often impossible. Adjustment necessary. Variety and relative nature of stresses making imperative change of attitude.

CHAPTER IX

I. Cure of neurotic symptoms by changing reaction patterns. Reaction patterns changed by retraining attitude.

II. *General Attitudes.* Early formation. Self perpetuating. Psychoneurotic attitudes: irritable, egoistic, over-emotional responses. Effect of home environment. Psychoanalytic explanation of origin of psychoneurotic traits. Residual irritations.

III. *Specific Attitudes.* Interrelation with general. Infinite number of specific attitudes. Contradictory attitudes.

IV. *Technique of Changing Attitudes.* Three-fold aim. Necessity for a catalyst, time, and persistence to make changes permanent. *Preparation of patient.* Overcoming antagonism. Value of thorough examination. Presenting psychoneurotic formulation of the illness. Value of reasonable explanation in eliciting cooperation. *Desensitization* through discussion. *Retraining attitudes.* General basic attitudes to be removed; general basic feelings to be inculcated. Technique: repeatedly applying *general principle to specific situations.* Value of intellectual understanding. *Conscious thinking* along new lines essential. Value of patient's *wishing to change.* Reassurance and encouragement. Inevitability of symptom recurrence. Avoidance of making moral issues. Aim of psychotherapy: teach patient how to think; to formulate general attitudes that will enable him to meet specific situations.

CHAPTER X

I. Habitual nature of general attitudes. Necessity of breaking old habits and establishing new. Many techniques of therapy. Primary requisites: *self reliance, awareness of limitation and assets, objectivity.*

CHAPTER XI

THE THERAPY OF THE NEUROSES AND PSYCHOSES

CHAPTER I

CLASSIFICATION OF PSYCHIATRIC STATES

FUNDAMENTALLY man is not a rational animal. Man's reactions to his parents, to his family, to his pleasures, to his friends, to his association with others, to social organization are far more dependent upon his "feeling tone" than upon that which he "reasons." Within each action primarily determined by the "way he feels," man may to some extent utilize his powers of thinking; but for the most part and in most persons, action based on logical, rational conclusions is rare. For every example cited where such is the case, one can cite in the same person many other examples wherein reason entered only secondarily in the determination of the action.

As a consequence, to understand the "normal" actions of "normal" persons, it is necessary to consider, not whether the actions are "right" or "wrong," not whether they are logical or illogical, but rather that which influences the emotional state. One needs to consider the environmental stress:[1] the danger to security, the wounding of the pride, the physical disturbances, the anger or pleasure of the wife, the approval and disapproval of one's fellow men, etc., before one can understand the reason for an action which may seem illogical or unwise. Moreover, these stresses exert their pressure upon persons who are different in their makeup, and will therefore have different results. In order then to understand how the "normal" man will act it is necessary not only to find out the existing irritations, but to study the person, the original type of constitution, the type of early training, the physical disturbances, and so forth. Man reacts to life, as the result of all these forces, and not primarily because of his thinking. As a result of these stresses and strains[2], man develops tensions and learns to express, by short cut symbolic methods, the multitudes of problems which

---

[1] *Vide* p. 39 *ff*.   [2] *Vide* Ch. VIII.

perturb him.   Thus there may be such general tension symptoms as anxiety, irritability, sensitivity, and worry; and more specific signs of tension such as tachycardia and moist palms.   Man may express his anger at some one person or thing, as a symbol for all the irritations under which he labors.   He may strive and work for a goal which is symbolically expressive of all his desires.   He may have fears which symbolize his anxiety over many problems.   In short, the internal and external stresses to which man is subject may produce "normally" symptoms of tension and symbolism.[1]

Psychoneurotic persons are potentially "normal" persons in whom the reaction to life is ill-advised, unhealthy, and disturbing. Psychoneurotic symptoms are expressions of the personality disturbance; and these symptoms differ from "normal" personality reactions not so much in quality as in degree and intensity of response.   Normal[2] persons develop tension symptoms, become depressed, irritable, develop headaches over worry, sinking feelings in the pit of the stomach when frightened, tachycardia when emotional, etc., just as do psychoneurotic patients, whose symptoms may involve not only the pit of the stomach but spread to involve the rest of the gastrointestinal tract, and whose symptoms in general are of longer duration than the comparable "normal" reactions of the "normal" person.   There is no border-line sharp and distinct between the normal and the neurotic.   There are many neurotic reaction patterns which may disappear and reappear into normal reactions.   Some of the reaction patterns of a "normal" person may be termed neurotic; while conversely, many of the reaction patterns of the neurotic fall within that range which is designated as normal.

The reaction patterns of both normal and neurotic persons are the result of the influence of stress upon the personality makeup. To understand the neurotic symptom one must understand the forces which brought it about; just as in understanding "normal" reactions one must know the background of the person.

Man's over-reactions to life situations may be not only psychoneurotic but also psychotic.   There are many categories of response which are usually listed as belonging in the province of psychiatry, though many of them should fundamentally be considered as part of general medicine.   The following outline with the brief explanatory notes is intended for only a perspective view of the psychiatric field, and of the relationship of the psychoneuroses to other reaction

---

[1] *Vide* p. 24 *ff.*   [2] *Vide* p. 259 (footnote).

patterns present in man. These diseases are not properly diseases, but are the type of *responses* of which man is capable when his system is modified by disease (constitutional or acquired) and by environmental pressure. The symptoms are personality reactions, which though ill-advised and unhealthy, are types of responses in and reaction patterns designed to meet problems of the existing situation. The personality pattern may thus be phrased in the formula: inherited constitution molded by environment (especially in childhood) under the influence of stress at a given time and in a given setting.

GENERAL OUTLINE OF PSYCHIATRIC DISEASE PROCESSES

I. Amentia.[1]—Amentic or mental deficiency is based upon an intellectual deficiency either congenital or acquired early in life. The pathology is a less than normally developed brain. The symptoms are characterized by various degrees of intellectual sluggishness. There are three generally accepted subdivisions: (*A*) Idiocy, wherein the mental age is that of a child less than two years old, irrespective of the chronologic age of the patient; (*B*) imbecility, wherein the mental age is between two and seven, and (*C*) mental deficiency, wherein the mental age is between seven and twelve. The personality reaction of these patients depends upon the degree of their mental deficiency, and upon the environmental stress. These patients may suffer from all the disorders suffered by "normal" persons, in addition to those to which they are constitutionally predisposed.

II. The Organic Psychoses.[2]—The etiology of the organic psychoses lies in any physical factor which will produce a diffuse disturbance in the function of the *cortex*[3] of the brain. The pathology of these conditions may be any of the pathologies found in general medicine, and involves such categories as: infectious states of the cortex, *e.g.*, general paresis; toxic states, *e.g.*, alcoholism and drug intoxication; degenerative, *e.g.*, senile and arteriosclerotic degeneration; traumatic; and neoplastic pathology. The

---

[1] *Vide* p. 413 *ff.*

[2] *Vide* Ch. XV, p. 342 *ff.* The term organic psychoses is used arbitrarily to denote those states resulting from actual pathologic factors as we now know them. It is entirely possible to include in this grouping many other psychoses which at present have no known pathologic processes.

[3] *Vide* p. 343.

symptoms fall into three categories: (A) those resulting from the pathologic disease itself; (B) those resulting from disturbances of the intellectual processes, such as orientation, memory, ability to calculate, general knowledge, and (C) those resulting from personality changes attendant upon the other two changes. It must be emphasized that to produce an "organic" psychosis, these pathologic processes must be relatively *diffuse*, and involve the *cortex of the brain*. For example, if a disease is not diffuse, such as may occur in cerebral damage following a depressed skull fracture, there may be no psychosis; and if a disease does not involve the cortex of the brain, primarily (*e.g.*, general paresis) or secondarily (*e.g.*, Schilder's disease), such as would for example occur in epidemic encephalitis where the basal ganglia are involved, there may be no psychosis.

III. The Constitutional Psychoses.—In the constitutional psychoses there is no demonstrable etiology, despite all the claims made about involvement of the third layer of the cortex, the disease of the hypothalamus, the endocrine dysfunctions, etc. Where the disease process lies is as yet unknown; there is most likely a strong constitutional predisposition, though it must be admitted that this supposition is as much of a theory as is any of the others. There are two major groupings under this heading; but though it is easy to find clear cut cases illustrative of each type, any one with clinical experience and an open mind knows that there are many cases which are difficult of categorizing.

The first group is *Manic-Depressive Psychoses*,[1] a disorder involving the intensity and direction of response of: (A) mood, (B) physical activity, and (C) thought processes. In the *manic* phase, these three primary functions are intensified and elevated; so that there is (with modifications[2]): (1) exaltation, (2) increased physical activity, and (3) rapidity of thought amounting at times to a flight of ideas. In the *depressed* phase, there is the reverse of this process: (1) depressed mood, (2) decreased physical activity, and (3) sluggishness of thought which tends to center about one or two ideas. These phases may alternate; but statistically it has been shown that the depressive phase is more common, is most frequent in the fourth decade of life (thirty to forty), and in over 50 per cent of patients occurs only once in a life time. Involutional

---

[1] *Vide* p. 355 *ff.*
[2] Occasionally manic patients instead of being happy may become very angry; their quick flow of speech may give evidence of delusions, etc.

melancholia is a form of depression characterized by agitation and hypochondriacal delusions.

The second group is the *Schizophrenic psychoses*,[1] (often called Dementia Precox) in which there is a strong tendency to utilize primitive thinking[2] and to react to life as it is phantasied rather than as it is. The "feeling tone" of the person is markedly involved, less in the form of mood swings and more in the form of "feeling" hurt, persecuted, and inadequate.[3]

There are four standardized (though inadequate) subdivisions of schizophrenia. (*A*) In Simple Schizophrenia the patient may be said to be a daydreaming, sensitive, inadequate person, who retires within himself to the point where society needs eventually to care for him. (*B*) In Hebephrenic Schizophrenia the patient is silly, (Hebe, the goddess of puberty) grimacing, childish, and with many vivid hallucinations. Deterioration tends to be rapid. (*C*) In Catatonic Schizophrenia the patient tends to be mute, refuses to eat, and demonstrates disturbances in muscle tone (waxy flexibility). This group has the best prognosis for spontaneous remissions. (*D*) In Paranoid Schizophrenia the dominating symptoms are projection mechanisms, suspiciousness, and a tendency toward systematized delusions. (Delusions and hallucinations are found to some extent in all the varieties.) A separate entity called pure Paranoia has been culled from this group, but is probably merely a form of schizophrenia.

It should always be borne in mind that *schizophrenic symptoms are only reaction patterns;* and are very much akin to "fever" in organic disease. In themselves, schizophrenic symptoms are not significant in determining the etiology. Some persons may develop schizophrenic symptoms as the result of severe psychogenic stress,[4] if there is any constitutional predisposition; while other schizophrenic symptoms may be the result of some organic process involving (according to one poorly defined theory) the thalamo-cortical processes. The entire symptom complex is poorly understood; though the lay person usually thinks of this category, when he refers to "insanity."

IV. Psychoses Associated With Other Organic Diseases. —In this category come the psychoses following disease processes

---

[1] *Vide* p. 378 *ff.*   [2] *Vide* p. 43.

[3] Textbooks speak of schizophrenic patients as having no emotional disturbance. This statement is a controversial point.

[4] *Vide* p. 114 (Case H. N.).

such as pregnancy, Huntington's chorea, multiple sclerosis, brain tumor, etc. In all probability this category should be a subdivision of the organic psychoses.

V. Psychopathic Personality.[1]—This group is more or less of a waste-paper basket category into which are cast such disorders as drug addiction, psychopathic emotional outbursts, alcoholism (not alcoholic psychoses), sex perversions, vicious criminal tendencies, etc. Many of these personality disorders may come under the category of neuroses; alcoholism, for example, may be one method of escaping from the troubles of an unstable neurotic personality. These disorders may also be classified under psychoses, as is the case with some psychopathic emotional states. Most of the patients who fit into this category have enough balancing factors in their personality to enable them to adjust, with effort, to ordinary social demands, for short periods of time.

In the above classification, which is a convenient method of describing various forms of human behavior, though it does not illuminate greatly the causes of that behavior, one may understand that the terms "neuroses" and "psychoses" are inadequate to describe the personality disturbance. As a consequence, it is better not to attempt to differentiate between the normal and the neurotic, or between either of these categories and the psychotic or psychopathic states. It is far better to describe just what the symptom complex is, than to attempt to force the patient into one or the other major category. A real etiologic and therefore truly descriptive category will be devised only when we understand more about the underlying constitutional forces, and the mechanism of environmental stress. For purposes of present day description and for therapy, it is better to speak of those etiologic factors we can find, and of observable behavior.

Moreover, it must be stressed that the *cause* of the psychosis lies often in the disturbance in the constitution and the molding forces. The *form* of the psychosis is, however, partially the result of the cultural pattern existent at the time. Thus schizophrenia may be said to occur because of constitutional inadequacy; but whether the accompanying hallucinations appear in the form of angels, and devils and a fiery inferno as was the case in such patients during the middle ages; or whether the patient's delusions involve being persecuted by radio waves, and mental telepathy, and electric wires, is the result of the culture which exists at the time of

[1] *Vide* p. 393 *ff.*

the symptoms. In the same way the *form* of the other psychiatric illnesses is in part dependent upon cultural stress, though the *cause* of the illness may lie in the determining forces of the personality.

We are as yet not entirely clear as to the reason for the different forms of psychiatric illness. If one reviews many cases of psychoneuroses, psychoses, psychopathic personalities, alcoholism, and so forth, one is struck by the fact that the psychologic and environmental forces which preceded most of these illnesses are as a group essentially the same regardless of the type of illness. Even more impressive is the fact that many persons who remain "normal" may be subject to stress of the same character and intensity as are those who break down with some form of psychiatric illness. There are only a few major categories of stress into which most of the individual variations fit. As a consequence, one is forced to the conclusion that the type of the "mental breakdown" is dependent less upon the environmental or existential pressure and more upon the type of person on whom this stress acts.[1] The person is in some way susceptible, either by heredity or training, first, so that a stress which would leave many persons "normal," will provoke a psychiatric illness; and second, so that a particular form of illness will result. It is the study of the make-up of the person, particularly the inherited constitution,[2] as modified by the early environment, which will give us an understanding of the various forms of illness.

The type of predisposition present in the make-up of the person is the major reason for the relative infrequency with which psychoneurotic patients develop psychoses. Only infrequently does a patient develop first a mild neurosis which later becomes more and more severe until a schizophrenic illness occurs. The patient's first reactions tend to be mild forerunners of the eventual illness; so that the earliest signs of a schizophrenic condition tend to be symptoms of withdrawal or suspicion; the early signs of a manic-depressive depression tend to be fatigue, insomnia, "decreased pep"; those of a neurosis tend to be mild hypochondriacal complaints, etc. However, there are many variations in such a formulation, for the border lines between the various forms of mental illness are broad and interdigitating; and though it is not the rule, not infrequently one may find neuroses as the earliest manifestations of a psychosis. In those instances where a neurosis does

[1] *Vide* p. 122.　　　　　　[2] *Vide* p. 182.

precede a psychosis, one can discern queer or distorted complaints, or the setting of other non-neurotic background.

VI. The Psychoneuroses.—The Psychoneuroses (or neuroses) are symptom complexes or personality reaction patterns resulting from the interplay between constitutional and environmental forces; are of an unhealthy and immature character, and differ from "normal" reaction patterns primarily in intensity of response and in diffuseness of response. As a consequence, many normal persons may temporarily have some responses which are intense enough to be termed neurotic; whereas many neurotic symptoms are difficult to distinguish from "normal" responses.

Psychoneurotic symptoms may thus be termed intense and diffuse reactions which are indicative either of (1) *Tension*, or of (2) *Symbolism*. Both of these types of symptoms occur among normal persons as well as among psychoneurotic persons. Psychoneurotic symptoms are better described individually by the terms tension, or symbolism or their combination rather than by attempting to group them arbitrarily. The traditional classification which includes, (A) neurasthenia; (B) hysteria; (C) anxiety states; and (D) obsessive compulsive or psychasthenic states, culls out conglomerations of syndromes which apparently have some relationship to each other but which, except for extreme cases, are of little descriptive or etiologic significance. Each subdivision of the neuroses may be represented as a dense conglomeration of symptoms lying within a diffuse matrix of emotional instability containing all the psychoneurotic symptoms. Within this diffuse base are many symptoms common to all the psychoneuroses just as fever, leucocytosis, anemia, anorexia, and constipation are common to a host of dissimilar physical diseases. At some points, certain symptoms increase in intensity and form syndromes. These syndromes differ from each other only in degree and selection, but not in fundamental character. It is suggested, therefore, that neurotic symptoms be no longer "lumped together," and that they be described as tension or symbolism symptoms, which terms are indicative of the mechanisms involved and which suggest the therapy to be followed.

A. TENSION SYMPTOMS

Tension Symptoms.—The symptoms presented by the patients suffering from psychoneuroses may be those of a state of general "psychological" tension or of tension (stretched, overly active) of the autonomic nervous and other related systems. (1) The *general tense attitudes* show themselves in irritability, anxiety states, "worry," over-concern about one's self, egocentricity, and even an *inability to concentrate* on anything unrelated to one's problem. These symptoms have their basis in emotional factors; and they tend to be present, in varying degrees of intensity, in all the forms of neuroses. Such signs and symptoms of tension are present, however, not only in patients who are neurotic, but in normal persons when they are laboring under strong emotional stress.

Focal Tension Symptoms.—The focal tension symptoms show themselves in the evidences of disturbed activity of the autonomic nervous system (and related systems). These are in addition to the general state of tension which manifests itself in the "emotional attitude" of persons. Although disturbance of the central nervous system may show itself in tension of striated muscles and although the over-activity of endocrine glands may be manifest through increased basal metabolism, hyperfunction of the adrenals, etc., generally such symptoms are expressions resulting from the over-activity of the autonomic nervous system. Speaking more succinctly one may say: though all integrative systems are to some degree involved in tension, most focal disturbances result directly or indirectly from disturbed activity of the autonomic nervous system.

As a consequence of such focal tensions, there may be disturbances in cardiac rate and rhythm, showing clinically as tachycardia, extrasystoles, cardiac pain resulting from spasm of the coronary vessels;[1] there may be respiratory disturbances expressed by deep sighs, a sense of oppression across the chest, chest pains, etc.;[2] there may be gastrointestinal disturbances such as hyperchlorhydria, spasms of the cardiac or pyloric sphyncters of the stomach, vomiting, spasms of the intestine, of the gall bladder ducts, mucous colitis, constipation, diarrhea, etc.;[3] there may be bladder disturbances such as frequency of urination, urgency, retention;[4] there may be sexual difficulties: impotence, priapism, dysmenorrhea, delayed or too frequent menstrual flow;[5] there may be disturbances in vision, in the functioning of the eye, ear, nose and throat;[6] there may be stammering and stuttering resulting

[1] *Vide* p. 292 *ff.*
[2] *Vide* p. 35 *ff.*
[3] *Vide* p. 300 *ff.*
[4] *Vide* p. 310 *ff.*
[5] *Vide* p. 325 *ff.*
[6] *Vide* p. 316 *ff.*

from tension of the speech muscles; there may be tics, perspiring palms of the hands, and soles of the feet, cold hands and feet. All these and many more symptoms for which no definite "organically" pathologic basis has been discovered may result directly from over-activity of the autonomic nervous system or indirectly via the influence of this system on the adrenal, pituitary, and other endo-crine glands. The fact that the autonomic nervous system co-ordinates all activity accounts for the widespread symptoms in the neuroses.

These general and focal symptoms occur in most of the psycho-neurotic patients: preponderantly so in those suffering from neur-asthenia and anxiety states, relatively less so in those categorized under the labels of hysteria and obsessive-compulsive neurosis in which states symbolic symptoms are more common. The tradi-tional description of neurasthenia which follows is an excellent example of the innumerable tension symptoms which may be "lumped together."

Neurasthenia (derived from the Greek meaning nerve without strength) is a syndrome characterized by weakness and hypo-chondriacal complaints. There is general muscular fatigue, there is lassitude, lack of interest, anxiety, and irritability. The hypo-chondriacal complaints may involve almost any part of the organ-ism and generally are widespread. There may be headaches; "eyestrain"; "sinus trouble"; soreness of the gums; a "lump in the throat"; abdominal complaints of all sorts including "a nervous stomach," "cramps," a spastic colon, constipation, diarrhea; fre-quency in urination; and vague aches and pains in the extremities. Indeed in some of these patients it is difficult to mention any part of the body that is not or has not been "ailing."[1] The following case is illustrative:

The patient, aged thirty years, single, female, came to the clinic complain-ing of a feeling of lordosis, an inability to straighten her back, a radiating anginal pain, a tickling of the nostril and a tickling in the eardrum, a con-striction in her head, difficulty in inspiration, a peculiar tightness of the abdomen, urgency of urination, and general weakness. She had been perfectly well until July, 1930, when her mother died. She then had attacks of belching, with eructations of sour fluids. In November, 1935, she entered business college, resolved to lead her class. She succeeded in doing so, but worried greatly about maintaining her scholastic standing. It was at this time that the symptoms mentioned above developed. She was unable to obtain work and had to be supported by a friend. A thorough physical examination revealed no organic findings.

[1] *Vide* p. 320 (Case W. H.).

Tension symptoms may become focalized[1] to any portion of the body. When the cardiovascular system is involved there is often associated a great deal of anxiety. This fact has led to the culling out of a so-called anxiety syndrome which differs only in intensity from the neurasthenic group just mentioned, and in actual practice is not always possible to differentiate, because of the presence of minor "neurasthenic" symptoms. Formally, *anxiety states*[2] are characterized by extreme tension, with fearfulness, apprehensiveness, and a number of striking vagotonic symptoms. Anxiety, it will be remembered, is found in most of the psychoneuroses, but in this subdivision is almost in pure culture. Most of these patients have no major cause for anxiety. In many, the anxiety seizes upon some accidental occurrence as an outlet, so that speaking in public, hearing certain noises, or even smelling or seeing certain objects may bring the anxiety to a climax. The anxiety symptoms, in addition to the subjective feeling of uneasiness, are often associated with a "sinking feeling" in the pit of the stomach, and with cardiac signs which may go to the point of extra systoles. Frequency of urination is often present.

Anxiety *attacks*[3] may occur; and not infrequently a patient will state that he was suddenly awakened out of a sound sleep with a strong feeling of apprehension, at times mounting to a fear of death. His heart will pound rapidly, and his breath will come in quick gasps. The patient will then get out of bed and walk around. When the physician arrives, there will be no physical evidence of any abnormality; and later the patient will fall asleep. Such attacks are characteristic. Attempting to elicit precipitating factors such as bad dreams just before the attack, emotional upsets, or other physical or psychologic causes, often fails. The immediate etiologic factor may precede the attack by one or more days and may be a minor incident. On the other hand, the anxiety attacks may occur during the daytime and may take the form of paroxysmal tachycardia. These attacks vary in frequency and often seem to occur without any cause; generally, however, in the background is some topic of concern over which the patient feels very apprehensive. Many of these patients appear to be perfectly adjusted though they feel insecure and inferior internally. "They worry inside."

[1] *Vide* p. 289–290.
[2] *Vide* p. 113 (Case D. J.).   [3] *Vide* p. 52 (Case B. U.).

Marie C., aged thirty-nine years, stated that her complaints were limited to definite attacks which occurred at night. She awoke with a feeling of anxiety and apprehension, usually about two o'clock in the morning. The attacks were not preceded by bad dreams, or by other emotional causes, that she recalled. During the attack she was conscious of severe palpitation, a marked feeling of suffocation, and she broke out into a profuse sweat. The attacks were accompanied by a fear of imminent death or of going insane. The intense reaction subsided within a few minutes; but the feeling of anxiety persisted for hours, sometimes throughout the night. She found that getting up and walking about tended to produce some measure of comfort. Returning to bed brought the attacks back in full force. During the daytime, the patient occasionally had a mild variation of the above attack, but these attacks were unaccompanied by the physical signs and symptoms. A thorough physical examination revealed no organic basis; and an electro-cardiogram showed the heart perfectly normal in spite of the fact that a physician noted marked extra systoles at night time during an attack. In the psychiatric examination, the patient stated that she was worried over financial matters and over the health of her three children. This condition, however, appeared rather superficial; and deeper questioning brought out the point that she was exceedingly concerned over the sexual act. She was Catholic, and had used only the so-called "free-period" method to control pregnancy. This practice had not been successful, and she had had three children within the five years that she was married. She reported that during the first two years she was unable to respond satisfactorily to sex relations, but afterwards, until the onset of her complaints, she had an intense desire for sex relations and responded to coitus with great satisfaction. In the early part of 1934, the patient and her husband decided to limit off-spring by abstinence. This proposal they could not carry out completely, and sex relations occurred two or three times a month, and were limited to the so-called "free-period." An intense conflict resulted from her desire for the act, her fear of pregnancy, and her wish to carry out the orders of her faith. This conflict was at the basis of her anxiety state.

B. SYMBOLIC SYMPTOMS

Symbolic Symptoms.—Many of the symptoms (reaction patterns) of neurotic patients are symbolic; that is, the symptoms represent in condensed and often obscure form, underlying emotional difficulties and conflicts. Frequently the symbolic symptom has elements of the disturbed function of one of the integrating systems, but more frequently it is a more or less pure ideational expression. Thus a patient may have a paralyzed arm, and yet no evidence may be found of any organic disease or even of any disturbance in the autonomic nervous system. A cure by psychotherapy will later confirm the diagnosis of "hysteria." The hysterically paralyzed arm is a symbol, a symbol which represents, *unconsciously*, to the patient, the underlying disturbing emotions. Moreover, the symptom enables the patient to focus his general unhappiness and distress on a concrete and tangible illness. This finding of an outlet for the pent-up internal emotions serves a function of release, expression, and the "taking one's mind off" the other and etiologic causes.

Miss I. D., aged seventeen years, came to the clinic complaining of a paralyzed arm. Thorough examination revealed no organic disease, and no evidence of any physiologic disturbance associated in any way with the arm. There were other symptoms of tension, of irritability, of depression with crying spells, of tachycardia, etc., but none of these other symptoms could explain the arm paralysis.

The paralysis was diagnosed as a symbolic representation of underlying emotional conflicts, and a further examination of her history confirmed the diagnosis. The girl lived in a very unhappy home; her father was a confirmed alcoholic who had mistreated the patient's mother "till he caused her death." The stepmother was cruel and mean, seizing every opportunity to berate and physically beat the child. The patient's sister had run away at the age of fifteen to get married, "just to get out of the home." The patient cried constantly, but could find no means of escape.

One day the mother began to beat Ida, and Ida put up her arm to ward off the blows. The blows struck her arm and the patient cried and sobbed that her arm was hurt. The mother, in a temporary state of alarm, stopped long enough to inquire about the arm, and Ida suddenly felt that she was powerless to move it. She was not seen in the psychiatric dispensary until a month later, but no improvement had occurred. Under psychotherapy, the paralysis disappeared.

In this instance, the symptom was primarily symbolic of underlying conflict and unhappiness, plus resentment of all the unfortunate occurrences in her family life. However, associated with this symbolic complaint, were many other symptoms of general and focal tension. Both of these general groups of symptoms resulted from a personality disturbance due to environmental pressure.

Many other symptoms are of symbolic nature: hysterical aphonia,[1] or inability to speak either at all, or only in a whisper; astasia abasia,[2] or inability to walk because of weakness in the legs, although there is excellent muscle power while the patient lies in bed; obsessive ideas[3] which cannot be eliminated from one's thought, such as fears, and peculiar ideas; *e. g.* compulsive actions such as continuous hand washing, or the compulsion to touch some object; hallucinations, and delusions. These are but a few of the

---

[1] *Vide* p. 323.　　　[2] *Vide* p. 30 (Case D. W.)　　　[3] *Vide* p. 113 (Case F. M.)

symbolic representations of underlying difficulties. Each one of the symptoms is meaningless in itself; but it has a great deal of meaning if understood as being symbolic. Such an understanding is essential for a dynamic comprehension of human activity.

Many patients who suffer from psychoneurotic symptoms are called hysterical, neurasthenic, or obsessive, without an understanding of the symbolic or tension nature of the symptoms produced. This tendency to categorize patients and to label them with arbitrarily selected names for arbitrarily selected groupings confuses both the mechanism and therapy of the illness. Moreover, in actual practice, it is the extreme case which fits nicely into one of the traditional patterns of classification; and expert, well trained psychiatrists will often disagree on the classification of cases except those which are sharply defined and entirely typical. The groups called "hysteria" and "obsessive compulsive states" not only over-lap, but are not too divergent variations of the same etiological forces.

Hysteria.—Hysteria is a symptom complex characterized by disturbance of any function which is not on an organic basis. Almost any function of the body may be involved. The function of motor activity, of sensory activity,[1] of the special senses, and even of psychologic processes may be involved. Usually cardiac, gastrointestinal, or respiratory complaints are regarded as not belonging to this group; but the definition of these groups is so vague that some physicians do include among the hysterias these disorders of the vegetative tracts. The Freudian psychologists speak of an "anxiety hysteria," but this classification but further complicates an already complicated syndrome.

Hysteria is the Greek word for womb, and the ancients believed that an hysterical symptom occurred at whatever site the womb, which wandered over the body, might lodge. Erroneous as we know this concept to be, there are two interesting connotations: first, that women more often than men are affected, and second that sexual difficulties play an important role.

Mr. D. W., aged sixty-three years, suddenly developed a paralysis of his legs which prevented him from walking. He had been perfectly well until four days before examination. He was in normal health in every other way, ate and slept well. Neurologic examination revealed no pathology. While in bed he could raise his knees and flex all his joints even against great resistance.

[1] *Vide* p. 114 (Case B. T.).

Mr. D. W. lived with his daughter-in-law. He was a cranky old man who had retired and was tolerated only because he had some insurance which would eventually benefit the daughter-in-law. On the day of the development of the paralysis, his will and policy had been found, and it had been discovered that he was leaving some charities as beneficiaries. In great rage, the daughter-in-law ordered the old man from her home; and the paralysis promptly developed. It was a typical astasia abasia.

In many of these instances it is difficult to distinguish between hysteria and malingering. Indeed it may be said that hysteria is unconscious malingering. In hysteria, the symptom is symbolic and dictated by fear or conflict rather than by conscious direction.

Symbolic activity may occur in the form of spasm. Torticollis is a good example. Because of the tendency of this symptom to resist therapy, many authors have insisted that it has an organic basis; but extremely few cases of pathologic lesions have been reported, and in those the evidence that there was a direct connection with torticollis is unconvincing. Moreover, physiologically it is difficult to explain what group of nerve cells could be so involved as to produce only this twisting of the neck and to leave all other muscles undistorted. On the other hand, I have seen cases which were unrelieved by such extreme operations as cutting all the muscles of the tense side of the neck, or cutting the high cervical or accessory nerves; while in other instances, repeated injections of novocaine or alcohol seemed to produce relief (as the result, however, of suggestion). So great is the propensity of these patients to twist their necks, that it has been said that if one were to denervate all the muscles of the neck, and bisect the muscles in addition, the patient would still be able to twist his neck by means of the carotid sheath and the esophagus!

Mr. T. Y., aged twenty-nine years, came to the London Hospital complaining of torticollis. He showed no evidences of organic involvement of the nervous system other than the twisted neck. The patient was put to sleep (sleep treatment consisting of putting the patient to bed for ten to fifteen days and keeping him asleep with sedatives, allowing him to awaken only for food and elimination) for twelve days; and in this deep coma, his head remained in the midline. When he recovered from the sleep treatment, however, his torticollis promptly returned. He was then put in a plaster cast, and so great was the rigidity that anesthesia had to be used to get his head to the midline. When the headcase was removed six weeks later, his head promptly returned to its former position.

This torticollis, unchangeable by mechanical or chemical means, was, however, easily remedied temporarily by hypnosis and suggestion.

Mrs. K. U. had worked for the same firm for twelve years. She was directly under the supervision of the vice-president, and soon learned to handle most of the responsible work. When he went on vacations, she was left in charge. Shortly before the onset of her symptom, this vice-president became exceedingly slovenly, unkempt, and in addition, began to make advances to the patient. The work, also, increased in volume and responsibility, so that any mistake would prove costly. She was informed that as soon as the vice-president retired, she would be given his position, as far as work was concerned. The prospect of having to shoulder all this responsibility made her over-concerned about mistakes. An irritable husband contributed to the picture. Her torticollis developed in this setting, and was symbolic of "avoiding looking at her work." The torticollis cleared up for one day under hypnosis, and was removed entirely when she was taught not to feel the responsibility so keenly as she did.

Sensory Functions.—Sensory functions may be involved. There may be anesthesia, hyperesthesia, or paresthesia. One part or many parts of the body are involved, and usually, inconstantly. The distribution of these anesthesias, as a rule, does not follow any of the segmental or nerve pathways. Often the anesthesias are not complained of, and indeed, not found until they are closely examined, so that the problem of how much they are suggested to the patient is an important one. Characteristic sites of the anesthesia may be the so-called glove anesthesia, involving the hands and wrists; the stocking anesthesia, involving the foot and half the leg; and hemianesthesia, involving half the body. Interestingly, in the last mentioned condition, half of the tongue and one side of the palate on the side of the anesthesia may be also anesthetic. In these instances, the motor power is usually intact, a rare state in organic conditions.

One patient, a girl aged twenty-three years, following an accident, suffered from anesthesia of the dorsal surface of the right hand because of the injury to the superficial radial nerves. This condition was complained of bitterly, and frequent visits to the doctor resulted. One day, quite by accident, the left hand was tested with the pin, in order to compare its sensations with the other, and the patient stated that she had no feeling whatsoever. It was found that her entire left hand, up to the middle of the forearm, had an hysterical anesthesia; but of this the patient did not complain. It was remarkable that such a complete, even though hysterical, anesthesia could be unnoticed by the patient; it is an example of Charcot's "belle indifference."

The special senses may be affected. In the eye, *visual function* may be disturbed,[1] and there may be partial blindness or complete blindness. Vision may be tubular, that is, all things may be seen

---

[1] *Vide* p. 316 *ff.*

as though through a small telescope, so that nothing in the periphery is visible. There may be diplopia, or seeing double; and charting of the visual fields often shows a spiral type of field. The function of *hearing*[1] may be involved so that there may be deafness, complete or incomplete; there may be constantly-heard noises or peculiar sounds which may border on auditory hallucinations. All these disorders are without organic basis, and are symbolic means of expressing underlying conflicts.

There are many hysterical (symbolic) movements, but these are legion, and description of the individual types is unnecessary, for the principle is essentially the same in all instances.

Miss L., aged thirty-eight years, came to the hospital in a taxi-cab and had to be carried into the clinic on a wheelchair because of her asserted inability to walk. She had been paralyzed for six months, according to her story. The paralysis was of the astasia abasia character. A neighbor, who accompanied the patient, gave the following information. The patient has always been a spoiled child. She lives with her mother, aged seventy-five years and crippled with arthritis, and with another sister who is a few years younger than the patient. According to the neighbor, the patient has a full domination over the mother. She is petty and spoiled; and on leaving the clinic once, came home, sat in a chair, and made her aged mother get up and wait on her in spite of the fact that her mother was groaning in pain from arthritis. The first symptom developed at about the age of sixteen. She was in high school and began to have some difficulty with her school work. She lost appetite, and vomited. She saw several physicians and improved temporarily. She worked from the age of eighteen until the age of thirty-three, but the positions which she held were more or less temporary. She would always become ill and have to leave work. She saw various physicians continuously, but improved only temporarily. In 1930, she was in love with a man, but she developed a terrific pain in her neck which she felt might prevent her from being a real mother to her children, and as a result, could not marry the man. The physician whom she saw at the time insisted that there was nothing wrong with her. When she spoke to her girl friends, she often resorted to a baby type of talk. Six months ago, a clergyman came to visit her, and when she complained of weakness in her legs, gave her much attention which increased as the weakness developed into paralysis.

Neurologic examination was completely negative, and after the examination, by means of hypnosis and strong suggestions, the patient was made to stand up and walk out. She visited the clinic thereafter for further psychotherapy, without evidence of paralysis.

So-called *mental processes* may be symbolically (hysteria) involved. Complete amnesia,[2] without ability to recall any part of one's history, may occur. There may be amnesia for certain events or situations. I have seen a case of vivid hallucinations in a

---

[1] *Vide* p. 318.   [2] *Vide* p. 76 (Case B. Q.)

3

young hysterical girl. Occasionally coma occurs with, at times, retention of urine for twenty-four hours. Acute and violent emotional outbreaks with very little provocative basis may also occur.

An interesting and extremely common form of the combination of tension and symbolism is to be found in the *speech disorders*. There may be *aphonia*,[1] whispered voice, hoarseness, or stammering and stuttering. In whispered voice there is a greater or lesser degree of failure in approximation of the vocal cords in their attempt at phonation. Aphonia of the whispered voice type tends to be a symptom primarily of tension and is usually associated with other physical and psychologic symptoms of tension. On the other hand, complete aphonia tends to be more symbolic, a "wish not to speak" or a "fear of speaking."

STAMMERING AND STUTTERING

Stammering and stuttering are extremely common expressions of tension. Speech is so commonly involved because tension is such a common characteristic of our present day society; and since speech is one of the latest phylogenetically acquired characteristics, it is therefore one of the first functions of the organism to be disturbed under conditions of stress. There are four general types of stuttering as related to tension states (there is only an artificial difference between stammering and stuttering), but they are not usually found in pure form. The average patient utilizes several forms, forms which differ not in etiology or mechanism, but simply in the particular muscles involved. Illustrative of the first form are those patients who start to speak and then hold their breath before emitting a sound which when uttered usually comes forth in perfectly formed words. In these patients the tension of the respiratory muscles prevents the relaxation and the release of air normally used in speaking. The second group of stutterers make many facial grimaces before vocalizing, and they may contract the muscles of the mouth, project and withdraw the tongue, wrinkle the face and forehead, before uttering a word which when uttered may be perfectly pronounced, or may be hesitant. The tension of the muscles involved in this grimacing is evident. The third and most common group consists of those persons in whom there is tension and spastic-like contractions primarily of the tongue but also of other muscles of speech such as the soft palate, the vocal

[1] *Vide* p. 324 (Case K. L.).

cords, and the lips. The muscles employed in the formation of words start to make the sound and then instead of relaxing so that the succeeding phonation can occur, become so tense as to interrupt the formation of the word. The effort of the subject to force the word through, results in further tension of the tongue and other speech organs so that the stuttering sounds are increased. The fourth type of stuttering is more of a temporary and emotional aphasia than a true stuttering. Patients in this group begin to speak and then suddenly forget the word which they wish to use. The word "is on the tip of the tongue," but like the aphasic patient who knows what the object is but cannot name it even though he recognizes when the object is incorrectly named, so this type of stutterer cannot recall the word he wishes to use. A substitute word will frequently come to the fore, and may be uttered simply and perfectly.

These several types tend to merge into one another so that one frequently sees a patient holding his breath, making many facial grimaces, not being able to think of the word he wishes to use, and then bringing forth a battered and unrecognizable form of a word. In practically every patient there tends to be marked general tension, which the patients too often insist is the result of their self consciousness, rather than the causal factor of the speech symptom. The tension of their speech muscles first originates from general tension; and although by the stuttering a vicious cycle is started in such a manner as to increase self consciousness, the element of primary importance to treat[1] is not the speech but the tension behind the speech.

Another traditional classification includes the obsessive compulsive group, which however are more obviously symbolisms than are the "hysterical" physical complaints because they tend to be confined to ideas or activities. Thus formally the *obsessive compulsive states* may be characterized by the word "must." On the one hand, these patients "must" think a certain thought; and on the other hand, they "must" perform a certain deed. In most instances, the person will spontaneously state that the thought or act is silly, foolish, and without reason or justification; yet he cannot prevent himself from carrying it out. If he attempts to avoid carrying out these acts, he will become exceedingly tense, restless, and if forcibly restrained, may develop a panic. There are various

[1] *Vide* p. 291.

degrees of obsession ranging from mild fears of disease, with compulsive hand-washing to clean off imagined germs or dirt, to a severe condition where persons "must" wash their hands two to three hundred times a day. These states are so deeply seated and sometimes so distorted, that they are often spoken of as being allied to schizophrenic psychosis.

Miss S. G., aged twenty-five years, came in complaining that she had an idea that she would kill children. The idea developed one day after she had read in a newspaper about an elderly couple who had killed their child. The idea came into her mind that she too might kill the children of the sister with whom she was staying. The idea persisted, and she could not get it out of her mind. She tried working hard, going to movies, going out with people; but wherever she went and whatever she did, the idea came to her. Associated with it were fear and panic. She told herself that the idea was absurd and crazy; that she had no reason for such thoughts, but the idea persisted anyway. It prevented her from sleeping, disturbed her appetite, made her extremely depressed, and finally forced upon her the idea that she should commit suicide lest she give way to an impulse and carry out the frightful idea that she had. Psychiatric examination revealed that the patient had been in love with a young man in another part of the country. The young man had to leave home in connection with his work. Just before he left, the girl had become pregnant, and her lover had insisted upon an abortion. The patient resented and revolted against the idea, feeling she was killing her child, but finally was persuaded to follow his wishes. When she came to Chicago to live, she was taken in by her sister, who knowing something of her history, soon became jealous and suspicious that she might seduce her husband. The girl was temporarily without means of support, and therefore had to live with her sister, but the friction between her and her sister mounted. It was with this background that she read of the couple's killing their child and that the idea occurred to her of killing her sister's children. She accused herself of already killing one (unborn) child and feared (unconsciously) that her antagonism to her sister might lead her to repeat the act.

The entire groups of "fear states" or phobias,[1] are symbols and may be included in this subdivision. There may be fear of dirt, of disease, of being in closed spaces, in open spaces, by one's self, in a crowd, and numerous other fears. As a rule, these fears are associated with anxiety over some more personal difficulty; and the person not being able to face the difficulty develops anxiety, which he then displaces to some incidental or minor irritating condition. Attempting to *eradicate the symptom is futile, unless one understands its symbolic nature and eradicates the basic causes.*

[1] *Vide* p. 53 (footnote).

It is hard to differentiate in a clear cut fashion between tension symptoms and symbolic symptoms, for in any given patient, both sets of symptoms are so intermingled that the task becomes one of separating the yolk from the white of a scrambled egg. Moreover, any given symptom may be at one and the same time an expression of tension and over-activity of the autonomic nervous system, and a symbol of some underlying difficulty. Thus one young woman complained bitterly of blushing spells which came on so frequently that she had become desperate. Since blushing is a vasodilatation in the face and neck, it must therefore be assumed to be a symptom of tension, a symptom of disturbed regulation of the autonomic nervous system. However, a further analysis of her history revealed that this young woman, married four years, had discovered her husband's infidelity, the woman in the case being her own sister. "It made me blush to think of it," besides making her furiously angry. The blushing was thus not only a symptom of tension but at the same time a symbolic representation of her emotional conflict over the entire sexual episode. In the following list, therefore, each symptom must be regarded not as belonging exclusively to one group, but as being usually of that group.

TABLE 1.—TYPES OF NEUROTIC SYMPTOMS[1]

Symptoms usually Symbolic[2] but not exclusively so	Symptoms expressive of General Tension	Symptoms usually expression of Focal Tension or of a disturbed Autonomic[3] Nervous System
Muscle paralysis	Irritability	Weakness, "being run down"
Muscle tics	Anxiety	
Anesthesias	Egocentricity	Easy fatigability
Hyperesthesias	Concentration difficulties	Cardiac symptoms
Paresthesias		Gastric difficulties
Tubular vision	Worry	Intestinal spasms
Phobias and fears	Over-concern about the self	Bladder irritability
Obsessions, compulsions		Uterine dysfunction
Abnormal sex interests	Anorexia	Pains and aches in limbs
Impotence	Insomnia	Headaches
Hallucinations		Perspiring palms
Delusions		Cold hands and feet
		"Eyestrain"
		"Ringing in ears"
		Stammering and stuttering
		"Lump" in throat

[1] It is assumed that there is no organic disease, and realized that only a few representative symptoms are listed.

[2] It must again be emphasized that many of the symptoms in this table are an inseparable admixture of tension and symbolism. Moreover symptoms classified as symbolic may simultaneously be focal tension symptoms and *vice versa*.

[3] *Cf.* footnote, p. 81.

In conclusion therefore, one may say that psychoneurotic symptoms are evidences of tension and symbolism which, though found at times in the normal person, tend to be carried to such an extreme as to be categorized as neurotic. The diagnosis of psychoneurosis is to be based not upon arbitrary groupings such as neurasthenia, hysteria, psychasthenia, and anxiety states which are greatly over-lapping and not contributory to the understanding, but upon the mechanism (tension and symbolism) by which the symptoms are produced. Tension symptoms may be general, or focal. The first expresses itself in general irritability, and the second in disturbed activity of the autonomic nervous system and other integrating systems. Symbolic activity may manifest itself through the use of physical symbols (usually termed hysteria) or through fears and obsessional ideas. Tension symptoms are the *physiologic* response, and symbolic symptoms the *psychologic* response to disturbed emotional states.

CHAPTER II

THE FUNDAMENTAL PSYCHOLOGY OF THE PSYCHONEUROSES

PHYSIOLOGY is based on the study of the functions of cells and organs and their integrative states; psychologic or personality reactions are based on the fundamental drives or tendencies of the organism as integrated in a complex society. The total personality is a function of a *socio-psycho-biologic unity in a given setting at a given time*, and can be understood only if studied as such. These five elements must be studied with reference to each other. It is not possible to draw general conclusions from a study of any *one* of the parts, even if the time and situation are considered; and in like manner, social analysis, psychologic analysis, and biologic analysis are inadequate to explain a person's symptoms unless reference is made to the other analyses; *i. e.*, of time and circumstance.

It cannot too strongly be stressed that it is *only for purposes of convenience and clarity* that a distinction is made between physiologic and psychologic reactions to emotional states. Of necessity they are discussed separately; but in actuality, *personality is a complex whole* responding to, being conditioned by, determining as well as being determined by the environment.

If one disregards all hair-splitting phrases and obscure terminology, it may be generally agreed that all psychologic reactions are built up, pyramided up on two fundamental drives—the drive for self-preservation (ego-maintenance) and the drive for race-preservation (predominantly sexual). In other words, man seeks security and satisfactions. For primitive man, "security" represented material self-preservation through the food-getting techniques and self-protection from the elements, wild beasts, and human enemies. His needs were more immediately acute and his methods more obviously direct than those of modern man living as he does in a highly complex world. There were no "middle men" for primitive man—he killed or produced his own food, and if he were physically stronger or more ingenious he killed or outwitted his enemies. Today man must be content with delayed satisfactions. He is trained more or less intensively over an

(39)

increasingly long period of time to learn some skill or profession by which he can secure the money with which to buy the food to give him strength to continue work to make more money. His enemies, too, are less subject to direct defeat. Today a person is relatively safe physically (unless he is a pedestrian), and his enemies become those factors or persons in his environment that offer danger to his ego, his pride, his ambition. Primitive man could not afford the luxury of pampering his ego; he was too busy seeking food and running away from physical danger. Desires and fears in civilized man, however, are no less exacting or painful because they are not, on the one hand, immediately capable of satisfaction, or, on the other, tangible and subject to escape; in fact, they are more so.

Physical security is basic; but mankind has gained a sufficiently adequate technique of control over the physical world to enable him to enlarge the *meaning* of security to include response, appreciation, recognition, approval, etc. In the same way, sex has come to mean far more than physical gratification; it has been idealized as love, a symbol of companionship, understanding, shared interests and desires, comfort, stimulation, and a host of other meanings. In other words, the quest for a satisfying and secure life has always been present as the driving urge; but as the concept of what constitutes such a life is enlarged and enriched, the technique of achievement becomes more involved, and the chances of frustration more numerous.

There are in actuality no rugged (or other kind of) individualists. *Every person is a part of the social whole;* and the *whole* modifies and changes the form of the *part*. Consequently the avenues of danger are multiplied, and pleasures become less direct, more symbolized. Life is an endless modification of one's "natural" tendencies so that man may live in the world as it is. These modifications, or more properly prohibitions which in normal growth become inhibitions, are constantly in operation, and each person must experience literally countless prohibitions during a lifetime. We must learn not to cry, not to snatch, not to demand. We must sit still, speak softly, say things we don't mean, refrain from saying those we do. We must eat food we don't like—even if we do like it we must eat it in a socially prescribed way. We must wear irritating clothes, pretend interests we do not have, conceal our boredom, mask our joy, restrain our anger, sorrow, or fear. The smiles of adults looking at a yawning baby have a certain nostalgic wistfulness for a lost freedom. Paradoxically, the only way a person can achieve even a modicum of freedom and security is by giving in to many of those restrictions and requirements. Society says "Which would you better?"; the individual man asks "Which would I rather?" Man is driven by felt needs; society furnishes inhibitions. To the degree that man can appropriate the superimposed patterns into his repertoire of personality reactions is he integrated; and conversely, to the degree that there is opposition and inability to make suitable patterns his own, there will be conflict and consequent tension.

Reaction patterns which are clearly developed and uncomplicated give rise to no disturbances after they have been established. The emotional outbreaks and irritations which may characterize their development disappear if the path is definite and consistently followed. Indeed it is possible for a person to hold apparently contradictory attitudes toward religion, politics, personal ambitions, etc., provided they are uncomplicated by inner turmoil.

Unstable emotional states, however, may result from ambivalent reaction patterns when contradictory attitudes are not harmonized, and maintain their opposing emotional drives. Ambivalency[1] (opposing tendencies or desires) may result from the reaction of the person to environmental pressure. Ambivalent persons swing from one extreme to the other. It must be remembered that individual differences[2] play a large role—that the same situation may not necessarily evoke indentical responses from different persons.

When they are complicated by internal turmoil resulting from indecision or strong desires, these contradictory attitudes tend to remain active in the personality reaction patterns. There results a situation termed "conflict," and the subject is unable to come to a final decision as to which of the two sides of the conflict shall rule. In the psychoneuroses this conflict is accompanied by great emotional tone and is indeed a conflict between two basic emotional tendencies (of basic desire to satisfy and of learned desire to restrain). Inability to make a decision in itself does not necessarily cause conflict; to vote for one party or another, to purchase a blue or red tie, to smoke a cigar or a cigarette; all these are primarily (though not exclusively) "intellectual" conflicts and are resolved without the development of symptoms. When, however, much emotion accompanies indecision, conflict results and the total

[1] *Vide* p. 76.   [2] *Vide* p. 240.

organism is in a state of unrest. Generally speaking, one may say that deep emotional unrest and conflict occur when basic drives have been involved; but conflict can result from relatively minor indecisions: as whether to take one's vacation in the mountains or at the seashore; to buy a car or save for a rainy day; to partake of liquor and suffer from an exacerbation of the ulcer symptoms or to abstain and feel better the next day. The intensity of the conflict is dependent on the attitudes and the amount of emotion present in an indecision. The causes of conflict often are found in the emotional tone developed early in life: the results of conflict are often the psychoneurotic symptoms discussed in the next two chapters.

Guided by the desires to achieve pleasure and avoid pain, the organism establishes certain *body attitudes*[1] or reaction patterns. The pleasure-pain concept is at first largely in terms of physical comfort. The reaction patterns of infancy are general and undirected; increasingly they become specific and localized. Certain behavior brings pleasurable results; consequently, the behavior is repeated until it becomes habitual.

Man has learned to make habitual[2] many activities, so that he is more free to focus his attention on objects of interest. Habitual responses require almost no thought, and are automatic and reflex-like in character. Without reflection man puts on the same shoe first each morning, or sits in the same place in classroom, church, or theatre, and moreover feels resentful if someone else "takes his place." It is desirable that much of one's life be automatic—provided the habits thus carried out are energy-saving ones. A man would never even reach his office if daily he had to debate with himself: to get up, or not to get up; to wash or not to wash; to shave or not to shave; to lead out on the right foot or the left; to read the newspaper or not to read, etc., etc. At the other extreme is the person who becomes over-routinized so that instead of action becoming automatic, and so a short-cut to achievement, the emphasis is shifted and the routine becomes an end rather than a means.[3] Habit has no value other than its pragmatic worth.

In the same way *much of what a person thinks and feels is automatic* and habitual, the pattern often having been laid in the forgotten past. The woman who sulks and pouts her way to a fur coat probably does not remember what she gained from her early

[1] *Vide* p. 78. [2] *Vide* p. 171.
[3] *Vide* p. 212 *ff*.

temper-tantrums; but her technique of control is the same. The man who feels that the world owes him a living no doubt could not recall the details of the over-protection and solicitude which inculcated in him the sense that the world is organized and run for his benefit; but the attitude is ingrained and operative.

Every person uses his past failures or successes as a standard by which to determine his present reactions. The more objective and "thinking" a person is, the more precisely and specifically can he evaluate his past experiences and "select" an appropriate response. The more emotional and subjective one is, the more immediate, strong, and general the response is, deriving its character from the kind and type of emotion associated with the stimulus on a previous occasion. This latter type of association tends to be *primitive; i. e., characterized by laws of similarity and laws of contagion*[1] (contiguity in time and space).

For primitive man, objects which looked alike were considered to be identical and to have each other's properties (law of similarity). Thus if one wished to dispose of his enemy, he need only make of wax or wood an image intended to resemble the victim and then melt it or stick pins through the heart section. In this connection one is reminded of football rallies in which a straw figure representing the "enemy" team is burned.

Similarly, objects which were in contact with each other or part of each other (law of contagion) were, for primitive man, of the very essence of each other. So if one could collect the cut-off hair, the nail parings, or even the possessions of the enemy, one could by destroying them rid one's self of the person of whom they had been a part. The veneration of relics or the cherishing of objects which have belonged to a great or loved person is the reverse and attenuated revival of this form of thinking.

Such primitive[2] reasoning is one of the bases for thought. In its unrefined form primitive thinking is present to a large extent in early childhood and in the child-like attitudes carried into adulthood. Wearing clothes similar to those of someone famous tends to endow the wearer with reflected fame; a military uniform helps one to brave deeds; meeting a great man gives one a feeling of distinction, etc.

[1] *Cf.* Frazer, *The Golden Bough.*

[2] Primitive reasoning is not necessarily found in primitive society; for modifications of such reasoning began even before men learned the use of sign language. Self-control necessitated by community life gave impetus to "logicality" of relationships.

Superstition is an excellent example of this type of thinking and is illustrated by the person who attaches importance to or even directs his life by broken mirrors, black cats, the location of the stars, the shoulder over which he sights the new moon, the number of letters in a name, etc., etc., etc. Society's concession today to this irrational conduct is evidenced by the absence of a thirteenth floor in practically all hotels and in many office buildings tenanted by "hard-headed" business men.

In distorted psychoses such as schizophrenia, one *reverts*[1] to primitive thinking and reasoning and does not, as A. Storch[2] suggests, *reproduce* the actions of one's primitive forbears. Primitive thinking is surcharged with emotion and does not allow for weighing facts critically and objectively. Consequently, the person who bases his judgment on this kind of reason is unable wisely to choose appropriate responses.

The tenacity with which reaction *patterns tend to operate long after the original stimulus is gone and forgotten* is one element of difficulty in understanding or modifying these patterns.[3] Another is the human tendency to *symbolize*. We learn to read special values and significance into certain objects and situations, so that they in turn come to represent meanings not inherent in themselves.

Whether a book is regarded as a weapon to be hurled, fire-wood to be burned, or a priceless treasure to be cherished depends on how it is used; just as a red light may mean variously danger or security depending upon whether it is part of a traffic signal or an exit indicator. We learn that an innocent-looking wire may mean death, that a reversed collar proclaims a certain profession, that a cross on a building indicates that it is a church, that a narrow band ring signifies marriage, etc. Symbolization which is a short-cut to realization and appreciation is essential, in a complex civilization, to progress and life, but like any other process if carried too far or not far enough defeats its own purpose.

Two of the major modifications to which symbolization is subject and which if illogically used may lead to the formation of fallacious conclusions are (1) Condensation, and (2) Displacement.

Condensation.—In condensation, several symbols and their concomitant feeling tones become condensed into one symbol.

---

[1] *Cf.* regression. p. 77.
[2] Storch, August: Nervous and Mental Disease Monographs, 1925.
[3] *Vide* p. 173.

Thus the desire for liberty, and freedom of speech, the right to earn one's livelihood, and the guarantee of protection may become symbolized by the country's flag.   When this condensation is utilized with an understanding of the meaning of the symbols behind it, it serves a useful function; when, however, persons react to the symbol itself and are carried away, for example, by a hysterical plea to "save the flag," and in so doing violate the very principles it symbolizes, then the symbol as such has proved a detriment.[1]   The dangers in condensation are that the values symbolized are obscured, and the symbol itself becomes an end rather than a function.   Many patients will undergo the most dangerous of operations and spend all their savings in seeking relief from a symbolic physical complaint without awareness or desire to correct emotional conflicts behind such a symbol.

Displacement.—Displacement which occurs when emotions involved in one symbol are transferred to another which may be related only by similarity or content, also has an objectionable character.   Freud, for example speaks of one young man who complained of intense nausea whenever he saw or smelled violets. The author had a patient who became deeply depressed whenever he was left alone in a room with an audibly ticking clock.   Examination of the histories of these patients revealed, in the first case, that when his proposal of marriage was repulsed with rudeness and contempt by the girl with whom the patient was madly in love, she was wearing violets.   The second person had, as a child, been terrified by threats of hell-fire and the story of the clock of eternity ticking off doom and damnation.   The one had transferred his feeling of wounded pride, the other his fear of the unknown to the associated objects of violets and clocks, respectively, and continued to respond emotionally to them.   Displacement is a common phenomenon present in every-day life and is utilized by dictators and politicians.   Dictators seek scapegoats, or begin wars in an effort to *displace* the irritability and anger of their people from some internal frustration to some external source.   Rationalization[2] will tend to fix and harden such displacement so that it may become a continuous source of irritation in itself.   Individual persons without such wide and dictatorial possibilities of scapegoats can still find many persons, many ideas, and many other symbols to hate and on which to displace emotional disturbance over their own

[1] A. Korzybski has elaborated a whole system of "Semantics" on this principle.
[2] *Vide* p. 71.

inadequacy or frustrations.[1] Psychoneurotic patients displace their concern over personal conflicts to concern over some psychoneurotic complaint.

So much of emotional stability in adult life is determined by the kind and firmness of the early reaction patterns, that it is clear that the family situation in which they are established is of primary significance. Long before a child develops conflicts of his own he is sensitive to those in his environment. If friction exists between his parents, for example—whether it be of the knock-down and drag-out type or of the grim suffering-in-silence variety, the child feels the tension and is torn between the parents. If each makes a bid for his affection, a conflict between two opposing patterns arises; and the person finding it difficult to choose, vacillates.[2] The result is tension. There are several possible results. If he loves one to the exclusion of the other, he accepts the conflict and tension of the loved one, and toward the other develops attitudes of hatred, shame, resentment, etc. He may turn against both parents; he may shut his eyes to the quarrels and be imperturbed; he may displace his irritability onto someone else.

Mr. B., with marked feelings of unreality, inferiority, and a drive toward suicide, comes from a home which was the foundation of his neurosis. To quote:

"Mother and Father used to fight all the time. As nearly as I can recall, I felt I'd be much happier if they would be like other people. One night my father struck Mother, and the neighbors came in; for weeks thereafter when I went to school I felt that every kid was pointing me out. Father used to drink for many years, but he changed a few years ago when he took up religion. Now he's always nagging on that subject."

Such a home situation left Mr. B. with a feeling of unhappiness, with insecurity and uncertainty as to how to face life. His future conflicts were based in large part on this home pattern of reaction. The panic Mrs. I. developed late in life also had much of its genesis in the family background.

"My mother isn't as intelligent as my father, but she is the only woman I know who would put up with his meanness. I always take her troubles to heart. He has made me so miserable all my life. I was always afraid of him. If I could only take the 'I don't care attitude,' but I can't. Everyone is afraid of Father. He has done much good; he gives money to strangers, and he provides a good living for the family. But he is so mean and has such a violent temper. Now I don't even talk to him."

[1] *Vide* p. 52 (Case N. O.).
[2] *Vide* p. 76.

If a parent, disappointed in his own emotional satisfaction, turns to the child for emotional release, centers his life in that of the offspring, binds him with "the silver cord," it is almost inevitable that indecision and maladjustment will follow.

L. K., aged twenty-six years, was brought in by his mother. He complained of having a "band around his chest," of being very self-conscious, of fearing to go out with girls, of being "nervous," etc. Early in life he had developed a cough and the tentative diagnosis of tuberculosis was made. His mother became over-concerned. The patient was hardly allowed to move. He was not permitted to work; and his mother would drag large buckets of coal up several flights and not allow him, at the age of seventeen, strong and husky, to exert himself. She supervised what he ate and how much he ate. She watched his hours of arising, of sleeping, his manner of dressing, and what friends he had. In all this solicitude she was earnestly serious, and she indelibly stamped the boy with concern over his own physical state. He was shy and uncertain of himself. He did not know how to mingle with people, what to say to girls, even what to do without asking the opinion and advice of his mother. His neurosis was life-long in duration.

The child will be as secure within himself as the parents are, and there is little hope of curing his behavior problems unless those of the parents first be treated.

Not only is the emotional atmosphere created by the parents absorbed and appropriated, but of equal importance also is the position of the person with reference to siblings. Is he the spoiled baby of the family? Is he of the preferred sex? Does he have a brother or sister held up as an example?

Miss C., aged twenty-two years, was the second child of the family. She admired and envied her older sister, and when she did not receive the same degree of attention tried to obtain it by getting in the mother's way. When her mother scolded her and then promptly forgot about the patient, she preferred to have constant scoldings rather than no attention at all. She grew up with the feeling of not being wanted; and when she was constantly compared with her older sister in an unfavorable light, she demonstrated her resentment by increased irritability. She was exceedingly unhappy, emotional, and finally committed suicide by an over-dose of nembutal which she took from her father's drug store.

This girl had never experienced real security. The original pattern of behavior started off unfortunately, and instead of being properly handled by the parents, was aggravated by their constant criticism, increasing her feeling of loneliness and "unwantedness"; they actually lavished more love on the patient's sister in an effort to get the patient to change, thereby emphasizing more acutely to the patient how unwanted she was.

The economic and cultural status of the family is of great significance in determining reaction patterns, for it will determine in varying degrees not only the child's attitude toward money but the emotional stability of his parents, the kind of neighborhood in which he lives, the school he attends, the play groups of which he becomes a part, etc. Whether he is socially acceptable in his group will have much to do with his successful emotional emancipation from the family, the development of his sense of personal worth, and his growth as a social individual.

Mr. M. with a painfully intense feeling of inferiority and with inclinations toward suicide spoke of his home in the following words:

"I never felt I could stand on my own feet socially and economically. Was always very dependent on my home; that is why I never moved away in spite of my troubles. Economic conditions at home in my youth were bad. I sold papers, shined shoes, sold gum, and did everything to earn a few pennies. I felt suppressed, and at the age of thirteen remember walking down a boulevard and looking into the windows. I tried to imagine how those persons lived and my imagination gave me satisfaction. I was always made to believe I must work for the home. Mother insisted that I give all my salary to her, but now she is bitter and only semi-reconciled that I just give her an allowance to pay for my room and board. My entire youth was unhappy. If I could only have had a happy home life, it would all have been so different.

If one knows the type of family life that exists, one can often make a fairly accurate prediction of what type of children will result. Thus the parents of Miss F. M. are described as follows:

"I am glad that my folks are away. My mother hasn't the slightest bit of insight into anything. My father has no friends. Mother has no tact, and nags consistently. My father seems to have the better personality, but mother has successfully dominated him. She just lives for me and my sister, and it just kills me. She wants to know where I go, what I do, comments slurringly on my friends, and once when I brought a young man home, actually insulted him. He never would call after that. She nags my father half to death. She is a perfect example of the old European disciplinarian school. She is the opposite of my father: she is immaculate and neat, while father has become slovenly. He once had marvelous possibilities but was disabled in the Spanish-American War and lives on his small pension; I believe Mother is frustrated and disappointed."

The patient, F. M., (aged thirty-two years), complained of marked feelings of inferiority, of persistent phantasying, of a constant feeling of depression, of a morbid interest in masturbation.[1]

[1] *Vide* pp. 70; 105.

All these symptoms could be traced to the patient's insecurity, lack of love and affection, and her seeking some sort of pleasure in day-dreaming and in masturbation, the latter having begun at the age of seven.

The conflicts which may arise in the family situations have been discussed in such detail because so much of future stability depends upon the *kind* of reaction pattern established and the permanency with which these patterns are ingrained.

As the person's horizon enlarges to include other groups than the family, *e. g.*, school, "gangs," etc., there is new opportunity for the development of conflicts. If a child cannot "keep up" with his classmates intellectually, socially, or financially, he may develop a sense of inferiority. If his training at home has been such as inadequately to prepare him for shared activity, he may find social adjustment difficult. However, even in these situations the tie-up with the family situation is clear; and the kind and stability of reaction patterns already in force will have much to do with how the new situation will affect him.

There are many complicating factors in connection with one's choice of life work. Is he financially in a position to train for his chosen work, or is he pressed into gainful occupation at the earliest possible age? Social approval is so important a part of the modern conception of security that the "caste system" of the relative dignity of various jobs and positions may force a person into lines of activity which though financially rewarding, leave him unsatisfied. Family pressure may also be brought to bear either in terms of need or insistence that a certain type of work is expected. The person is fortunate but rare who knows what he wishes to do, is able to prepare adequately to do it, and finds creative pleasure in the doing.

Of all the inhibitions superimposed by society, none are more tension-producing than those set up by some religious teaching and by sexual taboo.[1] Not only are so many of the formalized teachings of religion contrary to "natural" instincts or desires but too often compliance is gained through the force of threats. A person follows his "natural" desires, and because they are contrary to what he has been taught is "right," develops a sense of guilt. If the ordinary mistakes of childhood are held up as "sins" and the wrath of God invoked to substantiate the parent's irritation,

---

[1] *Vide* p. 54 (Case D. N.).

4

the almost inevitable result is a distorted sense of values. Most of the sexual maladjustments[1] have their origin in this conflict between what the individual person desires and what society says he may have, between his urgent needs and what he is taught is right.

The organism expresses its psychologic entity through its reaction patterns; and to the degree that these patterns are security-yielding and satisfaction-giving will the individual have psychologic wholeness or integrity. Where there is sufficient conflict to produce tension, aberrant reaction patterns will be developed; and the degree of their departure from the norm will in each instance be determined by the amount of stress both as it actually exists and as it is "felt" by the patient.

[1] *Vide* pp. 104; 107.

CHAPTER III

PSYCHONEUROTIC (SYMBOLIC)[1] SYMPTOMS EXPRESSED PRIMARILY BY PSYCHOLOGIC FACTORS

MANY of the symptoms present in psychoneurotic patients are in the nature of "organic" complaints which are associated with such physiologic changes as tachycardia, hyperchlorhydria, spastic colitis, etc., which are, in turn, the result of emotional stress. A second group of symptoms inseparable from and found always in conjunction with the first may be termed "psychologic."[2] These latter symptoms, such as feelings of inferiority, fear, and certain hysterical reactions, as the former, result from emotional disturbance and have as their basis conflict and tension.

The symptoms resulting from these emotional disturbances and conflicts are expressed by various psychologic mechanisms. To treat the symptoms in themselves will usually be a futile undertaking, in so much as they are permanently removed only if their underlying cause is cared for.[3] Psychoneurotic symptoms are legion and only a few of the more common are discussed herein. However, the *symptom in itself is relatively unimportant*, for though it is annoying to the patient, it is usually only a superficial expression of very disturbing emotional states in the background. In many instances, anxiety and fear are often associated with psychoneurotic complaints. Fears in the neurotic patient usually have their origin in emotional turmoil over unsolved problems and conflicts. Although the ideas involved in the conflict are as a rule successfully repressed, the pent-up emotions, like constantly heated and compressed steam, may escape into consciousness. Even this "escape of steam" is not direct, for all that the patient is aware of is a general feeling of concern, anxiety, or fear. Such patients often complain of being afraid, though they readily admit that they "have nothing to be afraid of." Such a fear is termed "free floating anxiety."[4]

[1] *Vide* p. 28 *ff.*
[2] It must repeatedly be emphasized that the distinction between psychologic and physiologic is but a matter of convenience and not of fact.
[3] *Vide* p. 291.
[4] *Cf.* Intransitive fear.

Mr. B. U., aged forty-three years, complained of a violent feeling of terror. He would be working in his store, and suddenly, "I'd get scared. It comes like a shock; the pit of my stomach feels tight, like a lump; then I become panic-stricken and have to rush out for air. I feel as if I were going to die. I can't explain it. I don't know why it should come."

Mr. B. U. was actually depressed over financial matters. His expenses were greater than his income and were going to increase, with the birth of an expected child. The future was very uncertain. He toyed with the idea of giving up his business, but could see no way of getting employment during a period when there were so many unemployed. He loved his family deeply; and the thought of what they faced—the poverty, the degradation, the attendant suffering—was more than he could bear. He tried to forget these matters, but when his mind was apparently blank he would be seized by this over-whelming fear.

This man complained of fear—just fear; intransitive fear without an object. The basis for it was his financial insecurity, the emotional tone of which was so great that it manifested itself, even when the mind seemingly was "blank."

The mind is so constituted that it is dissatisfied with that which it cannot understand, and consequently there is a tendency to "invent" reasons if the true ones are not apparent. As a result, the patient may "select" an object of fear, and focus on this "selected" idea all the emotion (displacement)[1] that has its true origin in the conflict or turmoil. There may be fear of impotence, of disease, of heart trouble, of dirt, or of any other of a myriad of ideas or objects. Often that which is feared is "selected" because it has some close relationship to the conflict, though the person may be unaware of the relationship.

Dr. N. O., aged twenty-seven years, an interne in a large hospital, had an intense fear of having rabies. Three months earlier he had been in the laboratory and had been scratched by a dog. He washed the scratch well (it was very superficial), painted it with iodine, and cauterized it with phenol. He became obsessed with the fear that he had hydrophobia. The dog seemed normal, but the patient insisted on getting a course of rabies vaccine. The dog was kept alive and showed no signs of rabies long after the incubation period was over, but the patient still feared he had rabies. He studied his throat, felt that he disliked water, developed headaches, and became so apprehensive and fearful that he could not do his work. He was sure he was going mad; and all reassurances and consultations failed to relieve him of his fear.

Dr. N. O. was a very conscientious interne. He had worked his way through medical school and had been able to earn good grades. He had left his family in anger. They had wanted him to quit high school and go to

[1] *Vide* p. 45.

work to help the family. They had refused to have anything to do with him while he was in school. He had finally reached his goal, and was going to go out into the medical world; but he had no one to turn to for help. He had no funds with which to rent an office or buy food. Moreover, he had fallen in love and was eager to marry. The young lady, who was his same age, had another suitor whom she liked less but who could provide a sufficient livelihood.

His turmoil was great, and he could not sleep for thinking of his problem. When the dog scratched him, all his anxiety was concentrated on the scratch as a symbol of the idea that his troubles were "driving him mad."

The occurrence of the scratch was seized upon to express his conflicts. He could not be convinced that there was no hydrophobia developing, because the constant flow of emotion from his own personal difficulties overcame his objectivity and offered a mode of escape (albeit a very inferior and inadequate one) from his seemingly unsolvable affairs.

The fears often have a definite relation to the conflict.[1] In unfounded fears of syphilis, the subject may be troubled by sex desires which he inhibits but which, nevertheless, are very demanding and which he is convinced need much inhibition. Fears of and actual impotence occur on a similar basis. In some instances the basis is a feeling of guilt over masturbation.[2] Many youths are seen who state that they are afraid to get married, because they "abused" themselves so much during childhood. When they think of sex and marriage, the fear inculcated in them becomes so great that it usurps the sex emotion, and as a result erections do not occur. If the guilt feeling is strong enough, even much sex play may not bring about an arousal.

Fears[3] of disease, of death, of going crazy are expressions of an emotional turmoil so strong, that the person, being unable to come to a clear, definite, and objective conclusion, feels that he "will go mad" or even "die from his worry." Or the situation may appear so complex that the patient wonders whether suicide is not the only real escape. When this question comes to mind, the fear develops that he may actually commit suicide, and this fear is the only idea permitted to consciousness, all the preceding emotions and thoughts involved being repressed.

[1] *Vide* p. 289.   [2] *Vide* p. 104 *ff.*

[3] The formal names given these various fears is made up of the Greek name of the object plus a suffix of phobia. Such names are in themselves meaningless and are not used herein. Some of the more common phobias are agoraphobia, or fear of open spaces or of being away from home; claustrophobia or fear of small or closed spaces, of crowded street-cars, etc.; mysophobia or fear of dirt, contamination, or sickness; anthrophobia or fear of men; erythrophobia or fear of blushing (redness); zoöphobia or fear of animals; pyrophobia or fear of fire; syphilophobia or fear of syphilis; and there is even a term called phobophobia or fear of having fears.

Along similar lines is the fear of being in a small place (claustro-phobia), for then one's fears seem to have no "room to escape," and the emotions are intensified. Some patients fear to be alone, because they fear they may attempt self-destruction, this fear in turn being the result of an unsolved conflict.

Some patients feel depressed on Saturdays, Sundays, and holi-days. This strange situation is the result of (1) more time to think of one's self, and insufficient occupation with activities which normally force one's mind off one's self, and (2) the contrast be-tween one's own feeling and the pleasures and relative freedom that he feels should be possible, and that others enjoy on these days. In manic-depressive depressions, giving patients cheerful and gay music or entertainment often deepens the depressive state because of the contrast, and the awareness of their own problem which prevents enjoyment.[1]

On the other hand, the fear of being in crowds may be associated with the idea that others will come to know of the desires one is trying so hard to repress. Fear of small spaces or closed rooms is often symbolic to the patient of being trapped by his emotions and of his inability to escape. Miss F. M., subject to this fear, com-plained: "People trap me. I'm afraid I'll give myself away."

D. N., aged twenty-eight years, single, came in, saying that she was afraid of men, afraid to be alone, afraid to be in any small room, afraid of thunder, afraid she was going crazy, afraid she had many diseases, etc. The more her case was discussed the more it became evident that she had fears in almost every field of human activity. She was working as a private secretary, but because of her intense anxieties, could hardly manage to keep her position. She wanted to "run away from herself." Her family life was distinctly unpleasant. When she was two years old, her father deserted her mother. The patient could not remember a time when she was not afraid of her overly-strict mother. At an early age she was whipped so severely that the whipping stick broke. At seven, she was sent to a convent where her fear-fulness caused a marked shyness which was interpreted as wilfulness; and harsh, disciplinary measures were applied. At eleven she was taken out of the convent, because the mother re-married. She felt unloved and unwanted. The tenets of the church were not taught her so much as they were "pounded" into her; and her fearful attitude made her think only of the negative aspects of religion, of sin, and hell, and guilt. A young man with whom she was going, and who had "serious intentions," would kiss her and "hold her close"; and the sexual thoughts aroused were to her unpardon-able, sinful, and so intense that she stopped seeing the young man in an effort to get rid of these thoughts. However, the thoughts instead of ceasing,

---

[1] *Vide* p. 362.

"irradiated," so that in the presence of any man she developed vague fears which sometimes produced a panic-like condition. The fears multiplied, and her "entire life was one mass of anguish." Her attitude toward life was that of fearfulness, developing inevitably out of her past, and coloring all phases from the most intimate sexual desires to the most impersonal letters she transcribed in her work.

The reaction patterns which grow out of conflicts represent the person's attempt to deal with the situation. If training has been improper or inadequate the patterns may be both immature and unhealthful, resulting eventually in inefficiency and unhappiness. The reaction patterns may, moreover, seem inconsistent and incongruous, if one fails to remember that each stimulus carries with it innumerable connotations and associations.[1] *The behavior which the doctor would call a symptom of disturbance is for the patient a concrete way of meeting a specific circumstance.* To the outsider the behavior appears inefficient and unrealistic; to the performer, meaningful and essential.

Mr. E. G., aged twenty-three years, was observed standing about the ward at 3 A.M. moving in the most peculiar manner. He would bow, and then step high and twist and turn. He would move his arms in a peculiar manner, and make sudden and quick motions, after standing still for awhile manipulating his fingers.

These actions were labeled just peculiar mannerisms. They seemed irrelevant, absurd, and without reason. Yet they were a reaction pattern which later the patient explained. "You see, there was this woman down the street who was trying to tie me up. All night long she wove these radio wires, and I could feel them tightening up on my legs and body. I got up and tried to untangle myself, and the more I tried, the quicker she spun. She got tired of it finally, but I still got the electric shocks."

His reactions in themselves were peculiar, yet to him they represented one means of escape from his imaginary torment.

Mr. S. U. was standing on the walk leading up to his ward. He was smiling, while making peculiar motions. With his left foot he was tapping on the ground while with his hands he would thrust suddenly ahead, hold still, and then thrust again. His actions were described as mannerisms and stereotypies. Yet they were also a reaction to certain ideas.

"Well down deep below where my foot is, is a cell. They're going to lock up those guys who are after me. Only the cell ain't ready yet, and I'm poundin' in the steel rods, and rivetin' them tight."

Mrs. B. T. was making circles in the air. She made this motion day in and day out. From the earliest moment of arising, she made these circles with her hand. It developed that the patient felt that she had committed an

---

[1] *Vide* p. 380.

unpardonable sin, and in praying for forgiveness, began to make the cross in the air. As she increased her speed in making this sign, it appeared to be a circle.

To the person involved it matters little whether the ideas are based on fact or on imagination; his reaction patterns seem to him the best and most adequate way of solving his problem, however fantastic they may appear to others.

There is always danger in attempting rigid classifications when one is dealing with aspects of personality; in so much as they of necessity remain highly individual, and each person's "case" has its own nuances and over-tones. The following discussion of some of the more common reaction patterns, therefore, is intended to be not so much exhaustive as suggestive and indicative. In general it may be said that most of *these mechanisms are "defensive" in nature,* and are designed to turn aside or render ineffective the dangers which the patient feels are threatening his security. The dangers are more subtle and more numerous than those which confronted primitive man, for they include all the elements of the environment which may threaten the ego.[1] The mechanisms employed to defend against criticism, for example, are in purpose identical with those used to ward off physical assault.

There are numerous symptoms which are expressed by other psychologic mechanisms. One of the commonest symptoms, for example, is the *"inability to concentrate."*[2] Most of the persons suffering from psychoneurotic disorders find it difficult to read any length of time or to pay attention to one subject very long. Their attention wanders. In addition, the memory seems impaired, and they "can't think as well" as they had previously. The reason for these symptoms is that the patients are overly self-conscious and pay excessive attention to these factors which they cannot solve and try to repress. Their worries and problems take up most of their attention; and as a result, external problems and subjects interest the person less than do his own; and the attention, even though started on a topic, wanders back. In other words, it may be said that the patient is able to concentrate too well, but on his own emotional self, rather than on that which he "chooses" to concentrate on.

Indecision[3] as expressed in the complaint, "I can't seem to make up my own mind," has its basis, as a rule, in the existing con-

---

[1] *Vide* p. 39 *ff.*   [2] *Vide* p. 279.   [3] *Vide* pp. 42; 370.

flicts. When there are strong and urgent problems which one does not know how to solve, or when there is conflict over some compelling desire which was inhibited by some intensive, restrictive force as of religion, there is much emotion associated with his inability to come to a conclusion.

The making of decisions is usually characterized by a certain amount of tension, the amount being in proportion to the values involved and the evenness of their distribution. For example, a man living in a community which he considers ideal so far as health and social contacts for his children are concerned but making only a meagre livelihood is offered a more highly lucrative position in a different locality. Since there are values to be gained and values to be lost whatever conclusion he reaches, there will "normally" be tension until a decision is reached.

Indecisiveness becomes pathologic when it irradiates to all of the processes of life. In depressive states indecision is common. Under ordinary circumstances, the depressed patient cannot make up his mind whether to buy something or not, to visit a friend or not, to go on a vacation or not; but the indecision may become so acute that some patients do not know whether to put on the right or the left shoe first, whether to lift the right or left foot first in stepping on a street-car, etc.

"I feel in a daze," is another common complaint. The patients are in such a state of conflict and indecision that they cannot think clearly, and appear to be "in a daze." Similarly those who complain that "everything seems unreal to me," are in a "daze" with an emotional clouding of consciousness. Reality appears almost meaningless when the entire mental life is occupied with all-pervading conflicts, and when the phantasy formation is in the ascendency.

The sensation of being tense, the fact that persons may "Try so hard to relax but can't,"[1] is also the result of the emotional tone associated with problems or conflicts. The continual awareness (even if the awareness is "unconscious") of possible dangers produces in the organism a state of preparedness to meet danger; such preparedness consists of alertness, tension, and energy mobilization.[2]

The very fact of trying hard makes relaxation difficult. Relaxation implies the absence of effort. In relaxing, one "lets go," and

[1] *Vide* p. 245.   [2] *Vide* Ch. XII.

permits ease and comfort to come; it is impossible to *force* it to come. The phrase, "You *must* relax,"[1] is a contradiction in terms. Moreover, physical relaxation is primarily a product of "mental" relaxation. Physical tenseness is the result not of local irritability but of general irritability. Such a general pattern of response as muscular tension has its origin in emotional tension; and these attitudes of tension should be "relaxed" in order that physical relaxation may occur. The good results reported from physical relaxation are primarily the result of the fact that the persons' *attitude* of tension was released. Being at ease implies peace and quiet and the absence of concern. Therein lies the real benefit.

As a matter of fact, one may be relaxed mentally, yet have temporary or localized muscular tension.[2] Some handball or tennis players are capable of almost drooping relaxation of their limbs during a game, until a moment before the ball is to be returned. On the other hand, business men, lawyers, etc., are often very tense physically without having done the slightest type of physical work; and it is very difficult to make them less tense, unless they can be persuaded to be less intense about their problems. Not only neurotic patients but also many "normal" persons show evidences of undue tension.

Oversensitivity.—It is against a background of oversensitivity[3] that most defense mechanisms are developed. Oversensitivity which is commonly characteristic of unstable persons may manifest itself in a variety of ways, but is always grounded in a sense of insecurity. This feeling of insecurity may be produced by chronic irritation or by a sudden and intense irritation later in life. In the vast majority of cases, it has its origin in a lack of security during the formative years.

Oversensitivity is characterized by: (1) an over-emphasis on *the person's inability* to meet difficult situations (hence the development of egocentricity and concern about one's self, and of the inferiority complex); and (2) an over-emphasis on *the difficulty that exists*.[4] Many persons will feel inferior in situations which to another would represent security; the difference lying not only on the level on which security has been placed, but also in the sensitivity to supposed danger. The multimillionaire who has placed his level of security very high feels insecure if his income, having been taxed heavily, is consequently reduced to a mere million or

---

[1] *Cf.* E. Jacobson, You Must Relax.   [2] *Vide* p. 251.
[3] *Vide* p. 209 (Case G. J.)   [4] *Vide* p. 153

two. On the other hand, the man-out-of-work, whose level of security was very low, feels secure enough to be married when he has obtained a job on W.P.A. The emotional disturbance in both these persons is affected by changes in the environment, but this in turn depends upon their pre-conceived ideas and attitudes toward the environment. To understand the oversensitivity of any person it is therefore necessary to understand not only his environment at the time, but his early environment and his attitudes.

Sensitivity is expressed in many ways. "I am always self-conscious"; "I seem to have nothing to say to people"; "I'm ill at ease in the presence of others"; "I won't speak for fear of saying the wrong thing": all such statements are indicative of such extreme affectivity and over-concern about one's self as to interfere with the efficiency of one's actions. These characteristics have their origin in a sense of insecurity which manifests itself in many directions. One of the commonest complaints is, "I can't stop thinking of myself," or "I'm not interested in anything except myself," expressing the person's inability to shift his attention to other persons or ideas. Other mechanisms such as criticism of others,[1] over-emphasis on the importance of one's own ideas, an ex cathedra fashion of stating one's opinions, etc., likewise are indicative of a basic insecurity.[2]

Mrs. I. Q.,[2] aged forty-eight years, was referred by her brother who said he was driven to desperation by the patient's constant criticism and general "nastiness." His sister always had a sharp tongue, and she was irritable, depressed, and very emotional. She had been this way for many years. The patient was a fairly intelligent woman who not only admitted her brother's accusations, but complained of being aware of and yet unable to prevent her actions. She was conscious of the irritability of others and the displeasure of those whom she visited; and though wanting to be liked, she could not forbear from making cutting remarks and insisting upon her own opinions. She had one younger brother. Her father was a wealthy and prominent man who could afford all luxuries, while her mother was "stingy" to the point of returning for cash the gifts given her by her husband. The patient loved but envied her brother who though younger quickly drew ahead of her in school. Both by implication and directly she had been told that she was "dumb and ugly." She wanted to be admired and respected, and having set her goal as brilliance and beauty, was attempting to achieve an impossibility. Her feelings of inferiority were accentuated by her mother's constant urgings and criticism. The mother also was "embarrassed" at the backwardness and awkwardness of her offspring. She was constantly correcting

[1] *Vide* p. 268 (Case I. L.)   [2] *Vide* pp. 73; 310.

the patient. The patient, whose ego was being constantly attacked, sought to salve her pride by finding fault with others. Eleanor received good grades because she was teacher's pet; Florence had boy friends because obviously she was a hussy, etc. So uneasy and unhappy was the patient that the feeling of inferiority manifested itself constantly. She not only became irritable and hypercritical, but began to boast what she could do and how good she was, in an effort to defend herself against the constant criticisms which in early adult life had begun to emanate mainly from her own conscience. An added blow which she has never forgotten was the marriage, arranged by her family, who despairing of her ever finding a husband, enticed a young salesman in the father's store to marriage. The marriage resulted in two children, was unhappy, and was a constant reminder to the patient that she had married beneath what she considered her station. She began to grieve over her lot and spoke constantly of her disappointments. As a result of this reaction pattern, she became emotional, developed trembling of the hands, poor sleep, and temper outbursts. Ironically enough, her elder daughter was a mirror image of the patient in looks as well as in thought; and to the observer it was evident the daughter was subject to the same merciless criticism by the patient.

This woman became very critical, egocentric, and subjective, as reactions of defense against intense criticism brought to bear upon her first by her mother and then by herself. At the same time she identified[1] herself with her mother and assumed a similar reaction pattern of criticism towards all persons as did her mother. Identification and internalization is a normal process—but when used excessively produces a neurosis. Efforts by the patient to control these symptoms were doomed to failure until the basic reaction patterns of inferiority and resentment and the identification plus the ambivalent rejection of the mother were resolved.

It is an extremely common finding that persons who are very critical of others, suffer from the very faults they are bitter about,[2] and that children who are a trial to their parents very often express those irritating qualities which are found in the parents.

By being *self-conscious*, the person may be expressing his awareness of and inability to escape from his internal conflicts. In other words, his consciousness over his appearance, his words, his actions is but an indirect expression of his basic feeling of inadequacy and inferiority, often existent since childhood. Normally, feelings of inadequacy are present in children and adolescents, but excessive self-awareness should disappear with the increase of social contacts and social situations. Every "normal" person has a certain amount of self-consciousness, and desirably so; but in oversensitive

---

[1] *Vide* p. 73.   [2] *Vide* p. 203 (Case T. C.).

persons this attitude is all-pervading. Most commonly it is the result of an instability and unsureness established in the child by his environment. Constant blame, nagging correction, feeling unwanted or unloved, demands beyond capacity, the suppression of normal tendencies: all tend to establish the pattern of uncertainty. Once the *pattern of insecurity* is established, it will tend to color all future reactions, regardless of how successful the person may be. The mind of the child is plastic, and impressions made upon it form grooves and ruts, which harden and last throughout life-time. Once a pattern of insecurity has been set, thereafter every attempt, even in the most simple situations, is accompanied by the "premonition" of failure so that the completed undertaking is always regarded as unsatisfactory in one way or another: in memory of childhood tasks which were continually criticized for flaws. Inferiority feelings when based on such early training tend to be general and all-pervading.

Such feelings as inferiority and oversensitivity are the basis for statements like—"It is hard for me to make friends." Persons who make such comments are too timid to make the necessary social gestures, and at the same time are so self-concerned that everything that is said is taken to have personal reference. They are "ill at ease in the presence of others" for the same reason. They "analyze" themselves constantly in a vague and generally poorly directed attempt to find the reason for their social failure. In extreme instances, this self-analysis and awareness may reach the point where the patient is 'conscious of every movement he makes;' e. g., "If I lift my hand to my face, I feel aware of it, for no reason at all." The oversensitivity may develop to the point where the patient "will leave the room whenever friends or company come."

Such attitudes of inferiority and sensitivity are generally ingrained from childhood, but they may develop later in life. Failures in accomplishment will bring on these attitudes, only in proportion to the degree to which the person evaluates and emotionally identifies himself with the failure. When there is much blame heaped on a person for a failure, whether it be outside blame or self-blame, then feelings of inferiority develop.

Self-blame,[1] another expression of over-consciousness of self, may be the result of inability to achieve desired goals and ideals; or, more seriously, the result of failure to solve conflicts. Here again

[1] *Vide* p. 202 *ff.*

the factor of irradiation (spread of emotional turmoil from one to other related or unrelated objects or facts) operates so that these patients blame themselves for failing in trivial, inconsequential tasks, or insist that they are responsible for various ill-fortunes. The basis is a feeling of self-blame over some internal conflict. There is intolerance of having faults, and of failure to achieve goals and ideals. Too often these persons have not crystallized their vague, indefinite desires, and strive aimlessly without any understanding either of their limitations, or the manner of possible further development.[1] Such persons may expect of themselves an "iron will," machine-like perfection, and irresistible and immovable determination.[2] They are usually doomed to failure, and so are left with self-intolerance and self-blame.

Mr. U. K., aged thirty-four years, complained that though he had many college credits, he didn't get the kind of position he wanted. He worked at places only a short period of time and left to seek something better. He wanted to be recognized as being "someone," and to be "looked up to." For over ten years he had been attending one of the night colleges. He started first in English, intending to be a teacher, but after a year and a half lost his interest and decided architecture would be better. However, the second semester of drafting was too difficult, and he changed over to law. This interested him and he did well until he spoke to some practicing lawyers who painted a black picture, whereupon he quit the law course in the middle of the semester and was studying civil engineering at the time of examination. His work record was about the same. He would start to work with a "feeling" that there was a future, and after varying periods of time would become discouraged. He blamed himself for being "dumb" and unintelligent, said his personality was at fault, that his face had too many pimples, etc., etc., all as excuses for his not "being looked up to."

Other factors may bring about similar tendencies. Boredom, for example, is evidenced by persons who are chronically dissatisfied:

Mrs. I. was a pouting type of woman who insisted on having her own way. Although her husband could not well afford it, she had a maid to do all the housework, and she did nothing. A hysterectomy for a fibroid tumor prevented the distracting influence of children. She waited all day long for her husband to come home, and when he did, fatigued and preoccupied with affairs of business, she was eager to go out for a good time. She wanted conversation, brilliant wit, engaging and entertaining activity; and not receiving it, felt frustrated and began the self-sympathy that led to constant concern over her physical and mental state, to feelings of being unloved and unwanted, and to constant self-blame.

Oversensitive persons, on being criticized, may become despondent, or they may become unduly irritable. Often they interpret

---

[1] *Vide* p. 205 *ff.*   [2] *Vide* pp. 212; 272.

the slightest gesture as being adverse criticism; and not uncommonly consider a lack of praise as being a direct insult. The more inadequate and inferior one is, the more potent and devastating will criticism be; for it confirms, as it were, and emphasizes one's own feeling of inadequacy and one's sensitivity to it.

The more common mediating mechanisms are of a defense pattern, developed to protect one from real or imagined dangers. The greater the oversensitivity, the more the defense reactions need to be called into play. *These defense mechanisms are substitutes* for a direct attack on the problem or conflict and because of their indirection lead to subsequent problems. Moreover, persons can become so sensitive that experiences long past may still continue to act as an irritant, and thus call forth defense symptoms.

Other mediating mechanisms include: *repression; defense by criticism; withdrawal; negativism; projection; phantasy-formation; attention-getting; identification; sublimation; conversion; irradiation; fixation; regression; ambivalence; dissociation;* and *compensation.*

It is often difficult in actual cases to isolate the mechanisms in pure form and the categories themselves are so over-lapping that any one symptom may be described under several categories. Moreover there rarely is a person who exhibits a single mechanism to the exclusion of all others. Many so called normal persons will use these mechanisms at one time or another. The case histories that follow are taken directly from my records; and the mechanism illustrated is shown as it "usually" occurs among patients.

Repression.—Repression is one of the most common methods of dealing with over-irritating memories. Repression is a dynamic forgetting,[1] *i. e.*, the irritating material continues to be regarded as irritating, but is put out of consciousness. Repression does not permit true forgetting.

Mr. H. I. had his leg amputated at the age of fourteen, because of a sarcoma. At the age of twenty-two, he was irritable, had acute feelings of inferiority, was very self-conscious, and "hated" girls. His artificial limb was almost perfect, and he walked with only a slight limp.

His over-sensitivity to himself and others was based on the feeling that he was a cripple, the term cripple implying for him some hideous deformity which no self-respecting person, particularly the opposite sex, could tolerate without a shudder. He could not "face" the fact of his amputation and allowed it constantly to irritate him. He refused to think of (repressed) his amputation, while at the same time reacting violently to any association connected with his difficulty. His feeling of self-consciousness, and

[1] *Vide* p. 65.

inferiority followed; his bitterness caused him to resent the imagined pity of girls; and although he gave many rationalizations, he could not explain convincingly his antagonism.

Whenever facts or possibilities are too irritating, the person tries to protect himself by removing them from his consciousness; unfortunately, these irritations may be removed just from immediate consciousness, but they are not really forgotten and so continue to act. Repressed emotions can be removed only when one's *attitude* changes toward the irritating material.

It must be remembered that that which is repressed is said to be in one's "unconscious mind" and is not forgotten. The person may not consciously think of it, but the memory forms a background which emotionally colors all his reactions. It may assert itself when the person is apparently "thinking of nothing." This phenomenon is important. Many patients will state, "My mind was blank when I got this feeling," for they do not realize that their repressed memories are just outside the door of consciousness (*i. e.*, technically unconscious) and make themselves felt "even when the mind seems blank."

Mrs. X. F., aged thirty-five years, married, with a child of three, complained of having had blushing spells for six months. The blushing was associated with a great deal of embarrassment and made her feel "almost hysterical." Examinations revealed no organic difficulty, and all sorts of "salty and other kinds of medicine" could not change the symptom. The patient was feeling desperate. It had even been suggested that the sympathetic nerves to the face be cut; and she was seriously considering the operation.

When an effort was made to find out the underlying psychopathology, the patient denied any difficulties. She was married to a nice, pleasant husband who made a comfortable living. She had a beautiful child and a comfortable home. There was nothing she could think of that bothered her.

Nevertheless, such denials served to emphasize the intensity of the repression. After she had been questioned further, the following story came to light. The patient was married at the age of twenty-six. She was a quiet, shy person who had been brought up in a religious atmosphere. She was more content to be with books than to be with people. Her husband was the opposite type of personality. He was sociable, had a large circle of acquaintances, liked to go out on parties, and associated with a group of persons whom his wife termed "roughnecks." Six months prior to her first consultation, she discovered that he was unfaithful to her; and what made the matter worse was that the indiscretion had occurred with her own sister. For days she seemed in a daze and could not reconcile herself. She condemned herself for not having gone out with him sufficiently and at the same time began to be excessively irritated at everything he did.

One month later, while she was at one of "his parties," and while playing bridge, her partner let out an oath on a false card play. She began to blush, and felt so self-conscious that she had to leave the table. Thereafter, whenever she thought of the incident she blushed; and finally it came to the stage where the blushing was continued even when "her mind was a blank."

Psychotherapeutic procedures (*que vide*) were instituted, and the patient was asked to return the following week at which time she stated her condition was unchanged. The next week, in the clinic, and before a group of students, she was asked about her symptom. She replied that she had been free of it since the first visit. When asked why she had made the statement the week previously that the blushing was unchanged, she replied, "Oh, I wanted to be sure that it was really gone."

The unfortunate incident which started this difficulty remained as an irritant in the patient's unconscious mind. She refused to think of it consciously or to face the fact that it had occurred, and that wherever the blame might be, she had to accept the fact and attempt to do something about it if she desired to continue her married life. She repressed the memory of the incident, which is to say she allowed it to rankle her continuously, although she avoided consciously facing it. The irritating repressed memory was, however, constantly in the background and made her feel irritable. She had already repressed the knowledge of her husband's infidelity when she heard the oath at the bridge table. The oath was all that was needed to start the blushing. The blushing continued, not because of the oath, but because of the background described. Insincerity was so much a part of her personality that she even refused to admit absence of her blushing on her return visit. The patient was relieved of her symptom of blushing because she came to understand the significance of the symptom and changed her attitude toward the irritating factor. Her preneurotic personality remained unaltered, however, and therefore subject to further neurotic complaints under appropriate stress.

Dynamic Forgetting.—Dynamic forgetting is in reality a subdivision of "repression." One has a tendency to "forget" when one owes money, or intends to do some distasteful task. Names of persons whom we dislike, objects that irritate may slip from memory. These items are not really forgotten, for by dint of suggestion or special technique they come to the fore. It is common to note that a "forgotten" item comes to mind long after its need has disappeared.

Mr. K. N. was disgusted with his wife. He was young when he married her, as the result of active pursuit on her part. He was flattered and praised and made much of it; and the marriage occurred without his having any real

5

affection for the girl. He continued to live with her and had three children; but not only was he not fond of her, but there was active dislike.

For the anniversary of his marriage, his wife gave him a sport shirt. He disliked it, primarily because she had given it to him. He asked his wife whether she minded his exchanging it for another shirt. He carried the shirt with him and "forgot it" on the street-car. He suggested that the real reason he forgot the shirt was that he didn't want it; and he did not call the lost and found department of the street-car company, because "I'm afraid they might have found it."

Attacking or Criticizing Others.[1] — This defense pattern grows out of a desire to ward off attacks before they can be made; *i. e.*, to hurt before one can be hurt, or out of the necessity of an outlet for one's own irritations. Not only is "attack" the immediate response, but the holding of a grudge is its corollary and its continued response. Such persons hate "anyone who criticizes me," and find fault with everyone.

This inability to forgive and to forget coupled with the desire for revenge is a basically immature and childish reaction. Grudge-carrying has the effect of constantly producing emotions of fear and rage which in turn have their physiologic concomitants in increased secretion of adrenalin, rise in blood pressure, tachycardia, etc. Hate is after all just chilled fear, for one hates that which might harm one; and the chronic fear (and its reaction hate) may be directed at its cause, or through displacement, at an unrelated object. Hate is an emotion which inevitably acts as a boomerang on its owner.

F. I., a man aged twenty-nine years, was still living in his childhood. "My whole early life was one of abuse. I was made to do all the dirty work around the house, was constantly scolded, had to clean the horse, polish the buggy, sell papers, wash dishes." He was never allowed to play with other children and was constantly criticized. "I was always told I was 'dumb' and never could learn anything." At least once a day physical punishment was administered. Now in adult life, he still carried the resentment not only against those who were unkind to him in youth but to anyone who, even in the friendliest fashion, advised him.

He was "getting even" with the way the world had treated him by treating others in the same way. By finding fault with others, he unconsciously criticized others before they could criticize him. In addition, his actions were imitations of others and were part of the reaction pattern he was trained in.

[1] *Vide* p. 59 (Case I. Q.).

Often nagging, hyper-criticism, fault-finding are used as a safety-valve for pent-up emotions or chronic irritability, and are evidenced in persons with insight by such statements as: "I stay mad at anyone who irritates me in the slightest way"; "I'm always picking on my husband"; "I'm very mean and not really livable with my husband."

There was the employer in an emotional storm over his own conflicts who scolded and then discharged a young man who he admitted was brilliant, but who shuffled his feet and "must, therefore, be worthless." This employer needed an outlet for his own unrelieved tension; so focused on some object or action which made him angry. There was, in addition, the sadistic satisfaction derived from being able to inflict pain, just as pain was he believed inflicted on him.

Mrs. N. D. was intelligent enough to know that her statements were contradictory when she said, "My husband's so good to me. He gives me everything I need and want; he is attractive and social. Yet I'm constantly irritated by him and am always picking on him." Inquiry into her background revealed three causes of her irritability. She had loved another man who had rejected her. Her marriage was to "show him that he was not the only fish in the sea." In addition, her parents disapproved of her husband who they said was her social inferior. Finally, sex relations (conditioned by the above factors) left her completely dissatisfied. Thus though she "consciously"[1] accepted her husband, her frustration was sufficient to cause the irritability manifested toward her husband.

Mrs. F. X., aged twenty-four years, came for relief from physiologic disturbances, and in her talk revealed clearly not only their basis but the cause of her excessive irritability: "I have a choking sensation in my throat, and pains in the chest. No doctor or x-ray has been able to find the cause. When I get sick, my breathing goes "haywire." The choking sensation in my throat comes on. Then I feel nauseated—it seems like there is something at the end of my tongue. I get short-winded and can't converse. My voice seems to grow weaker. I get chills up and down my spine and head. I can't relax, can't sleep, get diarrhea one day and constipation the next. I have pains in my stomach, and went to twelve doctors in the last two months, but no one can find the trouble. I can't take a deep breath, and feel so miserable as if I were going off my nut because of constant thinking." Inquiry revealed that her "constant thinking" was about her mother-in-law's "meanness." The following words indicate the depth and bitterness of the resentment she felt.

"How mean my mother-in-law used to be to me. Why she was so mean

---

[1] "Subconscious" and "unconscious" are used throughout this text not to indicate separate parts of the mental process, but merely as the periphery of consciousness. Consciousness, among other things, is the state of being aware of, and that which one could recall but does not, is said to be in the subconscious. (Psychoanalysts [Ch. XVII] use these terms differently.)

we had to get married in court without telling her. She said she'd kill herself if her son married. After we did get married there was more trouble with her because we weren't married in church. She's a nag and insanely jealous. She'd tell me about actions before his marriage, how he couldn't live with one girl, and didn't really care for me. She puts crazy ideas into my head. 'Are you worrying where he is now?' she'd keep saying, until now when I wait for my husband to come home and he is not exactly on time I get panic-stricken and think maybe he is out with another woman; then I can't eat. She was jealous when we didn't live with her and unhappy because I won't call her 'Mother.' She tries to get all she can out of him, and every time we leave her home we quarrel. I know I'm mean and not livable with my husband but it's her fault. She's caused every aggravation I've ever had. She tries to be nice to me now, because she knows she's the cause of my illness; but I hate her, and it won't help now."

The effect of her intense emotion on her physical organism is obvious; and it can easily be seen why this girl developed chronic irritability which she vented on her husband, who, incidentally, while realizing the situation still was closely attached to his mother, and thus intensified his wife's irritability.

Withdrawal.—Withdrawal[1] as a protection against possible hurt is a common pattern of reaction. If a situation becomes too irritating a person will remove himself from it. Such withdrawal would not be unwise, though it is usually better to face and fight out such irritations, were it not for the fact that so often it is not so much the situation itself, but rather the patient's attitude which causes his irritation. This attitude may or may not have been conditioned by some unfortunate experience; and if it has, the subject fears repetition. There are many young women, for example, who will not permit themselves to become fond of anyone, because they were deeply wounded on losing someone whom they loved dearly. There are other persons who refuse to talk about or even to think of controversial topics so as to avoid feeling "upset." Still others sequester themselves from society, because of the turmoil, strife, and obligations inherent therein.

Withdrawal may be physical, the result of simply staying away; or it may be psychologic, the result of "refusing to pay any attention to." In the latter situation it may lead to refusal to face the facts of a situation; to introversion; and the seeking of satisfaction in phantasy and in auto-erotic behavior; e. g., masturbation.[2]

One patient, married, aged twenty-eight years, stated: "I want to run away from myself." She had set up her father as an ideal, and had married

[1] *Vide* p. 378.   [2] *Vide* p. 104 *ff.*

a man who fell far below this ideal. In addition, she was in love with a man who was married to someone else, and sex relations with her husband were unsatisfactory. She was constantly torn by these conflicting emotions and "could not get away from herself to forget."

Withdrawal from one's self is very difficult. One can not run away from one's own conflicts. Patients who seek to solve internal problems by leaving home or by taking trips must learn that solution can come only through changed attitudes and reaction patterns.

Many youths come with the complaint of "What's the use?" Their feeling of futility is the result of inability to solve the conflicts and the turmoil within them. The conflicts may be over specific difficulties, and the feeling of futility in trying to solve a particular difficulty radiates to include everything in life. Tensions at home, desires for independence, ambitions: all or any may be at the bottom of the general futility. They "give up" the struggle and *withdraw* into a realm of self-pity.

Mr. K. B. did not speak with his mother, father, or elder brother. When he came home from school, and later from work, he offered no word of greeting and received none. He would get up out of his chair at the dinner table and walk to the other end to get bread or salt, rather than speak to them. He was irritable, unhappy, and "hated" them, yet still kept on living there. He tried to withdraw from contact with them because of fancied and actual insults.

This problem of not speaking to members of one's family[1] is unfortunately fairly common, and is an attempt to withdraw, as well as in some vague way to hurt; it is an inferior and immature way of handling a situation. Incidentally, it throws light on the emotional reactions of the other members of the family. Persons who withdraw are usually shy and sensitive and have a feeling of being unloved and unwanted. Their wishes are satisfied in daydreams; they are uneasy and unhappy when confronted with reality. They "feel 'lonely' even in the presence of others," and not infrequently they "leave the room when company comes." They tend to "avoid 'sad' movies and 'emotional' stories, and even refuse to read the newspaper because it has so many items 'about death and suicide and horror'." Statements of this sort are frequently heard in conversation with these patients whose only mechanism of defense is withdrawal. When emotional instability is great and the sense of conflict intense, then any additional emo-

---

[1] *Vide* p. 191 (Case K.).

tional disturbance, even so remote a one as reading of an accident in a strange part of the country, is sufficient reminder of personal difficulties.

Miss F. M., aged twenty-eight years, complained of being more or less constantly depressed and of feeling almost hopelessly inadequate for the ordinary routine of life. Ever since childhood she had felt tired and inadequate. She believed she was ugly, and so kept away from people. She became very lonely. She admired one girl and imitated her in all vices and virtues in an effort to be like her. She wanted to be loved by "anyone" so that she might feel more worthwhile. Her work was efficient, and she was in charge of a small office force; yet she fancied her employer thought she was inadequate. "I don't have a feeling of belonging. I always compare myself with others and find myself wanting. I am so tired and am always afraid, but no one knows it. I can't sleep nights thinking over the little things I said or did that were wrong and which might have been left unsaid, or done in another way. I've cried myself to sleep often, but even in sleep had horrible nightmares. Boys go out with me, but I often feel they really don't care for me. My reason tells me I over-emphasize many of these thoughts, but I can't help it."

Her home life was the basic cause for these feelings. Her father was a weak man, living on a war pension, dominated by a nagging, dissatisfied wife. There never was a kind word spoken. The children were punished—often unjustly, and often as an outlet for the parents' pent-up emotion. There never was any feeling of love or of affection. The patient was told she was spoiled and petulant and ugly. Constant pressure of this sort forced the patient to withdraw into herself, and even at the age of six and seven she remembers crying herself to sleep. At seven, she found that she could get some pleasure from masturbation, and this she continued for many years, feeling intensely guilty over the act, and yet being unable to restrain herself. She expressed this conflict by saying it had "a horrible fascination" for her. So deeply ingrained were her feelings of being unwanted that neither her work nor her social successes meant anything to her. She constantly felt inferior.

Conversion.—Conversion is a mechanism in which psychologic states are expressed symbolically by physical reactions. Thus, paralysis, anesthesia, aphonia, tubular vision, etc., may be without organic basis and may rather be expressions of the patient's anger, fear, conflict, or other emotionally toned ideas. Ida D. converted (expressed) in a paralyzed arm her resentment over her mother's violence.[1] L. converted her general dissatisfaction with life, her mother's domination, and her failure to get married by paralysis of her legs.[2] D. W. converted his refusal to leave his daughter-in-law's home into astasia abasia.[3]

[1] *Vide* p. 29.   [2] *Vide* p. 33.   [3] *Vide* p. 30.

Mr. S. Z., aged seventeen years, complained of terrific pain in the back of his neck. He was brought to the psychiatrist, because no organic pathology could be found. His mother explained at great length about her son's debility and showed much concern. The boy finally was able to tell his story in the privacy of the office. He was a healthy, normal youngster who desired to do all the things ordinary boys do. He wanted to play, ride, play ball, and be on his own. His mother was very fearful, however. He might strain himself if he played too violently. He might be injured in the ball club; and she would discuss at great length the danger of "swimmer's cramps," etc. She was, as his boy friends termed it, a "pain in the neck." The boy's pain in the neck developed as a conversion of the psychologic "Pain in the neck"; and both disappeared when the situation was explained to the mother and son, and the mother withdrew her octopus solicitude.

Negativism is not so common in the neuroses as in the psychoses. Children may on occasion be negativistic. Patients who are negativistic will do the opposite of what is asked. Schizophrenic patients will often do the opposite of what is expected of them. This reaction pattern tends to arise, on the one hand, out of the desire to assert one's self; and on the other, from the need for revenge, or of "hurting those who hurt."

Mr. N. T., aged twenty-seven years, was seen at the request of his mother. N. T. was not informed of the physician's visit, because he refused to see anyone. He had just come back from New York City and had gone to his mother's home. He secluded himself in the attic and slept on bundles of old clothes that were permeated with a stench. He even slept in these clothes. He refused to eat food cooked by his mother, and on receiving a $10 gift from his sister, bought a case of several hundred oranges, and after tasting one threw the rest away. He went to great lengths to do the opposite not only of what his mother told him to do, but of what he "felt" his mother wished him to do.

Rationalization.—Rationalization[1] is utilized in everyday life, and is in effect the person's invention of plausible reasons for doing that which he wishes to do even though he knows they are not the real reasons. Rationalization is a method of justifying wishful thinking, a means by which one provides himself with a fallacious reason which permits him to escape facing the real issues involved.

In the examples cited above where hate or irritation is vented on another, the real reason for the emotional outbursts is usually hidden and the person justifies his symptom by the invention of a socially acceptable and ego-maintaining "reason." Mrs. I. Q.[2] vented her feelings of envy and inferiority on her more successful

[1] *Vide* p. 121.   [2] *Vide* p. 59.

friends; but she "said" she disliked them because they were vain, or sly, or unfair.

Miss V. W.,[1] aged twenty-three years, fought violently with her family. She would throw dishes at them and call them all sorts of names. She said that they had never taken proper care of her, that they had engaged a poor doctor to sew up her harelip, that they didn't acquaint her with the right friends, etc. She had, at the age of nineteen, fallen in love with a young man and had pretended she was wealthy. When he found that her father was a simple laborer and had no funds, he left the girl for another. Since that time, she blamed her parents for his desertion, even though it later developed that he was a thief.

It appears that the human machine needs to maintain its pride (*i. e.*, its security), and any idea which tends to break down this pride or security must be resisted, even if the resistance is but a false and flimsy front that merely shuts the danger from view without really curbing it. Rationalization is thus used. It is an immature and ineffective way of dealing with any situation. Miss V. W. blamed her rejection by the young man upon innumerable incidents which had no relation to his action.

Projection.—Projection is a mechanism by means of which the person refuses to face his own fears and desires, and instead believes that they emanate from someone else. In its most serious form, it is seen in the schizophrenic patient.[2] Delusions are often the result of projection, and when a patient hears a voice coming from the next room saying, "You are a common criminal," he has projected his own conscience. An old-maid matron of a girl's school was projecting her own desires when she forbade one girl to wear pajamas and her roommate to wear a nightgown, since wearing such clothes suggested to her a sexual relation.

Such projections may show themselves in many ways and may become involved, complex, and seemingly ununderstandable. The patient who said, "I dislike persons who are free and easy," could find numerous rationalizations for his feeling this way; but fundamentally this person was, as most such are, very inhibited. Seeing others who express themselves in an uninhibited manner arouses in them, or makes them more aware of, their own desires. As a result their inhibitive tendencies are called into stronger play, and this situation is irritating. They project not only their own desires but their own inhibitions of them. The dislike of others' freedom is but a projected irritation and dislike of their own inhibi-

---

[1] *Vide* p. 396.   [2] *Vide* p. 389 *ff* (Case A.L.).

tions, and in a complicated fashion, an associated tendency to dislike their own desires because the inhibitions tell them "they ought not to like it."

Identification.—Identification[1] is the process of assuming the characteristics and emotions of another person, or of an ideal. Some patients assume the troubles of their parents; the daughter, for example, suffering all the anguish of the mother who may be in difficulty. In some instances, the child may feel actual pains complained of by the parent. Identification with some older person who is considered a community hero is common among adolescents. Gangs as a whole may come to express a certain type of morality with which each member identifies himself. Boy scouts may carry out acts which are considered as "noble"; members of a city gang may refuse "to talk" about who shot them, because they have so identified themselves with the prevailing morality of the group that it is impossible for them to act as individual persons; but always their performance must reflect the group ideology.

Psychoneurotic patients not uncommonly identify themselves with their parents,[2] and imitate their behavior; or identify themselves with anyone who seems to be in trouble, and assume all the woes of that person as their own.

Mrs. I. Q.,[3] aged forty-eight years, had suffered from a life-long psycho-neurotic personality, with many symptoms of instability. She cried frequently, spoke loudly, nagged constantly, and had many aches and complaints. Among other things she told of becoming terribly upset because she read in the paper about the accidental drowning of a child; of breaking down into tears because some friend of her's developed cancer; of suffering to the point of insomnia and inability to eat, because her sister's child had a bad cold. Her family, and the relatives of the friends involved, told her that she suffered far more than they. In each of these instances, the patient identified herself with the one who was suffering, and suffered on occasion more than they.

Identification is based on primitive thinking,[4] the person feeling and suffering in a fashion similar to the one with whom identification occurs. Pity, sympathy, hero worship, and provincialism are some of the states based upon the identification mechanism.

In some, the ego is so starved for attention and recognition, that all manner of techniques are employed to gain them. These *attention-getting* mechanisms are found particularly in the child

---

[1] *Vide* p. 292 (Case A. S.). [2] *Vide* p. 200 *ff.*
[3] *Vide* p. 59. [4] *Vide* p. 43.

who feels unloved.[1] At first the child will attempt to do whatever
he feels the parents like *and* which will gain their attention. In
many instances, if one parent tends to reject the child (as in the
case of a father who has only daughters and wishes a son) a special
effort will be made to please that parent. Feelings of being rejected
may be particularly acute if another child in the family receives
attention. If attempting to please the parents does not gain attention, then the child may develop *temper tantrums*, preferring displeased or even harshly disciplinary attention to none.

Likewise in adult life there are persons who constantly strive to
be the center of attention, and who will go to great lengths to develop some talent or capacity whereby to assure themselves of such
recognition. Similarly, men have become political ringleaders,
have led emotional cults, have been martyrs, etc., in order to satisfy
their desire for attention and flattery. If attention cannot be
gained by acts which are socially constructive, such persons may
perform irritating and anti-social acts; for it is better, they feel,
to be a despised hero than to be a nonentity. In some instances, the
sense of loneliness, of being unwanted, and the inability to gain
recognition and attention may lead to suicide.[2]

N. O., aged twenty-three years, had a great feeling of inadequacy. She
quarreled, cried, and spoke dogmatically about subjects she knew nothing
about. She tells of how her father wanted a son, and when she came, the
second girl, he was very disappointed. He gave his children no affection and
was curt and preëmptory toward them. He did not notice them. Nora did
everything in her power to attract his attention. She became the most
notorious tom-boy of the neighborhood, and climbed trees and played ball
as well as any male of her age. "I did it hoping he would pay more attention
to me, but he didn't."

This girl went to great lengths to try to please her unreasoning
and unundertanding father.

Phantasy Formation.—Phantasy formation, day-dreaming, or
building castles in the air is normal in childhood and even adulthood. When it continues in excess, or when it comes to be used as a
means of escape from reality to the point where it interferes with
living efficiently, it becomes pathologic. Day-dreams are the stuff
from which ideals are spun, and to that extent they have an enor-
mous benefit to the human race; yet patients too often use them to
wish themselves heroes, or to wish destruction of their enemies,
meanwhile ignoring any concrete or factual methods of carrying

---

[1] *Vide* p. 127.   [2] *Vide* p. 47 (Case C.)

out what they really wish.   Schizophrenic patients typify the extreme, and have withdrawn so entirely into phantasy life that they disregard real life in its entirety.

Phantasying is not always concerned with pleasant topics.   After a period of time, unpleasant memories and anticipations come to the fore, so that the phantasy then turns out to be a liability to the subject, for patients them begin to suffer from the distressing possibilities built up in their own phantasy.[1]

Chronic worriers[2] who are always concerned about what may occur have developed this kind of phantasy.   These persons have become over-sensitive to the possibilities of danger and instead of dealing with actual facts as they are, let their imagination "do its worst."

Problems should be solved by reason and not by emotion. Feeling tone, which, however, should be taken into consideration, often warps the decision and tends to result in worry.   In worry, correct solutions are made difficult, because one confronts one's self continually with the same fact, "feels" the inherent emotion, and over-emphasizes the dangers that might possibly arise.

A second component of worry is the lack of courage to "face the situation,"[3] and accept the fact of the difficulty.   Too often when an unpleasant situation exists, rather than understand it and do something about it, there is the tendency to deny its existence and try to forget it by denying it.

Mr. K. N., for example, was greatly irritated with his wife.   He developed a chronic resentment against her which gradually chilled and crystallized into a hatred.   She was an undemonstrative type of woman whose interests were directed along social lines; he was an affectionate man who was idealistic and more concerned with ideas than bridge parties.   He expected affection and interest in his affairs, and could not understand why it was not forthcoming.   He took her lack of interest in his problems as a personal affront, and in turn became irritable, demanding, and domineering.

This man refused: (1) to face the fact that his wife's temperament did not permit what he wanted, and (2) to accept this difference and try to make the best of it.   His resentment was productive of nothing but self-pity and a futile insistence that everything be done and perceived in his way.

Another way of expressing this same worry is typified by the statement, "I always anticipate the future."   Here again the person is over-sensitive and phantasies excessively about the future.

[1] *Vide* p. 193.   [2] *Vide* p. 194.   [3] *Vide* p. 205 *ff.*

Basically, such persons are tense, unstable, and inclined to have other symptoms that go with a neurotic illness. Not only is there an excessive fear of failure, but as is the case where there is one extreme, the opposite emotion also tends to be present; and there is over-gratification at the slightest success or praise. The anticipation or the "worry" that occurs in these persons is not an "objective" facing of the possibilities of the future, but an emotionalism and apprehensiveness about the most remote possibilities of the future.

Dissociation.—Dissociation is present in cases of symbolic amnesia.[1] In these cases, one's usual personality seems to be forgotten and a "second" self emerges. This split is only an apparent one and is frequently the result of a "desire to forget."

Miss B. Q., aged seventeen years, was brought to the clinic in a complete state of amnesia. She was found at a church, in a disheveled state, and could not tell who she was. She spoke coherently, but did not know her name, her address, who her relatives were, how old she was, where she went to school, or any other fact about her past life. Her mental processes were otherwise intact, and she could read, write, and discuss specific problems intelligently.

Under hypnosis, the essential history of her past was brought to light. She and her sister lived with their widowed father. He was a domineering, sadistic person who demanded implicit obedience and exact accounting of the household budget. On the day the amnesia developed, the patient was given the money for rent, and when she arrived at the agency discovered the money had been lost. The fear and panic that seized her was so great that rather than go back and face certain and severe punishment—she "forgot" all about herself.

Such dissociation is an unconscious escape mechanism, but practically it is very difficult to differentiate from the more conscious malingering.

Ambivalence.—Ambivalence[2] is the simultaneous existence of ideas or complexes charged with opposite emotional tones. There may be love and hate, trust and suspicion existing side by side. There is lack of a stable balance between the opposing tendencies; and ambivalent persons oscillate between extremes. It is not uncommon to hear a story like that of Mrs. N. D.

Mrs. N. D., aged twenty-nine years, complained of the host of symptoms classified as anxiety attacks. She stated: "My husband is the best husband a person could have. He is kind and considerate; he makes a good appearance and supports me well. A woman couldn't wish for a finer man. But why does he get me down? (Patient cries.) I can't stand him around me. Yet I love him because he's so good to me and so considerate."

[1] *Vide* p. 33.   [2] *Vide* p. 200.

There was a strong incompatibility between the temperaments and interests of husband and wife. The patient vacillated constantly between her feelings of appreciation for his good qualities and her equally potent exasperation and irritation.

Ambivalence differs from *dissociation* which permits the existence side by side of diametrically or logically opposed ideas or actions. It differs from ambivalence in that it is not a vacillating reaction to a particular situation or idea but rather the holding of inherently inconsistent ideas. Usually this dissociation exists for a few ideas; but it may be so deep as to "split the personality." There are many persons who condemn or even demand severe physical punishment to a dull-witted thief, but are aroused to great indignation at cruelty to "dumb" beasts. Some "great scientists" who have contributed materially to the world's welfare and who insist on strict scientific procedure may entertain ideas of spiritualism. The basis for such dissociation is that one set of ideas is determined by what the person *wishes*, and on the basis of which he has rationalized.

Regression.—Regression[1] is the reversion to infantile forms of behavior. Regression often occurs in old age when senile changes in the cortex are responsible for an impaired intellect. In these instances there is a development of what has been called euphemistically "second childhood."

Regression may occur, however, from psychologic difficulties. In the schizophrenic patient there is frequently a reversion to extreme infantile levels, with lack of control of the bowel and bladder. Occasionally the patient may regress to a vegetative state, be mute, unresponsive, even to pain, and refuse to eat.

In physical illness, one often witnesses the petty irritability and childish attitudes of otherwise mature persons. In this temporary regression, the patients whimper over slight pain, over lack of sufficient attention, require comforting and repeated reassurances as if they were children. True here as with other neurotic traits, the more emotional a person is, the greater the tendency to regression.

Irradiation.—Irradiation[2] is a psychologic mechanism by means of which emotional tension associated with one person or incident spreads to include other ideas or persons that may be connected in some way with the turmoil, or that may simply be associated by being physically present, or against which or whom there may

[1] *Vide* p. 437. [2] *Vide* p. 174.

be some slight irritation from some other cause. A business man who becomes angry at the loss of an order may become angry with all his employees. The father who has just learned of the arrival of his first-born son passes out cigars and greets everyone cheerily. The emotional state irradiates from one focal point outward to many. Conversely, several points of reference in a given situation may be over-looked by the person who prefers instead to lay all blame on one source. This process might be called *convergence*. Many irritations flow inward to one focal point. Business persons may attribute all financial distress to one political figure or party; a disgruntled wife may blame her husband for all her irritations and unhappiness; a drunkard may say he is so because his wife doesn't appreciate him. This device is used politically[1] to divert people's anger to *some* "manufactured" incident. Many symptoms of displacement and projection originate in the mechanisms of irradiation and convergence.

In addition to the defense mechanisms by which we seek to protect ourselves against danger, there are many reaction patterns by which we obtain pleasures which are denied to us by the environment or by our own conscience. In many instances, it is actual pleasure that is sought; and in many others, it is a release of tension created by the inhibitions attendant upon social training. Each living organism has a certain amount of energy which expresses itself in the ordinary pursuits of living. Should this energy be thwarted and prevented from coming to the fore, tension results; for the energy has not been dissipated; it has only been compressed and stored up.[2] As a matter of fact, *the greater the inhibitions, the more compressed and explosive the energy becomes*, and the more symptoms are created. Release of this pent-up energy or tension is pleasurable. It is difficult in any given case if not impossible, to tell whether pleasure is so because it is primarily pleasure-giving in itself—or tension-releasing.[3]

Moreover, pleasure is a relative term, its specific meaning dependent upon what the person considers to be pleasurable. The determining force is not so much the situation as it is the person's attitude. Pleasure tends to become a postponed feeling tone. For example, the child does the unpleasant task of washing dishes for the "pleasure" of her mother's approval and gratification; or the adult takes pleasure in doing much and hard work, because of the anticipated pleasure to come when the work is finally completed.[4]

---

[1] *Vide* p. 251.   [2] *Vide* p. 241.   [3] *Vide* p. 101.   [4] *Vide* p. 242.

There may, indeed, be more pleasure in anticipation than in realization insomuch as the imagined pleasure may have many of the vague but pleasing feeling-tones which are conjured up in our dream state but these phantasied feelings are rarely realized in sharply defined reality.

Fixation.—Fixation consists of centering one's emotional drives on one idea, action, or reaction pattern. A person may have a "mother fixation"[1] and be unable to express any affection toward any other woman; he may have a "racial fixation" and feel that all who belong to a certain race should be destroyed (or if he is a member of that group, be given an exalted place); he may be fixated on masturbation and be unable to enjoy normal sexual intercourse. In other words, such persons are tied by their emotional conflicts, and in an obsessive-compulsive manner persist in spite of reason in their "fixated" course. The fixation in itself is an immature, or pathologic reaction, although it may be justified by rationalization.

Persons may have a "fixation" at any level of development and not progress afterward. Immaturity is a fixation below the adult level, and various levels of immaturity may be maintained throughout life. Moreover, since fixation involves primarily the emotional connotations, there may exist side by side mature "intellectual" concepts about politics, business, etc., and immature concepts on life, love, or the pursuit of happiness.

There are some women who remain fixated at infantile levels as indicated by their constant use "of baby talk" even in ordinary conversation. There are men who take a childlike pleasure in being members of secret organizations and attach great importance to the "signs," "passwords," etc.

Many patients who are overly emotional remain fixated on a pattern of response begun in early childhood. Pouting, temper tantrums, carrying grudges, etc., are evidences of such fixations. Mrs. I. Q. shows many evidences of such childish and immature responses, though she has reached middle age.[2]

Sublimation[3] is a mechanism for releasing to another outlet the energy originally directed toward the fulfillment of a goal. It does not differ materially from substitution. In civilized life, there are many desires which cannot be expressed directly and which need some outlet. A salesman of medical specialties tells of once having desired to be a physician but being unable to complete the

---

[1] *Vide* p. 437.   [2] *Vide* p. 59.   [3] *Vide* pp. 116; 249.

course because of financial difficulties entered his field because, "It was as close as I could get to the practice of medicine." Music is an excellent form of sublimation, and almost any form of recreation or constructive enterprise may be listed as such. Some persons write poetry to sublimate their energies, and the world benefits thereby. Others invent, build, paint, or run large business enterprises as part of the same drive.

Mr. Q. M. suffered from marked inferiority feelings. He related, among other things, his invention of a special bicycle lock which would put an end to his financial difficulties. He had a small candy shop in a poor neighborhood, and feeling inferior, sympathized greatly with the poor waifs that came in. One day a child came in crying bitterly at having his bicycle stolen. So much did the patient take the child's crying to heart (identification) that he resolved to put an end to such stealing, and by dint of much application, invented a bicycle lock which was patented and which a manufacturer agreed to market. This man was capable of sublimating his suffering for the child into concrete action.

Compensation is a *substitution* process like sublimation but results frequently in *over*-responses. One may compensate for a short physique and its attendant feelings of inferiority by being dominant, aggressive, and loud-voiced. The blind compensate by a further development of the sense of hearing as well as their kinetic sense. Parents who struggled in childhood compensate by attempting to give their children "everything"—without understanding the deleterious effects. Such over-compensation is common, and it may be direct, as in the examples cited, or it may be indirect and via such mechanisms as defense, withdrawal, etc.

SUMMARY

It must again be stressed that the various mechanisms herein described are rarely found in pure form, and that any one symptom may be the result of several mechanisms. Indeed, it may be said that all these forms of psychologic activity are but subdivisions of the general tendency to "think emotionally"; *i. e.*, to utilize primitive reasoning by similarity and contagion.[1] All persons use some of the mechanisms at some time or other; and any individual person may be considered normal or neurotic depending upon the selectivity, intensity, and extensity of his use of these mechanisms.

[1] *Vide* p. 43.

CHAPTER IV

PSYCHONEUROTIC (TENSION)[1] SYMPTOMS DUE TO DISTURBANCES IN THE AUTONOMIC NERVOUS SYSTEM[2]

THE indecisions and conflicts inherent in many reaction patterns may find expression in symptoms of disturbed function of the integrative systems, including the autonomic nervous system, the cardiovascular system, the endocrine system, the postural system, etc.; or through psychologic mechanisms. The former symptoms have usually been described as psychoneurotic, simply because no organic etiology could be determined. The effect of emotion on the physiologic function of the body is too often minimized. Endocrine glands, for example, are influenced by emotion, as is commonly seen in lachrymation, salivation, menstruation, etc. Experimentally, Cannon[3] and others have found that rage and fear are accompanied by increased secretion of certain glands, notably adrenalin. Dr. Irene Sherman and the author[4] found that many symptoms termed psychoneurotic could be produced in normal subjects by the intravenous injection of adrenalin. Disturbances may occur in practically every part of the organism as the result of strong or chronic affective states. Much experimental work on human subjects has confirmed this theory. In this investigative work, extensive use has been made of hypnosis,[5] in which state it has been possible to suggest that the subject feel fear, love, hate, or any other emotion; and by this procedure the effect of these emotions on the body has been determined.

The experimental work and the conclusions of investigators in

---

[1] *Vide* p. 24 *ff.*

[2] Although the autonomic nervous system is mentioned alone, the meaning implied throughout this book is that of the entire integrating organismal structure. The central nervous system, the vasomotor system, the circulating blood and its contents, the endocrine glands, and any other integrating mechanism is involved in varying degree with the autonomic nervous system. It appears probable, however, that the autonomic system via its ganglia in the periphery, in the hypothalamus, and possibly even in the frontal cerebral lobes initiate and correlate all other systems as related to emotional changes.

[3] Cannon, W. B.: Bodily Changes in Pain, Hunger, Fear and Rage. (Appleton Co., 1929).

[4] Kraines and Sherman: Neurotic Symptoms and Changes of Blood Pressure and Pulse, Jour. Am. Med. Assn., vol. 114, pp. 843–845, 1940.

[5] *Vide* p. 227.

this field of psychosomatic function are listed below. This statement is not intended to be in any way exhaustive, but simply to indicate a few of the fascinating correlations which are opening new fields of study.

METABOLISM AND BLOOD

The basal metabolic rate can, for example, be lowered by hypnosis. Numerous experiments have been done along this line. Gessler and Hanson conducted experiments with a subject lying naked in a room the temperature of which could be decreased. In one subject, with cooling of the room temperature to about 16° C., the increase in O_2 consumption was 11 per cent; with cooling to about 13° the increase was 16 per cent; in hypnosis without suggestion, and the room temperature of 16°, the increase was only 4 per cent (instead of 11 per cent); in hypnosis, with simultaneous suggestion of warmth and room temperature of only 12°, the increase of O_2 consumption was only 3 per cent (instead of about 18 per cent). In other words, with hypnosis alone there was such a decrease in the activity of the heat regulating mechanism that (in view of the intense cold stimulus of 13°) one could call it an almost complete cessation of heat regulation.[1] These authors conclude that heat regulation depends not only on external conditions, but also on the subjective evaluation of the outside world.

Similarly, calcium content of the blood was brought down by hypnotic quieting, from 10.56 to 8.40 mg. per cent.,[2] and this observation has been confirmed a number of times. Ehrström concludes that psychic states that can be characterized as states of calm begin usually with a decrease of blood calcium, and periods of restlessness begin with an increase.[3] Similarly, various investigators point out the influence of emotion on cholesterol, acid base equilibrium, and sugar metabolism.

The role of sugar metabolism in the psychoses is unclear; but Cannon's classical experiment showed that glycosuria develops in cats in rage, and that the promptness with which sugar appears in the urine is directly related to the emotional state of the animal. Cannon and his co-workers examined the urine of 25 Harvard football men after the most exciting contest of the season and found sugar present in 12.[4] Interestingly and instructively, 5 of these

[1] Gessler, H., and Hansen, K.:   Deutsch. Arch. f. klin. Med., **156**, 352–359, 1927.
[2] Glaser, F.:   Med. Klin., **20**, 535–537, 1924.
[3] Ehström, M. Ch.:   Acta med. Scandin., **74**, 378–395, 1931.
[4] Cannon, W. B., et al.:   Am. Jour. Physiol., **29**, 280–287, 1911–12.

positive cases were among substitutes not called upon to enter the game, thereby showing the influence of excitement even in the absence of great physical activity. Several workers have found sugar in the urine of students both before and after examinations; and G. Bucciardi reports a considerable increase in the blood sugar of the 12 students he examined the day before, immediately before, and immediately after taking an examination. After the examination, the blood sugar fell in all but 2 students, who for good reasons remained in an agitated state of mind.[1] Similarly, hyperglycemia has been found in aviators, normal as well as neurotic soldiers, and in patients before operation.

In diabetes, it is possible to reduce the blood sugar by hypnosis. Povorinskij and Finne,[2] after performing carefully controlled experiments under hypnosis, conclude:

"1. The blood sugar content can be *increased by the suggested idea* of the intake of a great amount of sugar or honey; and the effect ordinarily produced by sugar intake can be very definitely *inhibited by the idea* of the absence of sugar in an actually sweet solution.

"2. Apart from the suggestion, the hypnotic state in itself tends to lower the blood sugar content.

"3. In persons with increased suggestibility, a change in blood sugar content can be produced also in the waking state.

"4. In one patient, the sugar curve rose more sharply in the case of suggested sugar intake than in the case of actual sugar intake. This increase suggests immediate cortical action as compared with the time necessary for the physiologic absorption of the actual sugar."

R. T. Woodyatt substantiates Naunyn, who "in his classic textbook on diabetes calls attention to the fact that the degree of diabetes exhibited by diabetic patients is proven to vary in response to nervous and emotional influences," and gives the following illustrative case:

A business man, aged sixty-five years, on a diet in hospital, and with small doses of insulin, was passing normal urine. Suddenly one day, with no change in régime, he passed 43 grams of sugar; and another day, 76 grams. The only cause was that he had just heard that his corporation was taking steps to retire him.[3] It has become increasingly evident that in the treat-

[1] Bucciardi, Giulio: Arch. di Fisiol., 26, 1–23, 1928.
[2] Povrinskij, J. A., and Finne, W. N.: Ztschr. f. d. ges. Neurol. u. Psychiat., 129, 135–146, 1930.
[3] Woodyatt, Rollin T.: Jour. Am. Med. Assn., 89, 1013–1014, 1927.

ment of diabetes one must, among other things, treat the individual's emotions. Some investigators have said that certain types of persons are more prone to develop diabetes than others, because of their "nervous irritability."

During excitement, the red cells in the blood stream may be increased. In cats, blood cells may increase 27 per cent in the presence of a dog,[1] possibly through the contraction of the spleen. Similarly, blood platelets and eosinophils may rise. The white blood count and the differential blood picture vary under emotions.[2] Mora and others demonstrated an absolute increase in the leucocyte count and a relative increase in the polymorpho-nuclear forms before an operation. Conversely, under hypnosis the reverse is true.[3]

CARDIOVASCULAR SIGNS OF EMOTION

The heart[4] and the gastrointestinal tract[5] are the most sensitive recorders of a disturbed emotional state. The intimate connections between the autonomic nervous system and the heart are so close as almost to justify the statement that cardiac rhythm and rate are a measure of the activity of the state of tension in the sympathetic and the parasympathetic systems. In primitive life this inter-relationship is of great value, for the efficiency of the circulation must be improved to meet the danger "perceived." When confronted by a fearful situation, the animal's primary integrative system, the nervous system, attempts to prepare the body for action; and the most important of all preparations is the ability of the circulation to supply sufficient blood to the various organs the actions of which are speeded up. The blood must bring increased amounts of oxygen to the muscles, and carry away increased amounts of lactic acid and other waste products. The increased flow of adrenalin and the consequent rise in blood sugar must be efficiently and quickly distributed. The carbon dioxide increase must be promptly eliminated by respiration, and the associated change in the blood speeds up the delivery of oxygen to the cells.

Anger, fear, and anxiety have the same effect on the civilized human as danger has on the animal; and increased cardiac irritability is manifested whenever these emotions are present. When

---

[1] Izquierdo, J. J., and Cannon, W. B.:   Am. Jour. Physiol., **84**, 545–562, 1928.
[2] Holler, M.:   Klin. Wchnschr., **3**, 1168–1171, 1924.
[3] Mora, Jacob, *et al.*:   Jour. Am. Med. Assn., **86**, 945–946, 1926.
[4] *Vide* p. 292.   [5] *Vide* p. 300.

these emotional states become chronic, the effect on the heart may become serious because of the constant bombardment of nervous impulses. Emotional tension need not always be in the foreground of consciousness; and the general pattern of irritability, the cause of which may not be in consciousness, may be sufficient to keep the heart in unrest.

An exciting experience was suggested to a subject in hypnosis, with the simultaneous suggestion of complete amnesia for it. Furthermore, the subject was given the post-hypnotic suggestion that with a certain signal (seemingly accidental showing of a handkerchief) the subject would have the same sensations as during the experience. When after hypnosis, the handkerchief was shown, there was a definite increase in pulse rate (maximum, 27 beats per minute), similar to that during the suggestion of the experience in hypnosis.

In other words, an experience which is no longer in consciousness may call forth the same reactions it produced at the time of its first happening.[1] Its effects may, in the long run, produce, or at least, precipitate actual physical disease. Werley phrases this concept well:

"It makes no difference if a highly sensitized coronary artery becomes spastic because of emotion or because of an overloaded stomach or physical exertion. The symptoms are much the same except for the emotional element or its absence. Even in true angina due to coronary sclerosis, the attack may be precipitated by emotional excitement. . . . That which has been said about the heart applies to the other viscera, because the mechanism of pain in them is the same. Contraction, over distension, pressure and pulling cause pain, and the result is very similar whether these conditions are brought about by local or organic disease or by overaction of the sympathetic nervous system under the drive of the emotions."[2]

Psychogenic cardiac death is regarded as an established fact by several authors.[3] In primitive tribes, vigorous and apparently healthy young adults have been said to die within a few days of over-stepping a taboo. Cases have been reported of patients in good condition dying on the operating table before the anesthetic was administered. The chief cause of cardiac failure seems to be the associated fear.

That the heart rate is increased by emotion is a matter of common, every-day experience. In some instances, bradycardia may result under tension. Extra systoles are fairly frequent in emotionally disturbing situations. Von Wyss quotes Wenckebach and

[1] Deutsch, F., and Kauf, E.: Ztschr. f. d. ges. exp. Med., 34, 71–81, 1923.
[2] Werley, G.: Southwestern Med., 15, 23–27, 1931.
[3] Dunbar, H. F.: Emotions and Bodily Changes (New York), p. 215, 1935.

Winterberg to the effect that over half of 278 patients with extra systoles did not show the slightest pathologic cardiac change.[1] It is probably the result of a disturbed relationship between the sympathetic and the parasympathetic systems. W. R. Houston discusses the whole syndrome of angina pectoris in terms of the "spasmogenic aptitude." He says: "If the spasmogenic aptitude is great a slight stimulus of neurogenic nature will suffice to evoke the spasm with its characteristic pain. If the spasmogenic aptitude is absent, the utmost stimulus will fail to evoke the spasm." This syndrome he finds essentially lacking in the Chinese, and it has been found lacking also in Negroes.   Both races are relatively insusceptible to angina, in spite of the fact that Negroes are particularly susceptible to organic heart disease.[2]

S. R. Roberts says: "Civilization as we know it in western Europe and America, the ambition, effort, and community state of mind of these areas, the increasing responsibilities that come with age, and aging circulation, apparently are the foundations for the increase in prevalence of angina. The inner adjustment to life, the real spiritual control of life whose outer evidence is a poise and tranquility of mind, is not very inviting to angina and the anginous life. . . . Racial susceptibility to the spasmogenic aptitude throws a new light not only on pyloric stenosis but upon angina, hypertension, nervous indigestion, and other spasms."[3]

K. Fahrenkamp points out that there are all possible transitional stages from the slightest disturbance of function in coronary circulation to the gravest pathologic-anatomic changes in the coronary vessels. "In all cases, next to physical exertion, psychic excitement is most likely to precipitate an attack."[4]

Similarly, study of the blood pressure[5] reveals the extremely close relationship to emotional states. There is a change in blood distribution under emotion in limbs and body surface on the one hand and in the viscera on the other; that is, with pleasurable effects there is an increased blood flow to the limbs and body surface and a decreased blood flow to the viscera, and *vice-versa* with unpleasant effects. The blood pressure response to emotion is utilized in the lie detector apparatus, measuring the subject's guilt feeling over his actions. This apparatus fails in its purpose should the guilty person be free of emotion; or should an innocent

[1] von Wyss, W. H.:   Körperlich-seelische Zusammen-enhänge in Gesundheit und Krankheit (Thieme), 1931.
[2] Houston, W. R.:   Med. Clin. North America, 12, 1285–1306, 1929.
[3] Roberts, S. R.:   Am. Heart Jour., 7, 21–35, 1931.
[4] Fahrenkamp, Karl: Der Herzkranke (Stuttgart), 1931.
[5] *Vide* p. 295.

person be very apprehensive. It is a common experience among physicians to find the blood pressure of a patient high on his first entering the office, and dropping often markedly after a short period of casual conversation. Farhenkamp, who bases his conclusions on the study of over 800 blood pressure curves observed over a period of six years agrees with others that in all hypertensive diseases the major emphasis should be laid on the treatment of the psychic element. In many patients a vicious cycle is produced; the concern over blood pressure causing further increase, which in turn may produce personality changes.[1]

RESPIRATORY SYSTEM[2] AND OTO-RHINO-LARYNGOLOGY[3]

Many patients suffering from neuroses show disturbances in breathing. Deep sighs are constantly present in moments of tension. Rapid and shallow respiration may occur in apprehensive states. Heyer had his subjects perform forced breathing, and the result of the extreme carbon dioxide output was a general nervousness which went into a state of excitement.[4]

Laudenheimer tabulates as follows the interrelationships of psyche and respiration in general:[5]

REVERSIBLE ACTION

of Psyche	*and Respiration*
1. Affect causes changes of the respiratory curve, depth, and frequency. (Zoneff and Meumann.)	1. Voluntary acceleration of respiratory rhythm cause Affect. (Wundt, Heyer.)
2. Pain or psychic excitement lowers the CO_2 tension in the blood (Straub-Beckman); the sensitivity of the respiratory center is increased, hence increased ventilation.	2. Hyperventilation, forced expiration (Heyer) increases CO_2 tension of alveolar air, produces Affective excitement and with appropriate breathing technique (in predisposed individuals) typical symptoms of asthma. (Tala, Strubing.)
3. Psychic stimuli may, via vaso-vegetative centers, spontaneously or in hypnosis, lead to most serious spastic - exudative (pseudo - anaphylactic) symptoms and to typical asthma.	3. Allergic stimuli may, over the reverse pathway (body fluids, colloidial disequilibrium, hormonal influence, etc.) lead to anaphylactic shock, bronchospasm, exudation, asthma, and anxiety.
4. Sleep, *viz.*, tiredness, increases CO_2 tension in blood (Straub), decreases the sensitivity of the respiratory center, hence produces slowing of respiration.	4. Slowing of respiration (with relaxation of respiratory muscles) through exercise or suggestion leads to tiredness, *viz.*, sleep and underhypnosis to lasting lowered sensitivity of respiratory center (cure of asthma).

[1] Fahrenkamp, Karl: Die psycho-physischen Wechselwinkungen bei den Hypertonie Erkrankungen (Stuttgart), 1926.

[2] *Vide* p. 296.   [3] *Vide* p. 316 *ff.*

[4] Heyer, G. R.: Das Körperlich-seelische Zusammenwirken in dem Lebensvorgangen (Munchen) 1925.

[5] Laudenheimer, R.: Therap. d. Gegnw., **67**, 339–344, 1926.

Mohr quotes in detail the case of a man who had suffered for ten years from headaches and violent coryza which were found to be psychically conditioned and thereupon cured. Similarly, he describes a case of sinusitis, the treatment of which (by a specialist) was greatly complicated by a swelling of the mucous membranes. This swelling, in the rhinologist's opinion, could not be explained on the basis of the previous operation, but it was shown to be psychically conditioned, and yielded to psychotherapy.[1] Hysterical aphonia with spasms of the vocal chords is commonly observed and cured.

Bronchial asthma[2] is a controversial subject. Much has been said about the influence of allergy, and almost equally as much has been said about the role of psychic factors. Hippocrates said the asthmatic must guard against anger. Freud mentioned asthma often in his earliest works on anxiety. Some authors classify asthma as a respiratory neurosis, a reflex neurosis, or a central neurosis indicating the role of the non-allergic forces. Costa points out that many neurodermatoses (urticaria, circumscribed edema, and eczema) precede asthma; others occur interchangeably, as for example mucous colitis and migraine. Costa feels that asthma becomes fixated only through the neglect of this psychologic etiology followed by an irrational polypragmatic drug therapy.[3] E. Moos reports 7 cases who "after complete or essential failure of medicaments, climate, breathing exercises, hydrotherapy and inhalation therapy were treated purely by psychotherapy, at first more because the writer was at a loss, and later because of the knowledge gained in the treatment of other organ neuroses." All 7 cases improved sufficiently to carry on their normal work. In 2 cases, there was sputum up to 200 cc. daily which completely disappeared. Simultaneously, eosinophilia disappeared not only from the sputum, but also from the blood (returning to normal from 16, 12.5, 10, and 7 per cent respectively).[4] K. Hansen asserts that for the majority of cases of true bronchial asthma, an allergic diathesis must be assumed. He believes that hypnosis acts by decreasing the excitability of the vegetative nervous system, and thus the sensitivity to allergen; furthermore, it acts by interrupting the conditioned reflex which can precipitate an attack, even in com-

[1] Mohr, Fritz: Psycophysische Behandungs-methoden (Leipzig), 1925.
[2] *Vide*, p. 298.
[3] Costa, N.: Deutsch. med. Wchnschr., 48, 1458–1459, 1926.
[4] Moos, Erwin: Münch. med. Wchnschr., 67, 805–808, 1926.

plete absence of allergen; he points out, also, that in all his "relevant cases the cutaneous reaction remained positive even after the elimination of the asthmatic attacks, *i. e.*, the allergic and specific constitution remained."[1] Brauns reports on 12 hay-fever patients treated exclusively by hypnosis, 10 of whom suffered no relapse (3 having been followed for three years, 4 for two years, and 3 for one year).[2]

GASTROINTESTINAL SYSTEM[3]

Nervous dyspepsia was first described as a disease entity by Leube, in 1879. Ewald (1884) and others did not accept the concept of nervous dyspepsia as a clinical entity. They stressed the concept of nervous dyspepsia as a symptom complex constituting a part of neurasthenia or hysteria, often even the *only* expression of such a neurosis. (Italics mine). This latter is the modern view. It is a common experience to find that persons who develop financial difficulties suffer from gastric disturbances, often until the financial state improves. On the other hand, it has been suggested that these gastric disturbances produce psychic alterations; but, as Dreyfus states, "one wonders how an innocent gastric catarrh or dilation could produce psychic turmoils (such as anxiety, depression, suicide) whereas they are never found in much more serious gastric conditions such as ulcer and carcinoma."[4] Being content to consider psychic changes as simply auto-intoxication, some investigators stressed doubly the importance of treating the stomach and not the psyche. Further, they maintained, the habit was established of seeing in psychic changes nothing but a "natural" consequence of the complaints; the psychic disturbance was only natural, even if it looked exactly like a melancholia; suicide was understandable, because the patient did not want to suffer any longer from his stomach. However, "it is not the gastric trouble that makes the patient a hypochondriac, but the hypochondriasis causes the gastric trouble."

Cannon expresses the same attitude: "An emotional disturbance affecting the alimentary canal is capable of starting a vicious circle; the stagnant food, unprotected by abundant juice, naturally undergoes bacterial fermentation, with the formation of gases and

[1] Hansen, Karl: Deutsch. med. Wchnschr., **55**, 1462–1464, 1927.
[2] Brauns, W.: Med. Welt, **7**, 559–562, 1933.
[3] *Vide* p. 300 *ff.*
[4] Dunbar: Op. cit., p. 270.

irritant decomposition products. These in turn may produce mild inflammation or be absorbed as substances disturbing to metabolism, and thus affect the mental state. . . ." "Just as feelings of comfort and peace of mind are fundamental to normal digestion, so discomfort and mental discord may be fundamental to disturbed digestion."[1] Mental discord can be of many varieties; for the stomach, like the heart, may react to almost every emotion and sensation that man is capable of experiencing. Depressing emotions appear to inhibit the gastric and even duodenal secretion. Exaltation seems to favor gastric secretion.

Salivary secretion is increased and made more acid by excitement. Bogen experimented on a child aged three and one-half years with esophageal stenosis and gastric fistula. Milk and food remained caught in the stenotic esophagus, but hydrochloric acid appeared in the stomach whenever food was given. Bogen sounded a trumpet whenever food was given; and soon thereafter, trumpet sounding alone produced gastric juice with free hydrochloric acid. Anger inhibited the secretion.[2] Under hypnosis, Heyer was able to produce secretion of gastric juice, which varied in amount according to the imaginary food the subject was eating. In another group of hypnotic experiments, it was found that relish in connection with food increased the acidity, disgust decreased acidity.[3]

Similar is the operation of other secretions of the gastrointestinal tract. It was observed, accidentally at first, that excitement in dogs decreased the flow of bile. Pancreatic secretion in a dog which had been stimulated by a plentiful meal was stopped when the dog was shown a cat, and on another occasion when the dog was suddenly shown a bitch in heat and prevented from going to her. In human subjects under deep hypnosis, it was found that even the type of secretion was dependent upon the type of food suggested, varying with the albumin and fat content.[4]

Other physiologic effects of psychic stimuli are found in globus hystericus, a spasm of the esophageal musculature; cardiospasm, which must be carefully differentiated from that produced by organic etiology, and inhibition of gastric motility is observable in emotional subjects under fluoroscopy.

[1] Cannon, W. B.: Am. Jour. Med. Sci., **137**, 480–487, 1909.
[2] Bogen, H.: Arch. f. d. ges. Physiol., **117**, 150–160, 1907.
[3] Heyer: Op. cit.
[4] Oechsler: Internat. Beitr. 2. Pathol. A Therap. d. Ernährungsstör., **5**, 26–30, 1913.

Peptic ulcer[1] has been thrown more and more into the limelight in studies of the psychosoma. Several points stand out: (1) peptic ulcer is not a purely local disease of the stomach. Cushing first observed 3 cases of early fatality due to peptic ulcers following operation on brain tumors. The constitutional factor in the predisposition of ulcers indicates the general correlations of the disease.[2] (2) In the etiology of gastric ulcer, the literature stresses the importance of disturbance in gastric secretion and motility. (3) There is increasing recognition of the role of psychic factors in the etiology of peptic ulcer, and the recurrent attacks thereof. In general, it is well to remember that *ulcer is the last manifestation of several processes* which have gone on before, including the predisposition, and the psychologic and physical disturbances which have brought about a disturbance of gastric motility and secretion. Pylorospasm, and spasm of the intestines are subject to similar analysis.

Spasm of the colon, mucous colitis, and spastic constipation are all subject to emotional disturbances.[3] Intestinal activity is increased at the sight of food and decreased in pain and anxiety. Depressive states are characteristically associated with constipation, which may at times alternate with diarrhea. Attempts to treat constipation by itself without reference to the accompanying emotional state are bound to eventuate in failure. Heyer through hypnosis was able to give a patient a large dose of opium, which is ordinarily constipating, and suggested to the patient that castor oil was taken; and the results were those ordinarily occurring with castor oil.[4] Mucous colitis is practically always associated with emotional states, and has been cured by psychotherapy alone.

Vomiting, particularly nausea and vomiting, has many roots in the problems of the psyche. Frequently the vomiting of pregnancy is on this basis and often occurs among women suffering from the stress and strain of marital discord.

GENITO-URINARY SYSTEM AND GYNECOLOGY[5]

The bladder is under involuntary and voluntary control, and thus has two avenues for psychologic disturbance. When tension arises, the bladder tends to empty itself frequently; while in hysteria, emptying of the bladder may be delayed an abnormally long

---

[1] *Vide* p. 292.
[2] Tscherning, R.:   Arch. f. Verdauungskr., **31**, 351–360, 1923.
[3] *Vide* p. 306.   [4] Heyer: Op. cit.   [5] *Vide* p. 310.

time. Schwarz cites cases of retention of urine in men concerned over masturbation and impotency.[1] Eneuresis on the other hand is practically always the result of a co-existing state of tension and emotional instability. Spermatorrhea similarly is common in persons with psychologic difficulties, particularly in those in whom there is much sex tension. Impotence[2] is far more often the result of psychic than of physical forces.

Nephrolithiasis has been listed among those illnesses which are psychically determined, secondary to disturbance in the chemical composition of the urine.[3]

Menstrual disturbances are exceedingly common in their relation to psychologic forces.[4] Patients with psychoses show a remarkably high percentage of anomalies of menstruation. Amenorrhea often occurs in women who are concerned over sex; for example, fear of pregnancy among unmarried girls. Pseudopsyesis, or grossesse nerveuse, or a delusion of pregnancy accompanied by amenorrhea, vomiting, and enlargement of the breasts is not uncommonly seen. In many of these cases, there is even an abdominal enlargement due to distension of the abdomen by gas in the intestine.[5] Hypnosis can often cure amenorrhea or profuse bleeding. G. R. Heyer says that he is frequently asked to postpone menstruation in artists when it would occur at the time of an important performance.[6] Dysmenorrhea can in many instances be improved by psychotherapy. Low back pains, and pelvic pain in many instances exist on a background of discontent and chronic anxiety. Labor pains are an excellent example of the influence of personality factors: some women experiencing comparatively little pain, and others apparently suffering beyond all relation to actual physical difficulty. Hypnosis is used successfully in effecting a complete amnesia and absence of pain in labor.

SPECIAL SENSE ORGANS

Headache[7] is one of the most common conditions for which patients go to the ophthalmologist, and glasses are frequently requested not to improve vision, but to relieve headaches. Head-

---

[1] Schwarz, O.: Psychogenese und Psychotherapie Körperlicher Symptome (Wein), pp. 273–294, 1925.

[2] *Cf.* Ch. V, p. 106.

[3] Groddeck, G.: Allg. ärztl. Ztschr. f. Psychotherap., **2**, 665–680, 1929.

[4] *Vide* p. 325 *ff.*   [5] Dunbar: Op. cit., pp. 346–348.

[6] Heyer, G. R.: Hypnose und Hypnotherapie (Leipzig), pp. 73–135, 1927.

[7] *Vide* p. 337.

aches due to emotional tension may be of any variety, but there
are three common types: (1) pressure on top of the head; (2) aching
over the occiput; and (3) a tight, band-like pressure as if the head
were being "squeezed." Obviously these headaches may be produced by many physical causes. However, even in emotional
states the headache is not "imaginary" but is probably the result
of some alteration in the vaso-motor function.

There are many ophthalmologic complications[1] in hysteria.
Blepharospasm, palsy, and spasm of the various extrinsic muscles
of the eye, monocular diplopia, tubular vision, and defects in the
visual field are common. Rutherford, investigating the records of
students at the University of Iowa who had been referred to the
eye-clinic over a two-month period, chose for study all those between the ages of seventeen and twenty-six who had no organic
ocular lesion. Out of 80 such cases, 63 complained of one or more
symptoms having no objective relation to any visual defects. He
concluded that astheopia or eye-strain needs to be considered as a
probable neurosis. He quotes Emerson as advising that "patients
should be examined as individuals and not as optical mechanisms
to be fitted at the test chart," and "that lenses should be fitted to a
patient's nervous system as well as to his eyes."[2] Non-visual disturbances include anesthesia of the cornea and are useful as diag-
nostic criteria of hysteria. Spiral visual fields may be an indication of psychoneurotic traits.

Ear disturbances[3] are frequently seen in the nature of hysterical
deafness, ear pains, and noises in the head. These symptoms may
be *"caused by"* intense emotional difficulties, and play their role
just as do the other psychoneurotic symptoms. On the other hand,
psychic disturbances *may result from* impaired hearing; and paranoid symptoms are not an uncommon resultant. In these instances, the psychogenesis seems to be as follows: The patients
hear what is being said, and become irritated both at the person
for not speaking loud enough and at their own inferiority in hearing. Many of these persons will insist that they are not hard of
hearing and that the trouble lies in those who are speaking. Delusions then occur that whatever is being said that cannot be heard
is said against them, and on this basis a system of delusions develops.[4] Persons who have worked with the deaf and blind often

---

[1] *Vide* p. 316.
[2] Rutherford, C. W.: Jour. Am. Med. Assn., **99**, 284–288, 1932.
[3] *Vide* p. 318.   [4] *Vide* p. 321.

comment on the extreme suspiciousness of the former as contrasted with the amiable behavior of the latter. Smell and taste are also subject to disturbances, particularly in the psychoses. Patients frequently complain of "tasting" dope in the food and "smelling" gas pumped into the room to kill them.

The skin[1] is one organ particularly sensitive to emotional disturbances. Many diseases of the skin are more likely to be expressive of general physiologic and psychologic disturbance than of local pathology. Among the more obvious psychic correlates of skin changes are the pallor from fright, blushing, erection of hair, cutis anserina (so-called goose flesh), and changes in sweat secretion. Commonly appreciated as a psychic factor is the increased amount of pruritis in emotional persons suffering from a mild dermatitis. In addition to these symptoms pertaining to the skin, there is a host of less well-recognized lesions which are the result of emotional tension. Urticaria, edema, and eczema are frequently found to be on a psychologic basis. Even skin blisters were produced by hypnosis under carefully controlled conditions by Doswald, Kreibach,[2] Heller and Schultz,[3] Schindler, and others. During hypnosis it is possible to inhibit bleeding due to a pin prick; and on the other hand, several writers have recorded "spontaneous ecchymosis in psychoneurotic disorders."[4]

The skin is overly sensitive to heat, cold, or stroking, in some patients. In some, stroking of the skin gives rise to erotic pleasure. In some, itching without any apparent cause becomes extreme. Pruritis about the genitalia and anus may in many cases be secondary to an erotic urge rather than to physical changes.

Congestion or pallor accompanying emotional excitement may occur in blotches about the neck and face. The tendency of the skin to pathologic blushing and pallor is often combined with an inclination of the capillaries to exudative processes on mechanical stimulation. Dermographism is a manifestation of this marked liability of the capillaries, and the difference between dermographism and urticaria is only one of degree. Many cases are reported of urticarial eruptions which occur in the course of emotional disturbance and which are cured by psychotherapy.

Eczema is one of the commonest diseases of the skin, and is

[1] *Vide* p. 312.

[2] Doswald, D. C., and Kreibich, K.: Monatshefte f. prakt. Dermat., **43**, 634–640, 1906.

[3] Heller, Fr., and Schultz, J. H.: Münch. med. Wchnschr., **56**, 212, 1909.

[4] Jacobi, E.: Arch. f. Psychiat., **88**, 631–645, 1929.

often the result of tension in the patient. Bunnemann reports a case of eczema treated locally two and a half years unsuccessfully and eliminated in three hypnotic sessions.[1] Bonjour recalls the well-known case of the Russian professor who suffered from chronic infectious dermatitis and returned home uncured after having been treated successively by Kaposi, Lassar, and Fournier. His family tried to induce him to consult a woman who cured eczema by prayer but, being an atheist he refused. Finally, sick of suffering, he went to see her. She took him to the church and asked him to wait at the door. After the first prayer, the pruritis ceased; and after the next day's prayer, the eczema was cured. This cure proves, says Bonjour, that the infection was secondary and the eczema was of nervous origin.[2] Many writers report cures of eczema by psychotherapy which could not be cured by any other means. Psoriasis is reported on a similar basis. Warts also have been known to be cured by suggestion, whether it is by means of prayer, hypnosis, or burying a black cat in the cemetery at the stroke of 12, as Huckleberry Finn suggests. Important is the fact that cure of warts by suggestion leaves the skin without a scar, a condition not true when cautery or surgery is used. Bonjour presents photographs of the manner of healing; most frequently it is a process of atrophy, in other cases, pediculization.[3]

The clinical and experimental studies cited above, are indicative of the oneness of the organism. An idea associated with fear, for example, involves a reaction pattern of the whole body, and not of the "mind" alone. Emotion is indeed more of a physiologic phenomenon than a psychologic one. Specific changes may occur anywhere in the body as a result; and although the first etiology may be some danger which we perceive in the distance (either distant in place or time), the symptom may have its origin in some altered function of the body. Therapy, to be successful, must bear this concept in mind.

[1] Bunnemann, O.: Ztschr. f. d. ges. Neurol. u. Psychiat., **78**, 115–152, 1922.
[2] Bonjour, J.: Schweiz. med. Wchnschr., **61**, 1255–1256, 1931.
[3] *Ibid.*, **54**, 748–751, 1924.

CHAPTER V

SEX DRIVES

THE relative ease with which society is able to produce food-stuffs and necessities renders the self-preservation drive less urgent, and permits increased attention to be given to the physiology, psychology and psychopathology of another fundamental drive—sex. The need for such attention is acute, for about no other aspect of life is there more wholesale ignorance and misinformation. It is of vital importance to health and happiness that a frank and objective understanding of sex—its nature, significance, manifestations, and potentialities—replace the all too common practice of treating it secretly, smirkingly, with an air of mystery, repression, revulsion, and taboo.[1]

Since the sexual drive is a part of the total organismic reaction, any phenomenon or stress which disturbs the organism may disturb the sexual drive. Consequently, in those personality disorders which we label "Neurosis" and "Psychosis," one frequently finds as *part of the total disturbance* a disturbance in the sexual function. When perceived from this point of view, sex can be understood simply and without excessive emphasis. It is indeed a mistake to place an over-emphasis upon sex and represent it as the most important factor, simply because there is a more obvious manifestation of its disturbance. From practical experience, one finds that many of the sexual disturbances return to normal if the stress upon the organism in other fields is removed.

However, sexual maladjustment in itself may be a primary stress which can lead to wide disturbances in the personality. The force of the sex drive carries it to some vicarious form of expression if the sex desire as such cannot find fulfillment. When this force is restrained or completely blocked by social prohibitions or individual inhibitions, the sexual force will express itself either constructively or destructively; in the former case, much of the drive for the work which is socially useful may be said to be, in part at any rate, a redirected sexual drive; in the latter instance, there may be sadism, emotional lability and symptoms of tension and symbolism. In any given case where one finds sexual maladjust-

---

[1] *Vide* p. 49.

ments, one must evaluate how much of the sexual disturbance is truly etiologic in character and how much is purely symptomatic of other stresses.

NORMAL SEX ATTITUDE AND PRACTICE

Children, as a rule, are not more interested in sex than in many other phenomena. In the multitude of questions that are asked in childhood, a number of them will bear upon the method by which children are produced. These questions, however, are merely part of the curiosity drive. If a child, for example, wishes to know where babies come from and is told that they are born inside the mother, such an answer is generally satisfying; and if the child asks how they come to be borne inside the mother, the answer that the father plants the seed is again often sufficient. The child often develops an over-interest because the environmental taboos make it obvious to the child that here is an interesting topic.

The amount of information given should be governed by the child's level of maturity. It is only as puberty approaches that more detailed and specific interest in the adult sex life is shown and understood, and it is at this time that the physician or some objective friend should explain to the child the physiology of sex: that males have the organ called the "penis" and that females have the organ called the "vagina" and that after marriage the penis is introduced into the vagina and thereby is planted into the mother's womb a seed which eventually becomes a child. Such an explanation, which then goes on to dwell upon physiology, makes the whole affair a matter-of-fact one.

If there is no atmosphere of tension or emotion about the informant, the child will accept such a straightforward explanation with the same dispassionate interest and satisfaction that he feels when he "learns the answer" to any other of the countless mysteries with which he is constantly confronted. A wholesome understanding of sex will have been implanted; and the child, feeling that he "knows all there is to know" on the subject, will quickly be engrossed in normal physical and social activities.

Such normal and ideal growth in sexual knowledge will be possible only if there has been created in the environment no emotional tension on the subject. If, however, as is all too common, there have been scoldings, secrecy, and shame;[1] if a child has been put

---

[1] *Vide* p. 101 (Case J. B.).

off with such answers as: "You are not old enough to understand"; "Nice persons do not talk about such things"; "Don't let me ever hear you talking about such things again," then he will surely acquire his "misinformation" in such a way as to think of the whole matter of sex as something "dirty" about which to snicker or to be ashamed. In such circumstances, sexual explanations, of necessity, carry with them an additional emotional tone.

The physician should attempt to make his explanations extremely matter-of-fact, while at the same time remaining sympathetic to the child's emotional state. The atmosphere of tension present in the child should be removed by frank and vocal recognition that "you seem to think of this sex problem as an emotional one, but you can handle it just as any other one." If the adolescent can be persuaded to take such a common sense attitude, much of his future discomforts will be eliminated.

Both the male and female may find accidentally that pleasure is derived from manipulation of the genitalia. In the boy there may be spontaneous erections which are followed by manipulation and ejaculation. This phenomenon is a normal one and generally occurs in most males for one or two years after puberty. It may occur one, two, or three times a week, and gradually disappears in one to three years as the boy becomes less interested in himself and more interested in the physical and social activities about him. Nocturnal emissions are normal and may occur for many years. They are increased by lying upon one's stomach or by the excessive use of condiments or large fluid intake just before retiring. Similarly, in the female, there may be massage of the clitoris, but only rarely is there any introduction of objects into the vagina. The parents, during this period, should encourage and facilitate all manner of social and recreational interests. Such masturbation is rarely accompanied by phantasy: it is simply an experience of physical pleasure.

As a child develops into and through adolescence, sexual desires may by varying degrees be aroused by the ordinary social contacts between girls and boys. The person's make-up, and his susceptibility to the more or less rigid moral standards set in the home and in society, will or will not prevent sex relations from occurring before marriage. Adolescents should be taught that the sex desire is perfectly normal; that no harm can come from continence; and that it is advisable to become actively engaged in physical and recreational activities, and to spend as little of the conscious time thinking about sex as possible. The energy directed along the channel of sex, it should be explained, can be redirected constructively into other channels—until marriage occurs.

When coitus does occur, very few persons understand the mechanism.[1] Ignorance of the procedure most calculated to bring about maximum satisfaction results in a great deal of sex dissatisfaction, on the basis of which the vicious cycle of matrimonial disharmony develops. It would be highly advisable for the physician to instruct all prospective wives and husbands in the phenomenology of proper sex relations. Many women are married with only a vague and often erroneous understanding of what is to occur. The male, being much more easily aroused than the female, and not appreciating this difference, often uses little consideration.[2] In many women an intact hymen or a small introitus may make coitus difficult. The male should be instructed to indulge in sex play, with much kissing and petting, before intercourse is attempted. Especially during the first intercourse, the male should introduce first one, then several fingers into the vagina so as to dilate it properly. Copulation should occur when both partners are aroused, and during the act of copulation the male and female should enter actively into it. A rhythm will eventually be established, if there are no disturbing emotional factors, so that the orgasm will occur simultaneously in both parties. The orgasm in the male generally occurs with the ejaculation, but it does not necessarily do so. In the female, the orgasm may be accompanied by some vaginal secretion; and in some cases, there may be actual uterine contractions, but as a rule *the orgasm is simply an intense nervous release of tension*.[3] The orgasm as such is an exceedingly important phenomenon. Essentially coitus is a building-up of tension followed by a sudden release or discharge. This release, or orgasm, is succeeded by a sense of marked relaxation. Should, however, the orgasm not occur, tension persists— often for long periods of time. Many women in whom tension is aroused but not released may cry and become very tense, irritable, and sleepless after coitus.

Sex relations may occur very frequently during the first few weeks of marriage; but thereafter usually take place two or three times a week. These relationships occur at this rate throughout the third and fourth decades, gradually becoming fewer until they average about once a month after the age of sixty. There are,

---

[1] *Vide* p. 159.   [2] *Vide* p. 162.   [3] *Vide* pp. 108 (Case T. V.); 241.

however, tremendous individual variations; and there may be very frequent or very infrequent sex relationships all through life.

Physical health is of importance. The male may be very aggressive sexually; or on the other hand, relatively passive. The same factors hold true for the female. When one partner feels an intense desire and the other does not, there may be cause for disharmony.[1] Again, not infrequently, there may be an actual physical orgasm, but extreme dissatisfaction remains if the emotional and psychologic relationship is not what is expected. Often men have ejaculations and orgasms, but are left with a feeling of dissatisfaction because of the irritability or lack of enthusiasm on the part of the wife. There are many variations of this phenomenon.

Sex desires tend to be more frequent at certain times in a woman's life, generally just before and just after menstruation. Sex relations are usually most enjoyed when there is a spirit of excitement preceding the intercourse. In the ordinary routine of the average married life, this excitement and excitability do not come about so often as they should, and *sex relationships become a routine matter*. It is this routineness which on a number of occasions may give rise to dissatisfaction in one partner or both. On the other hand, complete sex satisfaction may do much to increase the love and affection between compatible persons. It adds a fulness and an emotional tone to marriage that can not be obtained in any other way.

The purpose of these discussions is not to describe all the sexual aberrations that may occur, but merely to mention the most common difficulties which are met with by the average physician. Moreover, in sex as well as in all other reaction patterns in life, there may be temporary maladjustments among some persons and more or less permanent ones among others. Many sexual factors adjust themselves with practice and with time. The fact that sex has too long been shrouded in ignorance, and that it has been dealt with as an indelicate topic, has resulted in the development of a great number of symptoms which could very easily have been prevented.

There are all degrees of sexual maladjustments. Often what is normal for one person is abnormal for another. Temperaments vary as well as the social conditions and the standards set by the individual families.

The physician should try to deal with sexual problems from the effect they have upon the physical or mental health of the

[1] *Vide* p. 164 (Case H. I.).

patient. It is inadvisable to go against the rule of the society in which he lives and to insist or advise the patient to break existing moral codes; for when difficulties occur, the patient often blames the physician. Rather should the actual facts be presented unemotionally and fairly, and the physician should insist that the patient, and the patient alone, decide his course of conduct. The physician is neither a moralist nor a clergyman:[1] he can only advise on matters of health.

SEX AS A TENSION-RELEASING MECHANISM

The sexual function not only serves the end of race propagation, but has other values. Proper sex relations, besides being pleasurable in themselves, are definitely (1) *tension releasing* in their effect, and (2) they are very often used as a *pleasure substitute; i. e.*, when other real satisfactions in life are denied the person—he or she—may turn to gratification in sex. Over-interest in sex may thus be indicative of a lack of other pleasures and of boredom. In addition, incomplete sex satisfaction, generally without an orgasm, is definitely tension producing.

As the person engages in sex play, whether it be only in phantasy or in actuality, tension is built up which, if unreleased, tends to have a vicarious expression.

EARLY SEX MALADJUSTMENTS

A great number of the difficulties due to sexual inefficiency in adult life can be ascribed to the pattern of sex laid down in childhood. It had been the tendency, and still is among a large percentage of the population, to take the attitude that sex is sinful; that one must never speak of it; that it is a hidden, lewd, and disgusting part of one's life which one should never even think of. Girls are told not to play with certain "horrible boys," and mothers often manifest an obvious prudishness and concern. In general, the whole phenomenon of sex is given a mysterious and unpleasant tinge. The result of this atmosphere is to make the child at once avidly interested in the subject and to build up inhibitions which have a far-reaching effect.

Miss J. B., aged forty-two years, was single, and "detested" men. Once when a man asked her to marry him, she became furiously angry that any one would think "such a thing of her." She had a few women friends but did not particularly enjoy their company. She much preferred to be alone.

[1] *Vide* p. 187.

Her early environment not only was unfortunate in its atmosphere of tension but was particularly poor in sex hygiene. Her mother was extremely sensitive and bitter on the subject of sex. The children were continuously filled with tales of the evil nature of men; and there were many insinuations of the evil intentions of women acquaintances as well. So strong were this mother's feelings that she never permitted the children to undress before each other, or even before her. The patient "came by her prudishness rightfully."

On the other hand, over-exposure to sex at an early age may also lead to abnormal reactions. In other words, over-emphasis in either direction is unhealthful. Sex hygiene should be as objectively considered and dealt with as physical hygiene, and any sort of over-evaluation should be avoided.

One might suggest the rule: The more the attempt is made to prevent the child from knowing about sex, and the more sex is surrounded with a shroud of evil, the more surely will the child be both interested in it and inhibited about it. The physician sees many women who think that kissing will cause them to become pregnant; who feel that intercourse without an orgasm is an effective way of preventing conception; who permit sex relations only for the purpose of having children; who deny themselves the pleasure of an orgasm because it is sinful, etc. Many women are prudish to the extent of being unwilling to undress for a physical examination, or of avoiding seeking a physician when there is any disturbance in the generative tracts. As a result, there develops an attitude of not facing the facts of sex; and this attitude so easily applied in the one direction, quickly extends to a general unwillingness to face reality in non-sexual directions. This reaction pattern of avoidance[1] of that which is emotional or irritating is common; and too often its genesis lies in the lack of courage to face the facts of sex frankly.

Mrs. C. O. was brought up in a very strict and domineering home. Her parents were exceedingly prudish, and she knew nothing of sex. She was not even informed about menstruation; and when menses first appeared at the time of puberty, she experienced a tremendous emotional shock. When she married, she was horrified at her husband's desiring sex relationships. She yielded only after her husband used physical force and she developed an intense emotional reaction characterized chiefly by marked trembling of her entire body, insomnia, anorexia, and crying spells. She impressed her resultant aversion and prudishness so much upon her daughter that at the age of sixteen the daughter, in reaction against this teaching, became illegitimately pregnant.

[1] *Vide* p. 205 *ff.*

Such phenomena are exceedingly common and are the answer to the query so often asked by friends, "Why should the daughter turn out to be 'so bad' when her mother is 'so good'?".

Mrs. S. L. had acute anxiety symptoms. She had marked choking in the throat, her heart beat very rapidly, she was frightened, and feared to walk out of the house alone.

Mrs. S. L. lived in the slum districts. Her father was an alcoholic and deserted the patient's mother soon after the child's birth. The mother also drank and did not work frequently. From the earliest age, the patient was accustomed to see strange men in the house, swearing and cursing the mother, and not infrequently was she aware of the illicit relations in the next room of their extremely small apartment. Her reactions to sex were intense, and she married only because of the persistence of her "boy-friend." Sex always reminded her of the horrible days and nights spent witnessing her mother's debauchery.

This case is an extreme one, but a similar situation may arise wherever the moral code is very lax. Indicative of what "goes on behind the scenes," and of the type of ideas children get is such a question as the following over-heard query: The speaker was thirteen-year-old Don, "John, whose wife are you going to kiss when you get big?"

Another factor in early sex maladjustment is sex trauma. Children may be exposed while young to some perverse person and have some unpleasant experience which may result in an abiding fear of, or distaste for, sex relations.

Thus, Mrs. W. O. came in with the complaint of headaches, occasional dyspareunia, and frigidity during sex relations. When she was eight years old, a middle-aged man exposed himself before the patient who became violently frightened, especially when he offered her money and tried to force her to play with him. She was uninformed about menstruation; and when it occurred, she developed severe guilt feelings, thinking that the blood was a punishment for this sexual experience. She never had recovered from the shock, in spite of her marriage and children.

Mr. P. O. was not conscious or aware of the significance of sex, and he was regarded by, and regarded his parents with affection. When he was seven years of age, he unexpectedly came into his parent's bedroom one morning while they were having sexual relations, and he assumed from the positions that the father was hurting his mother. He was badly frightened and upset. From that moment he detested his father, and even after he intellectually "understood," he could not get over his dislike. He felt even more guilty because he was like his father, and he wished that he were not a man.

MASTURBATION

One of the most common of sexual difficulties grows out of the phenomenon of masturbation. As has been previously pointed out, masturbation is in itself a normal phenomenon, occurring shortly before and after puberty, and tending to disappear as the person becomes more engrossed in social and physical activities, and finally, as satisfaction is obtained through coitus in marriage.

The attitude of society, however, in many instances has been to condemn masturbation. It is to the interest of society and of mankind to discourage such practices which inherently have the tendency to prevent propagation. The way in which masturbation is discouraged is, however, often very unsatisfactory. The person, understanding neither his own desires nor the prohibitions placed on them, tends to develop guilt feelings. He is often told that masturbation is "awful"; that a person who practices it may develop disease; may become exhausted and get tuberculosis; will develop insanity and lose his mind; will injure himself physically; will lose his sexual potency, etc. The attitude of the parent often seems to be based on the desire to terrify the child. This frightening experience is worse than ineffective, for generally the physiologic drives are strong enough to force masturbation in spite of the fears which have been set up; and were it not for the frightening experiences, the tendency and desire for masturbation would usually disappear more quickly. The *feeling of guilt*, however, focuses attention upon sex; and because of the interest centered therein, makes the masturbation tendency continue long after its normal period of cessation, while at the same time producing many emotional and physical symptoms.

Thus, for example: Mr. D. D., aged thirty-one years, complained of having had a feeling of pressure on top of his head since the age of sixteen. This pressure was associated with the sensation of a band squeezing around his head, and with insomnia. This man had begun to practice masturbation at the age of sixteen and was discovered early in this practice by his father, who had told the boy that he would certainly go insane. Immediately upon hearing this prediction, the patient developed a pressure in his head and thought so much about his masturbation that he could not sleep. His entire interest became centered upon sex, and he could not develop the normal interest in physical, social, and recreational activities. He began to feel that people knew about his practice, and condemned him, and he grew very sensitive and was on the defensive whenever any of his non-sexual wishes failed, feeling that failure was entirely the result of his autoerotism.

It is important, therefore, in preventive therapy to see to it that the child has a normal understanding of masturbation, and that he be provided with sufficient energy outlets so as to become interested in things outside himself. Masturbation, he must be told, has no effect whatsoever upon the mind or body unless the patient feels guilty and is concerned about it. But he further must be told that masturbation in itself is a symptom of puberty, is immature, and dies out as soon as he becomes more mature and interested in outside events.

Release of Tension.—Release of tension may occur through masturbation. As has been pointed out, during sex relationships, tension is first built up and then released at the orgasm. Similarly, in certain anxiety states where tension is built up by other causes, such as concern over finances or social situations, some release of this tension may be obtained by orgasm.

Patients suffering from anxiety depressions sometimes utilize masturbation as a means of releasing some of their tension and anxiety; but this release is brief, and usually masturbation is not a predominant symptom.

Masturbation may be used as a *compensatory mechanism*[1] for obtaining pleasure whenever the person feels depressed, or un-loved, or cruelly treated. This use is more generally made by children than by adults.

Miss F. M.,[2] aged thirty-one years, had been practicing masturbation since the age of seven. She was brought up in an extremely unstable household. There was a domineering mother and a weak, disgruntled father who sustained himself on a small pension fund. The children were made the butt of the dissatisfactions present in the parents. The girl was constantly scolded; ordinary toys were denied her because of lack of funds; her clothing was unkempt; she had a feeling of being different, and was despised by the other children in the school; she felt lonely, had no one to turn to. She discovered masturbation accidentally, and the pleasureable relief obtained thereby gave her some compensation for the unpleasant life she led. At the same time she felt extremely guilty over the act and tried to stop the practice. This conflict between her guilt feelings and the desire to obtain some pleasure led to her using the words "horrible fascination" to describe her attitude toward masturbation. She developed fatigue and insomnia which were chronic.

This tendency to seek pleasure substitutes coincides with the phantasy development which is so common in children, and both are employed as an escape from reality.

[1] *Vide* p. 80 (Case F. M.).   [2] *Vide* pp. 48; 70.

There are some persons who may be termed "chronic masturbators." Many of these persons have a sallow, dreamy-eyed appearance and are very introvert in their tendencies. On analysis, it appears that their entire life is spent in a mixture of fantasy and reality. Their wishful thinking is such that they border very closely upon the schizophrenic reaction types.

One such male, aged thirty-one years, practiced masturbation three or four times a day for a period of fifteen years. He obtained no sex satisfaction from sex contact with women. He had never concentrated upon any work and fell into that class often diagnosed as Simple Schizophrenia.

In the psychoses, masturbation is often a common concomitant, particularly in Schizophrenic reaction types; and it follows the same principles as in the chronic masturbator: namely, a narcissistic "love of self" and fulfillment of desires in phantasy.

IMPOTENCE

Impotence in the male may result from such physical factors as illness, fatigue, syphilis of the spinal cord, tumors of the spinal cord, and local lesions. Physical impotence is rare in young healthy persons; and whenever it does occur in men under fifty, it is in the vast majority of cases the result of psychologic factors.

The ability to have an erection is the result of a desire for sex satisfactions. Should conflicting emotions stronger than the sex desire come to the fore, impotence may result. Thus a person who may be disgusted with his sexual partner, or who may feel antagonistic, may fail to have an erection; those who are in a state of fear may temporarily be impotent. Concern over masturbation is a very common cause of impotence. Many men are afraid to marry because they feel that masturbation has "robbed them of their manhood."

Other factors which will influence the male are: (1) a frigid wife with whom sex relations are unsatisfactory; (2) an overburdened conscience; (3) placing the wife on a pedestal so that she cannot be regarded as a human being but only as an ideal; (4) overaggressiveness of the female in a relatively non-passionate male; (5) concern about business[1] or social situations, etc.

K. Y., aged thirty-four years, complained of pains about the heart and of impotence. He had been married for fourteen years and had two children. For the past three months he had been impotent, although up until that time, sexual relations occurred normally two or three times a week. Six

[1] *Vide* p. 167 (Case S. O.).

months before, the man had been discharged from his employment and had been unable to find other work. The financial situation became exceedingly acute and the patient, who was proud, put off asking for charity. However, because of the need for his wife and children to eat, he had to go on relief, and it was on the background of these worries that impotence resulted. A different attitude toward his financial state and the partial relief thereof caused the impotence to disappear.

C. T., aged thirty-four years, complained of having had for four years a pain in one testis. Four years before, he had been married and living with his in-laws. His wife whom he respected discovered him with another woman; and his conscience troubled him to the point that he found, immediately thereafter, that he was completely impotent.

FRIGIDITY[1]

Frigidity, or lack of sexual satisfaction in women, is an exceedingly common phenomenon. It is far more common among women than is impotence among men. Frigidity, or sexual anesthesia, may be partial or complete. When it is partial, some satisfaction is derived during coitus, but no orgasm results. When it is complete, there is a marked tendency toward frustration symptoms. The causes of frigidity are several:

1. Early training[2] is the most common factor. Too often girls are taught by precept and example to be prudish. Sex is not placed upon a normal plane as something which is a pleasant part of marriage, and which is perfectly normal and natural, but is rather taught as being something which is "not nice" or even "wrong." Inhibitions which are thus built up carry through from early childhood to marriage.

2. The first introduction into sex relationship if improperly done often gives rise to a conditioned response of dissatisfaction and pain. The virgin female often is very tense during the first approach. This tension, in combination with an intact hymen and undilated introitus, may make for a very painful sex relationship, which may be further complicated if the husband in his approach is exceedingly direct and makes no attempt to arouse his wife and obtain relaxation. Many women on experiencing this very unsatisfactory first sex relationship become disillusioned, particularly if they have built up a set of romantic ideas about sex satisfactions.[3] Instruction to both the male and female before marriage is often a very important factor in preventing frigidity and thus preventing matrimonial disharmony.

[1] *Vide* p. 161 *ff*.   [2] *Vide* p. 102 (Case C. O.).   [3] *Vide* p. 270.

3. Roughness and precipitancy of the husband frequently make for rigidity. The female requires a longer period of stimulation in order to become properly aroused. The male, becoming aroused much more quickly, may not consider these factors; and the result is an unprepared wife who comes to fear sex relations as well as to be frigid.

A number of women stay up late into the night and avoid going to bed on one excuse or another, rationalizing that they have work to do, but really wishing to avoid this unsatisfactory sex contact.

Thus, Mrs. T. V., aged thirty-seven years, married, with two children, complained of nervousness, irritability, crying spells, fears of "doing something wrong" with weapons. Physically, she was in excellent condition. The patient stated that she nagged at her husband over little things and knew that she was wrong in doing so. She was an accomplished musician, played over the radio, but had to leave work because of her irritability. The husband, nine years older than the patient, made no attempt to arouse her. As a result, she had never reached an orgasm during the entire seventeen years of marriage and consented to intercourse only to oblige her husband. After intercourse, she was left tense, irritable, and frequently trembling all over.

4. Fear of pregnancy[1] is a common deterrent to sexual satisfaction. The pains during labor may be so intense that they leave a lasting impression upon the woman, and as a result, anything which concerns sex and pregnancy tends to be unsatisfactory. In a number of instances, children are not desired, and the fear of pregnancy operates in a similar way.

Mrs. D. I., aged forty-four years, had one child, at the age of twenty-three. Labor was extremely difficult, and it was five days after the onset of her pains before she gave birth to her child. Since that time, sex relations have been extremely unsatisfactory, and symptoms of frustration developed. When menopause set in at the age of forty-two, the patient knew she could not become pregnant again; and since that time the symptoms of frustration have entirely disappeared.

I. C., aged twenty-two years, married for four years, complained of difficulty in catching her breath and of being very excitable. She was perfectly all right until one night, a year and a half before, when she went to a movie, and on leaving, she began to yawn and since that time could not catch her breath. Sex relations were perfectly satisfactory until after the birth of her first child; but their financial status did not permit them to have more children, and being Catholic, she would not use any contraceptives. The result was coitus by withdrawal, and the patient developed symptoms of frustration. The symptoms began three months after the first child was born. When the patient was instructed in the method of "safe period," her symptoms disappeared entirely.

[1] *Vide* p. 164 (Case H. I.).

5. Irritations over non-sexual factors frequently leave the woman as well as the man in a state of mind where sex desire is absent. As a consequence, coitus during such a time may bring about only partial satisfactions, and the memory of this partial satisfaction may carry over into the succeeding sex relations and impair succeeding orgasms. Persons should be instructed to avoid sex contact should they find themselves unable to give up their concern over financial, social, or other problems.

6. Insufficient love-making by the husband is a very important reason for frigidity. The male of the species seems to be able to develop an erection and excitement within a relatively short period of time. Women, on the other hand, are for the most part, in need of a great deal of love-making before they can become adequately aroused. Moreover, in the female the physical element of sex relationship is in itself not sufficient.[1] Great value is placed upon the evidences of affection and care. There are many girls who have an intense, and some who have definite, nymphomaniac desires, but who will not have sex contact unless there is the emotional tone present. In women whose frigidity can be traced to such a factor, it is important to speak to the husband and obtain his cooperation. Frequently a cure can thus be obtained.

7. Improper coordination during coitus itself is an occasional cause of frigidity. Many women with the background of prudishness and inhibitions restrain themselves during the act. This restraint definitely impairs the satisfaction which can be derived. It is a common experience to hear men say, "She lies there like a board," a somewhat crude statement which nevertheless is a pithy condemnation of the wife's reactions.

One woman, for example: Mrs. F. P., aged thirty-seven years, expressed intense dissatisfaction over sex contact. This distaste carried to the point where she developed psychoneurotic illnesses such as pains and aches abdominally, which were used as an excuse to avoid sex relationship. It was found that when she was first married, she lived with her parents and was so intensely concerned lest they hear noises in her room that she made every effort during coitus to restrain not only her movements, but her husband's movements. Obviously no orgasm could be reached; and the habit pattern finally became so firmly established, that when their own home was acquired, coitus could no longer be enjoyed.

In a number of males, there is premature ejaculation and this, of course, leads to a lack of orgasm on the part of the female and,

---

[1] *Vide* p. 163.

consequently, to frigidity. On the other hand, some women are satisfied only when there is multiple orgasm present during each coitus. When this multiple orgasm does not occur, the feeling of tension results in a desire to avoid any arousal, and consequently brings about frigidity.   Many of the factors which influence impotence in the male may also affect the woman, and they all must be considered in getting at the etiologic mechanism.

The treatment of impotence[1] and other sexual difficulties has been indicated in the discussion of the causes of the various maladjustments.   Removal of the cause is important if a cure is to be obtained.   Insomuch as most sex problems in adult life result from attitudes, it is the correction of these attitudes which is of primary importance.   However, the tremendous variations in the amount of sex drive from person to person, and the fact that persons with different amounts of drive may be married, make any general formulation of treatment a difficult one.   Moreover, in marriage for example, the lack of excitement, the routineness of sexual activity, and the fact that *once a habit pattern of sexual reaction is established it is most difficult to eradicate* make the therapy of such sex problems as frigidity arduous and often unsuccessful. On the other hand, problems of masturbation and impotence are easily dealt with provided there are no serious complications.   In impotence, for example, the explanation of the mechanism of emotion, and reassurance, are valuable adjuncts to the removal of the particular cause involved.   In addition, in cases of impotence, if the patient is forbidden to have sex relations for a week (assuming as it were that his impotence will disappear) while indulging in much sex play, it will be found that freedom from the necessity of having sex relations combined with the stimulation from the sex play, will tend to make the patient so potent and eager as to make him disregard the command to wait for a week.   Once sex relations have been consummated, impotence generally disappears.   However, the success of such therapy varies in proportion to the duration of the illness.   In those instances wherein impotence has been present for a few days or even weeks, such as not infrequently occurs among susceptible youths when first married, a cure can usually be accomplished in two or three visits.   When, however, the impotence has lasted many months, as was the case of Mr. C. B., aged thirty-five years, who had been married for six months and had been unable to have sex relations during that whole time, the

---

[1] *Vide* p. 167 (Case S. O.).

therapy lasted over a period of three months before he was successful and his wife became pregnant. In this case, however, one had
to deal with the fact that the patient had masturbated every night,
with practically no exception for twenty years, and had never had
sex relations. In still other cases a man may be potent with one
woman and not with another, and here again it is essential to deal
with the etiologic mechanisms. Premature ejaculation is a problem of concern and differs only in degree from impotence. The
treatment again is concerned with the causative forces; though it
may be added that many men try to develop increased ability to
resist ejaculation until the wife reaches an orgasm by avoiding sex
relations, when the therapy should be the reverse of having more
frequent sex contacts so that the person becomes less sensitive to
stimulation and consequently less premature in his orgasm. Premature ejaculation is particularly common among tense, anxious,
irritable, and restless persons "who cannot sit still even for five
minutes."

Frustration.—Frustration (L. Frustratus Frustra, in vain)
symptoms show themselves in many vicarious ways. In the field
of sex, for example, when an orgasm is not reached, or dissatisfactions occur in some way or another, the person may show symptoms
of irritability, tension, anger, or an entire psychoneurotic complex.

Irritability.—Irritability is the most common symptom of sex
frustration. Often after an unsatisfactory sex act, persons, especially women, are left tense, emotionally disturbed; and occasionally they may tremble from head to foot, and cry. In most
instances, following such a frustrating experience, the person may
not be able to go to sleep for an hour or two; however, in many the
irritability remains far into the succeeding days and expresses
itself vicariously. Some women develop nagging qualities; are
fault-finding; constantly critical; they become suspicious, carry
tales, and spread rumors. They often cannot say a kind word, but
are full of animosity and irritability. These reaction patterns are
the indirect methods of expressing the frustrations due to inadequate sex contacts.

One woman, Mrs. K. D. L., writes the following letter which is exceedingly
graphic: "Upon the advice of the doctor, I came back to town last spring to
resume my household duties and to attempt another adjustment to married
life. Since my advent here, I have improved in some respects, but in others
have made no advance. I have taken more interest in my household duties,
and have shown more pride in keeping the house clean and in preparing tasty

meals, and in keeping up the sewing and in my personal appearance, and in mixing with people. On the other hand, my unreasoning resentments have grown apace, and I seem to be unable to control my spiteful behavior and seem unable to adjust to the conventional life of a married woman. I have caused him much needless worrry and embarrassment.

"I get a strange thrill out of trying to see whether I can provoke him to the point of losing his temper, and wait with bated breath for the consequences and tingle all over with a pleasureable sense of excitement and suspense. If he does lose his temper and an altercation follows, one side of my nature gets a strange pleasure out of that. It is true that all this is repugnant to a part of me, and yet these other tendencies seem the stronger, and I am apparently unable to check them. It is just as if I were putting a bomb on a railroad track and dreaded and yet at the same time, wanted to see the wreck. I know this sounds crazy, but I feel you will know what I mean.

"I seem to be irresistibly drawn and tempted to provoke and make trouble in thousands of little ways, just as though I were being drawn by a magnet against my will. I just can't help doing everything I can to pester and annoy my husband. I am ashamed of myself and know I am in the wrong and yet something drives me to it until at times I almost feel possessed.

"Outside the home I am extremely shy and bashful and unsure of myself. I feel tongue-tied and self-conscious and awkward. While I think I have improved to some extent in this respect, I am still very much ill at ease among people, and I believe that this feeling I have in public partly contributes to my unpleasant disposition in the home.

"My destructive tendencies have improved. I cannot understand these things. Sometimes I am aware of what I am doing, and yet seem to be driven by some force against my will to do them, and other times I am not at all aware of having done them until afterwards, when I am confronted with the obvious.

"In regard to my sexual life as a married woman, as mentioned in the above letter, because of my physical make-up, it is impossible for me to perform the normal sex act. This doubtless partly explains my condition. Perhaps the fact that I was a premature child, upon whom a previous attempt at abortion had been made, may also partially account for my condition.

"For these reasons I feel that I am definitely in need of institutional help and as my husband cannot with his present salary afford a private sanitarium, I would like to apply for admission into one of the state hospitals for observation and treatment, and to secure a court order for my commitment."

In the above situation, Mrs. L. had a congenital hip deformity which so bound her leg to the midline (by adhesions between the head of the femur and the pelvis) that entrance of the male organ was almost impossible. Nevertheless, contacts were attempted but were doomed only to arousal without satisfaction. There was no need for institutionalization, and all that was needed to make the symptoms disappear was to clear up the physical deformity.

Tension.—Symbolic symptoms[1] (frequently classified under the terms anxiety states, obsessive compulsions, neurasthenia, hysteria) and even psychotic reactions may result from sexual frustrations. So-called anxiety states are rather frequent and occur particularly when conception is avoided by withdrawal of the penis before orgasm is reached. The lack of orgasm in these situations is particularly intense because, although ejaculation occurs outside the vagina, there is concern over the possibility of pregnancy.

Thus Mr. D. J., aged twenty-eight years, single, complained of inability to concentrate, sharp pains in his head, insomnia, and intense anxiety which frequently caused him to awake in the middle of the night with a very rapidly beating heart and a fear of death. He had been seriously concerned and interested in sex for many years; but on first attempting relationships tried to prevent conception by the withdrawal method. Although ejaculation occurred, he was left tense, excited, and exceedingly uneasy. He ascribed this emotional reaction to the masturbation he had practiced as a child, and continued to get the same anxiety state whenever he practiced the withdrawal method.

Simple advice was curative.

Mrs. F. M., aged twenty-nine years, with three children, stated that sex relations had always been unsatisfactory. She said that though she was not very passionate, she tended to be aroused toward the end of coitus. She had experienced some orgasms before the first pregnancy, but none since then. When they tried to use a condom as a contraceptive, her husband became impotent. On the other hand, when sex relations occurred otherwise, she "did not feel him inside her." The patient developed fears of all sorts. She became afraid to go out alone; she would not go into the bathroom unless someone was with her, lest she take poison from the medicine cabinet. She would not go into the drug-stores, because poison was available there. She feared that she might kill her children; she cried constantly. Her fears, she spontaneously said, were unreasonable and without basis, and yet they persisted in spite of what she did.

In this case, perinorraphy plus the use of a pessary eliminated the obsessive symptoms.

Mr. J. D., aged twenty-two years, came in complaining of having had pains in the right side of the abdomen for six years, which lasted from three days to a week and subsided only to occur after several days. In addition, he had a dull ache in his back, felt weak and fatigued, and could not sleep well. These symptoms were markedly aggravated after masturbation. He felt much stronger if he could resist this auto-erotic tendency for a week or two. When the problem of masturbation was cleared up, his neurasthenic symptoms disappeared.

[1] *Vide* p. 24 *ff.*

8

Miss B. T., aged twenty years, complained of numbness in the entire left side of the body and face. This numbness was present for six months, came on suddenly, and was present only on retiring. There was no motor phenomena, and the neurologic examination was negative. This young woman planned to work in a restaurant as a waitress, but her mother objected because of the fear that men might make improper advances. The patient stated that she had no friends, because whenever she went to a dance, or elsewhere, boys made requests of her for sex relations. She had always refused, and the boys then no longer sought her company. When the patient goes out at night, the mother sits up and waits until she returns, and then questions her at great length about possible sex delinquencies. The patient stated, "Maybe she is afraid I will change and give in."

In this perfectly normal young woman, the intense concern over sex on the part of the mother and the abnormal interest thus aroused resulted in frustration symptoms which manifested themselves in numbness.

In some cases, actual psychotic reactions may occur, if there is sufficient constitutional predisposition.[1]

Thus, Miss H. N. was found to be acutely excited; pounding on the walls; stating that she heard the voices of men calling her names; and feeling electricity constantly in her genitalia. These symptom reactions and others pointed to the diagnosis of Schizophrenia. On more detailed examination it was found that this woman had had sex contact at an exceedingly early age and had developed nymphomaniac desires. She nevertheless would not allow herself to have any intimacies unless she could convince herself she loved the man. She was unable to obtain sex contacts; became exceedingly irritable, and phantasied constantly during the day and far into the night about sex. She masturbated, but got no relief. The tension mounted constantly until the symptoms mentioned above appeared.

Sadism and Masochism.—Sadism and Masochism may be expressions of sex-frustration. The desire to hurt, and inflict pain upon one's sexual mate is often an expression of anger at not receiving sex satisfaction. In the more violent forms of sadism emotional and sexual trauma[2] in early childhood play an important role. Similarly in masochism, the desire to be punished before having an orgasm may find its explanation in early conditioning.

Thus, Mr. K. U., aged twenty-seven years, stated that he could not have an orgasm unless he was beaten by a ruler across the buttocks. When the pain reached its maximum intensity, an orgasm followed. On detailed inquiry into the history, it was found that as a boy in school he was very fond of his woman teacher. He worshipped her and followed her about. On one occasion, after he had committed a misdemeanor, she placed him

---

[1] *Vide* p. 262.   [2] *Vide* p. 103.

across her lap and proceeded to spank him with a ruler. During this act, the friction engendered by the teacher's knee against the genitalia was followed by an orgasm. The patient's masochistic desires are definitely traceable to the memory of this incident.

Nymphomania and Satyriasis.—Similarly, nymphomania (intense and constant sex desire in the female) and satyriasis (intense and constant desire in the male) may result from emotional blocking of a psychoneurotic nature. These emotions then seek expression in sex as a pleasure substitute or as a vicarious release of general unrest.

Alcoholism.—During alcoholism[1] there is often an intense desire for sex contact; and on many occasions, especially in chronic alcoholics, there is a relative inability to have an erection. The combination of the increased desire due to decreased inhibitions and of impotence often leads to projection mechanisms wherein the alcoholic says, as it were, "It is not my fault; it is your fault,"—and then accuses the wife of infidelity.

Homosexuality.—Homosexuality may be overt or latent. In many men and women, intense love of one of the same sex may be the manifestation of a hidden homosexuality. Overt homosexuality may take various forms. There may be mutual masturbation, fellatio, cunnilinguism, or even pederasty. Many homosexuals have no feelings of guilt about the action; but the majority are constantly at war within themselves, feeling that their desires are entirely wrong, and yet being unable to restrain themselves. Not infrequently such guilt feelings will lead to projection mechanisms. Homosexuality is not uncommonly found in Schizophrenia.

One may divide homosexual drives into three groups:

Social.—Wherein homosexual contacts occur among large groups of men or women who, because of circumstances, have no association with the opposite sex for long periods of time.

Constitutional.—Wherein there are many physical characteristics of the opposite sex. Thus, a number of men have a very slight growth of hair upon the chin or chest; have long eye-lashes; a rounded figure; a highpitched voice, etc.; and *vice versa* in regard to the female. These extremes, however, are not in the majority.

Psychosexual Homosexuality.—Wherein there has been sex trauma of sufficient intensity to cause the person either to hate members of the opposite sex, or to like abnormally members of the same sex.

[1] *Vide* p. 402 *ff.*

Miss S. S., aged twenty-four years, stated that she had an intense desire to be with women; actually, physical intimacies occurred. She was very nervous, easily irritated, afraid that one side of her face was different from the other, and was sure that everyone stared at her. When she was eight, her brother, aged twenty-one years, forced intercourse upon her. The patient was so much in fear of him that she submitted to it without revealing the intimacy. Later, a second brother also engaged in relations with her; and this practice they continued until the patient was fourteen years old. Since that time, she feels no emotions save disgust in the presence of males and develops actual nausea if men try to flirt with her.

Mr. K. T., aged thirty-six years, liked to dress in women's clothes, and he came to the clinic with the request that he be operated on and have his genitalia removed and a vaginal-like orifice substituted. He was not psychotic, had a responsible position, and apparently adjusted well, except for his concern over the above-mentioned problem. His mother was very eager to have a girl child, but had four boys, the last one being the patient. The mother, feeling disappointed, kept the patient away from boys and dressed him like a girl. She gave him dolls to play with and taught him all the arts taught to a girl. This farce was kept up to the point that when he was six, he was sent to a girl's school, dressed as a girl. When he was seven, "I had the greatest disappointment of my life. My father took me to a barber and had my beautiful hair cut off. When I got home, both my mother and I cried. The next day I was sent to a boys' school, and I did not like to be dressed as a boy. My pants were rough, and the blouse was coarse, and I delighted in going home, taking off these clothes, and putting on my bloomers and dress, with its bows and ribbons."

It is obvious from the above statement that the attitudes inculcated by this mother were of vital importance in causing this man to have the ideas he had at the age of thirty-six, when he came to the clinic. In many instances the fact that the homosexuality is psychogenic in origin provides a basis for therapy.

The healthy male or female when frustrated may consciously direct his reactions into constructive sublimation.[1] One may speak of frustrations as arousing energy (in this case, by sex dissatisfaction), which needs to be expressed.[2] If a person can direct this energy wisely, no unhealthy symptoms will appear. Violent physical exercise is only a partial relief; but work of intense and interesting character frequently furnishes an excellent sublimation, as do social and recreational activities. All are outlets for energy which is not adequately relieved through sex contact. It matters little what form the energy release takes *as long as it interests* the patient and gives him a feeling of pleasure.[3] The more these sublimated activities give one a "kick," the fewer unhealthy

[1] *Vide* p. 79.   [2] *Vide* Ch. XII.   [3] *Vide* p. 250.

frustration symptoms will there be. It is these suggestions which the physician must give to those for whom adequate sex contact is not available.

It is well to stress the desirability of self-discipline in sex and other pleasures, as opposed to ignorance, repression, and external discipline. *Self-discipline consists of the ability to postpone immediate gratification and to do whatever may be necessary, even if it is unpleasant, for the sake of long-term satisfaction.*[1] Self-discipline, therefore, means more than a simple determined following-out of a set pattern of behavior, regardless of temptations. It implies, most of all, that the mental process be so disciplined that facts will be faced as they are,[2] and that rationalizations[3] will be minimized. One of the most difficult tasks to perform is this *mental self-discipline.* On occasion, it may be carried to an extreme, in the so-called "iron-willed"[4] person, who takes the attitude that most things that are pleasurable are to be avoided, and delights by such denial in proving his "own strength." Such exaggerations carry dangerous connotations for ultimate personal and social happiness.

In knowledge and action involving sex, it is far more valuable for the person to be able to understand his limitations, capacities, and long-term satisfactions with self and society considered, than for society, by its taboos, to keep information and discussion away from him. The first course is conducive to self-direction and sympathetic control; the second to repression, vicarious satisfactions, distorted emotional relations, and the need for excessive external control.

---

[1] *Vide* p. 242.   [2] *Vide* p. 205.   [3] *Vide* p. 71.   [4] *Vide* p. 212.

CHAPTER VI

THE PRINCIPLES OF PSYCHOTHERAPY

SINCE neurotic symptoms, expressed through both tension[1] and symbolism,[2] are immature or unhealthy personality reactions to stress, the fundamental treatment of neurotic symptoms should be directed at: (1) removing excessive stress, (2) eliminating immature and unhealthy personality traits, and (3) substituting mature and healthful reaction patterns with which to meet future stresses.[3] It will be noticed in this statement that no mention is made of treating the symptom of which the patient complains. Symptomatic therapy when used alone, as will be discussed later,[4] usually fails, for the cause of the symptom continues to operate. Symptomatic therapy may be used in conjunction with "causal" therapy; but the patient should understand the temporary nature of superficial therapy, and should direct the greatest part of his efforts in the more important direction. The physician can explain to the patient that one treats the tuberculosis and not its symptomatic cough; that one treats the pneumonia and not its associated fever; that one treats the basic emotional and unstable reaction patterns and not the neurotic manifestation. One of the great difficulties in all therapy is the tendency to treat the symptom without getting at the cause thereof.

A SOCIO-PSYCHO-BIOLOGIC ANALYSIS[5]

Personality reactions, mature or immature, healthy or unhealthy are the result of the constant interplay of biologic, sociologic, and psychologic forces. Consequently, in order to understand the normal or the neurotic personality it is important that there be a thorough study of the person from the physical, social, and psychologic aspects.[6]

A diagnosis of symbolism[7] or of tension symptoms should always be deferred until a thorough *physical examination* has been made.[8]

---

[1] *Vide* p. 24 *ff*.   [2] *Vide* p. 28 *ff*.   [3] *Vide* Ch. VIII,   [4] *Vide* p. 180.
[5] *Cf*. Ch. XVII (Psychoanalysis).
[6] There are other important aspects of influence. Dr. W. F. Petersen, for example, has pointed out the significance of meteorologic changes in the formation, growth, and disease of organisms. At the moment, however, these factors are not understood sufficiently to suggest therapeutic measures.
[7] See Chap. I for a discussion of the nature of neurotic symptoms.
[8] *Vide* p. 176.

Not infrequently "neurotic" symptoms turn out to be in reality the earliest signs of an apical tuberculosis, or an exophthalmic goitre. It is the mild lesions of a toxic or infectious nature which are so often responsible for errors in diagnosis. Consequently, the physical examination of the neurotic patient should be even more thorough than that of the patient who is obviously physically sick. One should not be wasteful of laboratory procedures; but if there is any suspicion of disease, then the X-ray, blood count, sedimentation rate, and any other procedure deemed necessary should be carried on. I have seen patients suffering with severe headaches and diagnosed as "neurotic" cured when X-ray showed the sphenoidal sinus to be "cloudy" and drainage was subsequently instituted;[1] patients with "emotional diarrheas" cured after the belated stool examination revealed ameba; patients markedly depressed and suicidal for over a year, cured in three weeks after the proctoscopic examination revealed an ulcerated bowel full of pus. Moreover in such instances, it is of the greatest value to have examined every possible cause of disease at the beginning of the treatment, rather than later; for the psychotherapeutic efforts are facilitated when the patient knows how thoroughly he has been scrutinized for any pathology.

There are some patients, however, who going to the opposite extreme, will insist that there is some physical basis for their ailment, despite all sorts of physical and laboratory examinations to the contrary, and despite many positive evidences of neuroses. These persons may attribute a major neurotic disturbance to some mild physical ailment. The physician must be prepared to *evaluate* the *relative* role of the pathology and the emotion: to exercise his judgment in the making of his diagnosis. Despite the significance of a careful physical examination one should not minimize the equal importance of emotional forces. At all times, common sense[2] must prevail.

Social Forces.—Social forces because of their extensive implications are of utmost importance in the formation of any personality. These influences, beginning with the parental environment, and extending through the whole gamut of life's forces, have vary-

---

[1] *Vide* p. 177 (Case of Bob H.).

[2] Common sense (though uncommon) is the ability to see the part in relation to the whole; it implies a true perspective of the relative importance of any fact or idea. Common sense is a comprehension of the total situation; and upon this faculty are elaborated the rules of science whose function it is to systematize and explain the details.

ing effects depending not only upon the nature of the social pressure, but also upon the state of the constitution at the time.[1] Each stress leaves behind some trace of its influence, and this trace continues to manifest itself in later life in proportion to the intensity of its effect and the susceptibility of the organism. Consequently, it becomes important to inquire into the social pressures (1) existing at the time the patient comes in for treatment, (2) those existing at the time of the onset of the illness, and (3) those which have existed as determining mechanisms from early life. This information can be obtained from the patient, from the wife or husband, from friends, siblings, or parents. In many instances, social agencies, school teachers, and others are of aid.[2] The more facts one has at hand, the better the diagnosis of what is and was wrong and the better insight will the physician have with reference to the characteristic type of response manifested by the patient. It is necessary to know what pressures exist at the time of treatment in order to be able to understand the obstacles to the treatment; knowing the social pressures existing at the time of onset of the illness will facilitate the explanation of why the particular tension and symbolic symptoms occurred; and determining the forces existing earlier in the patient's life will enable the physician to understand the susceptibility of the patient.

Psychologic Aspects.—Finally the psychologic aspects, usually the most important to investigate, reveal much of the susceptibility of the person to the stress. Practically, the physician needs to determine *what emotional reactions*[3] resulted from the stress; in other words, he must remember that that which might be a serious blow to a person at one time might at another be considered a casual incident. For example, one patient lost $20,000, his life's savings, in the 1933 bank crash, and accepted the loss with resolute equanimity; whereas one year later, when the patient lost his executive position, he became acutely neurotic, and developed a symbolic aphonia.[4] It is not the stress as such, but that which the stress represents to the person that is significant as to the results produced. The loss of the job may have been the "last straw," or the person may have changed, or the values may have been different. In any case it is significant that the stress itself is important only as related to the patient's attitude toward it.

---

[1] *Vide* p. 39.   [2] *Vide* p. 152.
[3] *Vide* Ch. VII (for technique); Ch. VIII (for significance of stress).
[4] *Vide* p. 29.

The patient's attitudes and the patterns of reaction which he has built up toward himself and towards others as a result of early training are the most important elements in the creation of neurotic tension and symbolism. Many of these attitudes are conscious and obvious to the person himself; but many attitudes are automatic and unconscious both in their expression and in their origin. Persons like, dislike, love, hate, fear, or enjoy specific ideas or things, without having any clear idea of the why of their emotional attitude, or with only some secondary and rationalized reason to explain their feelings. In the neurotic patient (indeed in many so-called normal persons), these unhealthy and immature attitudes and their attendant reaction patterns are responsible for the appearance of tension and symbolic symptoms. It is important to determine these underlying attitudes,[1] because irritations which have existed from earliest childhood may continue to exist in memory and continue to act just as if they were still actually present. In order to remove an unhygienic pattern of reaction it thus becomes necessary to remove the continued underlying irritation. These irritations are spoken of as being frequently "unconscious";[2] yet these unconscious memories may be elicited by conscious discussion with the patient as well as by other techniques (free association, dream analysis, etc.).[3] When the word unconscious is used in this sense, we do not mean that which is forgotten; it is rather used in the sense that the patient is unaware at the moment of the unconscious force which leads to symptoms. Thus an employee may become furiously angry over some trivial incident at home, without being consciously aware that he is releasing hitherto unexpressed anger evoked by his employer's criticism. At the time of his outburst against his wife, the employee is "unconscious" of the fact that his real anger is against the man who abused him. Ordinary discussion with the patient would quickly elicit the fact of his emotional suppression. In the same manner, though in far more detailed fashion, and searching far back in the patient's life, the physician attempts to unearth the "unconscious" mechanisms which without the patient's awareness play their role in producing symptoms of tension and symbolism.

A SOCIO-PSYCHO-BIOLOGIC RESYNTHESIS[4]

However, the mere making of such a thorough analysis of physical, social, and attitudinal factors is in itself not sufficient.

---

[1] *Vide* p. 134.   [2] *Vide* p. 67 (footnote).   [3] *Vide* Ch. VII.   [4] *Vide* Ch. IX.

It is not enough to understand intellectually what is wrong and what is right. It is essential for this therapy that each person apply and make automatic that which he understands. Many patients will spontaneously state that they are not acting as they should and they know what they should do; but they are unable to apply their knowledge. Consequently, the physician needs to resynthesize the patient's attitude and reaction patterns in such a way as to eliminate immature and unhealthful responses, and inculcate mature and healthy reactions.

As one analyses the causes, one provides for the therapy of the physical "dis-ease," advises on the treatment of the social problems, and outlines a procedure for retraining the attitudes of the patient. The physical disturbances should be dealt with according to their requirements,[1] and at the same time the patient should be made aware of just how much of a factor in his illness is his physical condition, and to what extent the social and psychologic forces are involved. In other words, the patient should be made to understand that the cure of his "actual" physical disease is inadequate to cure all his physical symptoms; he must learn the necessity of curing the emotional disturbances as well. Such emphasis is of vital significance as we shall see later. The medication used should be as specific as possible for the ailment; and, moreover, adjuncts which are of doubtful value should be avoided, in order to emphasize doubly the need for the patient's cooperation.

The social stresses present a special problem. Just what constitutes a stress is a problem to be considered. Many patients will attribute their illness to financial difficulties, to social pressures, to domestic squabbles, to employment; yet on longitudinal examination of the patient's life, one will often find that the patient has in the past suffered similar difficulties without developing symptoms of tension or symbolism.[2] In other words, the patient is at the time of development of the neuroses, more susceptible because of intrinsic changes, because of the cumulative effect of stress, or for other reasons. Moreover, many of the stresses which according to the patient produced the illness, often are not stresses to the average person. Most persons are under constant environmental pressure of various intensities without going into "nervous breakdowns." "Normal" persons may be unhappy and distressed over unfortunate situations, but tension symptoms arise only tempor-

---

[1] *Vide* p. 155.   [2] *Vide* p. 24 *ff.*

arily and the situations are quickly adjusted to. The psycho-neurotic patient is, in the usual situation, more susceptible than the "normal" person to stress.

Consequently, in dealing with social stresses, the physician should determine in his own mind, whether the particular stress is justifiably strong enough to produce symptoms in the "normal" person. If the stress is unduly severe, then the second portion of the therapy; *i. e.*, after treatment of physical disorders, is aimed at removing the stress, removing the patient from the stress, or advising the patient how to deal with the stress. If these efforts fail, or if the stress is one which occurs in the usual scheme of things and cannot be eliminated, then it becomes necessary to attempt to retrain the patient so that he will be able to avoid developing neurotic tendencies when he is under difficulties.

One may *remove the stress*[1] in such instances as those wherein there are cooperative relatives who though well meaning, are themselves sufficiently unstable as to create the social pressure that produces emotional tension in the patient. In children's behavior disturbances[2] the most effective therapy consists of removing the stress which lies frequently in the parental maladjustment. In actual practice in children's cases, one treats the parent much more than the child. When the situation is such that one cannot remove the stress, one may often *remove the patient from the stress.*[3] Not infrequently, for example, the patient labors under adverse working conditions, which may produce harmful emotional results; removal of the patient from such employment is often of great value in therapy. Finally, in the treatment of social factors, one may give the patient some *common sense advice*[4] *on how to deal with stresses* which cannot be removed. One can instruct the maladjusted adolescent on how to live with neurotic parents, one can advise the patient on diplomatic methods of dealing with unreasoning employers, one can recommend the study of another trade or profession, and so on. There are many limitations to and even dangers in giving such advice, as will be discussed more fully in

[1] *Vide* Ch. VIII.

[2] It is interesting to note that in children unhealthy reactions are spoken of as behavior disturbances; whereas in adults similar though more involved reactions are termed neuroses. *The adult's neuroses are indeed behavior disturbances;* the adult's symptoms are those of tension and symbolism just as are the child's behavior difficulties. Many persons have attempted to read mysterious causes into the adult neuroses, instead of recognizing the same pattern of behavior in the child and adult, differing only in complexity.

[3] *Vide* pp. 156–157 (Cases N. H.; L. S.).   [4] *Vide* p. 165 (Case F. S.).

the next chapter; but when used judiciously such advice may be invaluable in the therapy of the neurotic patient.

The main efforts at therapy, however, are to be directed towards the *changing of the susceptible personality*. This susceptibility stems (exclusive of constitutional predispositions) from the immature and unhealthy attitudes and patterns of reaction instilled in the person from early childhood and throughout life. Many persons with neuroses are trained by circumstance to over-react, to react by being fearful, to be egocentric and subjective in their evaluations, and so forth. These reaction patterns have become automatic within the patient, so that when a new situation arises which carries some form of stress, the patient responds almost reflexly in an immature and unhealthy manner, and with the side symptoms of tension and symbolism. The principles of this therapy consist of: (1) bringing to conscious attention in specific detail the unhygienic attitudes and their attendant irritating memories, (2) removing the emotional tone attached to the memories by intellectual understanding and by desensitizing[1] the patient through repeated discussions, and (3) retraining the patient so that he will react automatically in a hygienic, efficient, and non-symptom forming manner to the various stresses of life. It is of the utmost importance to remember that the person needs to learn to respond automatically in a healthful manner; consequently, intellectual understanding of what one should do is insufficient.[2] This automatic response is *learned by the adult only by persistent conscious effort.* The rapidity of such learning is dependent upon the number and intensity of the immature attitudes, the cooperation of the physical and social forces, and the amount of effort exerted by the patient. Time is an important element.[3] When these basic attitudes and reaction patterns are made normal, the individual responses will no longer carry undue signs of tension or symbolism and the patient's neurosis will cease to exist.

In actual practice it is not always possible, and often it is not advisable to attempt a thorough retraining of general and specific attitudes. Such attempts require a tremendous amount of effort and expense, and often seriously interfere with the patient's pursuit of the requirements of ordinary life. Consequently, in many instances if one is able by determining the immediate causes of the symptom and removing them, one may thereby produce a clinical

---

[1] *Vide* p. 179.   [2] *Vide* p. 193.   [3] *Vide* pp. 132; 206.

recovery.[1] In many patients the background is so unstable as to facilitate a quick recurrence of another neurotic symptom; but there are many other patients who have sufficient recuperative powers, and who are sufficiently stable to make a satisfactory adjustment with comparatively little therapy.[2] In these latter instances, it is the stress which is usually more severe than usual; and the treatment of such stress and the inculcation of adequate attitudes toward it often are all that is needed for the immediate recovery.[3] Despite this "short cut" method, however, one should always bear in mind that the more thoroughly one follows the principles described above, the more stable will be the personality and the more resistant will it be to future stresses of similar intensity.

TECHNIQUE OF ANALYSIS AND RESYNTHESIS[4]

The technique of analyzing the physical difficulties falls within the realm of general medicine. The usual physical examinations plus laboratory studies should be made before psychotherapy is seriously instituted, so that the patient will not be able to say that there is no proof of his lack of physical disease.[5] The analysis of the social factors can be done by obtaining information from persons who know the patient, or from the patient himself. The former technique consists simply of questioning relatives, friends, and others about specific points in the development of the particular patient and about any other information which they may give. In such interviews, it is important that the consent of the patient be obtained, and that the physician be careful not to violate the patient's confidence in any manner. Moreover, the physician should refuse to "label" the patient with some name, for too often friends and relatives will use such information to berate or reproach the patient. A more detailed discussion of this social analysis will follow in Chapter VIII.

Determining the basic attitudes[6] and reaction patterns depends for the most part on eliciting subjective information from the patient. In this portion of the analysis, the physician needs to understand what motives guide the patient, and what he "feels" in his reactions to life situations about him. In the last analysis, a situation is irritating or not (except for actual physical danger) in proportion

---

[1] *Vide* p. 257.
[2] *Vide* p. 301 (Case K. D.).
[3] *Vide* p. 135 (Case F. B.).
[4] *Cf.* Ch. VII.
[5] *Vide* p. 176.
[6] *Vide* p. 171.

to individual sensitivity and attitude.[1]   Most of these attitudes can be *determined by direct discussion*.[2]   If the patient is permitted to tell his own story, and the physician is trained to recognize the significance of slips of the tongue, over-emphasis, associated mannerisms, etc., most of the pertinent information can be quickly elicited.[3]   With practice, the physician can soon learn to put the patient at ease, and to make the patient feel that he can unburden his troubles without fear or restraint.   When the patient has apparently exhausted his information, the physician can then question him about early childhood relationships, school difficulties, adolescent problems, social, marital, financial, and other difficulties.   One should be careful not to hurry the patient.   This directed examination is in most instances entirely adequate, but should additional information be necessary, other techniques, such as free association and dream analysis[4] may be used.

Treatment.—Treatment of the physical difficulties (like diagnosis) is in the realm of physical medicine.   However, in view of the tendency of many psychoneurotic patients to over-emphasize the presence of any illness, it is wise to state, in a casual and under-emphasizing manner, the nature of the illness and the procedures to be followed in its cure.   Reassurance that the therapy will be effective should be given repeatedly.

The therapy of *social stresses* has already been outlined.   Much can be done via the cooperation of the mate, the parents, the friends, the relatives, the employer, the social agencies.   Though the physician should not hesitate to utilize all these sources in the therapy of the patient, it is nevertheless true that most of the social therapy will have to be along the circuitous route of first changing the patient that he may in turn ameliorate the social situation.

The therapy of the patient's *attitudes and patterns of reaction* which are at the basis of the neurotic predisposition is directed at: (1) *Specific attitudes*[5] which are removed and replaced by: (*a*) intellectual understanding of the *cause* of the attitude; (*b*) desensitization toward the old and emotional acceptance of this newer outlook,[6] and (*c*) conscious redirection of thought and action processes so as to break unhealthy *habits* of thinking and feeling and instil healthy ones, and (*d*) use of adjuvants as drugs, suggestion and hypnosis, and (2) *general attitudes*[7] and patterns of reaction

[1] *Vide* p. 154.   [2] *Vide* p. 136 *ff*.   [3] *Vide* p. 139.
[4] *Vide* p. 140.   [5] *Vide* p. 174 *ff*.
[6] *Vide* p. 193.   [7] *Vide* pp. 171–174.

which are removed and replaced by consistent and persistent training.[1]

As the discussion reveals specific attitudes or reaction patterns which are in themselves unhealthy and which have contributed to the emotional instability of the patient, the physician enlists the cooperation of the patient in ascertaining *the origin of the particular attitude*. When the cause, or more usually causes, are determined, the patient's reaction to the causes is discussed, and the better attitudes which should have been used are suggested in order to remove any resentment still existing in the unconscious. Repeated discussions will desensitize[2] the patient to the irritations dynamically forgotten.[3] Thus one patient had a dominant reaction pattern of automatically criticizing practically everyone she knew.[4] On investigation it was found that one of the causes of this reaction pattern was the attitude of her mother, who had constantly berated her as a child and had produced an intense sense of inferiority. In compensating for this inferiority the child had developed the pattern of attacking others before she could be attacked and criticized; and this pattern had carried over into her adult life. The patient still carried with her memories of her mother's nagging and condemnation, and continued unconsciously to react to them as if they still existed. The discussion that ensued demonstrated to her, not that she should avoid being condemnatory (for the desirability of this avoidance was obvious), but that there was a definite origin for the pattern, and that instead of reacting to the memory of her mother's criticism in an unhealthy manner, she could learn to react to this particular cause by understanding its origin, and by assuming a non-hostile but understanding attitude toward her mother. In other words, each specific attitude or pattern of reaction is dissected, and its origin traced. The patient is then trained by conscious direction to face in an adult and mature fashion the original cause of the difficulty. It cannot be emphasized too strongly, that general advice is almost valueless. Specificity of analysis, dealing with specific situations, and giving specific advice and comments are essential. In most instances, the more detailed the information given the patient, the easier is it for him to follow. Rather than tell a patient to "keep busy,"[5] one should discuss with him what he can do, and when he can do it. Some patients require an hour by hour schedule. Good results often are

---

[1] *Vide* p. 176.   [2] *Vide* p. 179.   [3] *Vide* p. 65.
[4] *Vide* p. 268 (Case I. L.).   [5] *Vide* p. 250.

obtained by such specificity when the giving of general advice would avail nothing.

The patient should understand intellectually the origin of each specific immature attitude, its function, how and why it is ineffective or harmful, and be shown a more mature method of meeting the specific situation. Here again it is important not to state merely that the patient's point of view and action are wrong, but to examine in detail just how the attitude arose, what was the role of the environment, of the parental attitudes, of the school situation, etc. Often a patient is emotional because the mother was emotional,[1] and the patient imitated the immature response. Often there was inculcated a feeling of inferiority, by condemnation, or by inadequacies in certain fields,[2] which attitude prevails in adult life. Often a person is sadistic because early in life he was cruelly treated and has compensated by treating others cruelly. It is just such facts which the patient should intellectually understand, and not simply be told that it is "wrong" to feel emotional or to feel inferior or to be sadistic. The very understanding of the cause of one's attitudes tends to remove much of their unhealthy force.

Intellectual understanding of the cause should then be followed by intellectual understanding of how he should now act and feel not only towards present conditions, but toward the memories of the original irritations. He needs to know not only that he has no basis for feeling inferior now, but that there was no real basis for feeling inferior then. He should not only understand that his own instability is probably a reflection of that of his parents, but also he needs to understand that most of the fears which have existed unconsciously since then should be faced now with calmness and decision. He should understand that his unhealthy "mental" attitudes towards all those things about which he has been concerned need to be discarded and healthy attitudes substituted. Actions which started in the past and which still exist should be discussed in detail and discarded where advisable. Detailed fears, hates, wishes, and emotions which are unhealthy should be examined and if they continue to exist, should intellectually, at least, be discarded. The patient should have a clear concept of what is expected of him in regard to these unhygienic attitudes.

In such intellectual appraisal of what is wrong and what needs to be done, it is important to avoid blaming the patient, or criticiz-

[1] *Vide* p. 158 (Case M. P.); 172.   [2] *Vide* p. 156 (Case O. N.).

ing him.   The physician is neither a moralist nor a judge; it is his duty to analyze causes and prescribe the remedies.   Such objectivity is important not only because it lessens the patient's feelings of guilt which tend to perpetuate the neuroses, but also because the objectivity of the physician is an attitude to be copied by the patient whose major fault usually is excessive subjectivity.   To tell a patient, for example, that his beliefs are childish and emotional and that they have no basis other than wishful thinking will do little more than put him on the defensive and call into play such mechanisms as withdrawal[1] and rationalization.[2]   On the other hand, unearthing the origin of the specific belief, and demonstrating its immaturity and inefficiency not only has the virtue of being a factual and truthful technique, but also makes the patient cooperative, and points the direction toward the better way of responding.

Intellectual understanding is, however, not enough.[3]   The patient must be willing to change the underlying attitudes and must *accept emotionally* that which hitherto he has refused to accept. Many patients will say that they know what to do, but they can not make themselves do it.   Emotionally their response has been so long in a direction opposed to the one offered by the physician that it is difficult for them to "feel" the way they have reasoned out they should feel.   Or to put it another way, one may say that despite the advice of reason, habitual emotional responses tend to direct the course of action.

To overcome this habit obstacle, the physician needs to establish sufficient rapport with the patient so that the attendant confidence, respect, and desire to live up to the physician's expectations will overcome the resistance of habit.   The degree and rapidity of cure are in large measure dependent upon the degree of rapport. *Rapport*[4] is more dynamic than simple confidence or trust.   Rapport implies a common meeting ground, a mutual appreciation, a "speaking of the same language."   The patient sees in the physician one who understands, sympathizes, and guides.   He feels that the physician has evaluated him and appreciates him for his assets, even though they may for the time be outnumbered by his liabilities.   Rapport has the quality of "liking" in addition to the factor of confidence.   When rapport has been established, the patient will have not only the intellectual realization that he should change,

---

[1] *Vide* p. 68.   [2] *Vide* p. 71.
[3] *Vide* p. 193.   [4] *Vide* p. 192.

9

but also the emotional "feeling" that the physician wishes to aid him in the change; he will have a sense of moral support while he is changing, and consequently, a conviction that his efforts toward change will be successful. The success of some physicians and the failure of others is often to be explained in terms of their ability or lack of ability to establish such rapport.

Indeed there is no other field of medicine in which the personality and attitude of the physician are of such great value and importance as in the treatment of the neuroses and psychoses. One physician may bring about a cure while another, apparently using the same method, fails egregiously. Charlatans and certain "faith cults"[1] are able to obtain cures (only of neurotic symptoms, however) in direct proportion to the magnetism of the associated personality and the "faith" it inspires. Such cures can be only temporary, since the basic causes of the neuroses are left untouched; but the fact remains—and it is a fact of transcendent importance— that emotional belief in a cure is curative in itself. If the patient believes strongly in a cure, regardless of its source, by his very belief he at once obtains sufficient moral support and courage to *face all his problems*[2] with some degree of equanimity; and in this way his specific problem loses much of its emotional (and therefore neuroses-producing) character.

Some physicians seem to have a natural "bent" for therapy, and are able to establish rapport and confidence more quickly than others. There is an "art" in psychotherapy, an art which like that of music or painting can be greatly aided by study and by experience. One of the most important factors in the development of this art is the physician's sincere interest in his patient's problems. There is no substitute for real interest in the patient as a suffering human being. Such interest makes the physician more than a doctor; he becomes a friend whose concern it is to help one extricate one's self from the morass of emotional conflict. The patient's response to such friendship is to do gladly what the physician advises, for the patient knows that the physician will aid, support, and encourage him.

Pampering is to be avoided. Helping a person who is ill, however, whether the fault be his own or some one else's, is not pampering. The patient must understand the fact that although the physician will provide moral support, give constant reassurance, advise on problems to the best of his ability, the patient must

---

[1] *Vide* pp. 219; 234.   [2] *Vide* p. 205 *ff*.

simultaneously make every effort to face the facts courageously, must learn to rely on his own powers of analysis and action. Honesty is respected and appreciated by the patient, if the explanation is tactfully and sincerely given.

Confidence is increased when the physician seems to be certain in principle what is wrong and what needs to be done. Definiteness in diagnosis (including definiteness in stating what one does not know) plus decisiveness in action provides encouragement for the psychoneurotic patient, who usually has an inherent lack of decisiveness. Realization that the physician has a clear cut formulation in his own mind communicates itself to the patient, and is extremely reassuring. Even where rapport is not established at first, confidence in the physician is established when the patient feels he is in capable hands. Hence, much training and experience are advisable for those who would deal with persons who suffer. On the other hand, dogmatism is far from reassuring for it indicates an inflexibility, built too often to over-come a fundamental insecurity.

Simultaneously with giving intellectual explanations and establishing confidence and rapport, the physician instructs the patient on how he can translate his intellectual knowledge of what is to be done into automatic responses of the personality. This technique involves consistent and persistent conscious efforts to apply the principles learned to every detailed and specific situation in life to which they can be applied. The patient must set up his goal, the attitude to be removed and the attitude to replace it, and continually orient himself toward such a goal. The patient must train himself to do that which he knows he should do, and only by effort can he carry out this training. There is no royal road to the development of a healthy and mature personality. Yet with the application of effort, the patient can learn to react differently. In actual practice, one finds that old as well as young persons can radically alter their method of response. Under ordinary circumstances[1] most persons can be successful enough to remove unhygienic and neurosis producing traits and develop the habit of reacting in a mature fashion. The physician needs to iterate and reiterate the necessity of continual application of the principles outlined.

The removal of the fundamentally unhygienic general reaction patterns is carried out almost purely by retraining. Each general

[1] *Vide* Ch. XIII.

attitude, such as discussed in detail in Chapter X, should be understood as to its origin as much as it is possible,[1] after the manner of removing specific attitudes; and then by dint of repeated analysis, of specific illustrations of this general attitude,[2] and by guiding the patient along mature methods of response, and by cooperation of the patient,[3] new reaction patterns will be formed. The most important elements in changing the fundamental, life-long general attitudes, is consistent persistency. If the newer and healthier form of response is clearly defined and illustrated in many ways by examples from the patient's own experience; and if these ideas are presented with sufficient repetition to the patient, he will eventually adopt the suggestions given. There are many handicaps, however, and these are discussed in detail in Chapter XIII, on prognosis.

At first the patient will fail.[4] The patient must be warned of his likelihood to initial failure; but he must also be reminded that learning a new trait does not differ essentially from acquiring a new skill, that one makes many errors before arriving at a successful outcome. A patient whose attitudes have been established after decades of experience cannot be remade in a few weeks or even months.[5] It takes time, much time, for the newer attitudes to become so integrated as to be automatic in their response.

Moreover, the factor of habit plays an important role. Once a pattern is established, it tends to perpetuate itself even though the underlying cause has been removed.[6] Only time and persistence toward the goal of a more mature habit can overcome the inertia which is associated with already established traits.

Adjuvant Therapy.—This consists primarily of the use of *drugs*, *suggestion*, and *hypnosis*.[7] These should always be used only as adjuvants in the therapy of the underlying immature attitudes. The drugs used, exclusive of those needed for actual physical pathology, are directed at the tension symptoms, and should be of the sedative type. When drugs are given, the patient should be informed of their purely palliative nature.[8] Suggestion and hypnosis are also of value; but here again, it must be remembered any therapy which does not treat the cause, is rarely permanently therapeutic.

The utilization of these procedures will facilitate the removal of

---

[1] *Vide* pp. 126; 189.   [2] *Vide* p. 180 *ff* (Case S. G.).   [3] *Vide* p. 224.
[4] *Vide* Ch. XIII (curve of improvement).
[5] *Vide* p. 110 (Case C. B.).   [6] *Vide* p. 281.   [7] *Vide* p. 227 *ff*.
[8] *Vide* p. 234.

the specific distorting attitudes and substitute hygienic and mature patterns of reaction. Yet each specific emotional problem has as its background some general emotional problem,[1] hence the difficulty in attempting to correct any specific trait without dealing with those general immature attitudes which constitute the unstable base upon which specific difficulties can arise. Therefore thorough specific therapy implies adequate general therapy; and thorough curative measures carry within themselves the basis for future prophylactic procedures. Psychoneurotic patients who are adequately treated learn not only to remove the particular emotional difficulties which appear to them to be uppermost, but also to lay the foundation for future emotional stability and mental hygiene.

[1] *Vide* p. 174.

CHAPTER VII

TECHNIQUE OF ANALYSIS OF PERSONALITY
DIFFICULTIES

EFFECTIVE treatment of the psychoneuroses is dependent upon the physician's ability to find the basic cause for the existent condition. He has special difficulties not present in other fields of medicine. There are no thermometers with which to grade spiritual fever; no x-rays with which to determine the extent to which a personality is broken. The analysis of the personality is an extremely personal problem; and the "art" of analysis is as important as the "science" of analysis.[1] This fact is even more true in the resynthesis of the individual personality, as we shall see later.

A person's reaction patterns are the result of three main factors: (1) stress[2] as it affects the (2) inherited constitutional pattern[3] which has been modified by (3) internal and external environmental factors. Understanding the "why" of a person's reactions, therefore, requires a study of these three forces[4] in the time and setting of their occurrence. In some patients in whom the maladjustment is mild, one may be able to ascertain the precipitating factors in one or two visits. In such persons, it may be totally unnecessary to go into detailed analysis provided there are sufficient elements within the personality to permit a quick reintegration, once the irritants are removed. In other instances, however, where the basic personality pattern has been unstable since infancy, or where it has existed a long time, it may be necessary to see the patient for many months. The difficulty in analysis lies in the tendency of the patient unconsciously to repress memories which are vital and continuously active in the person's reaction patterns. It is the unearthing of these (dynamically)[5] forgotten memories that necessitates the use of some of the special techniques described in the following pages.

---

[1] *Vide* p. 130.

[2] Stress is obviously an environmental factor which having acted, becomes integrated with the personality experience. It must be recognized that man acts as an integrated organism, each succeeding environmental or external influence becoming an integral part of the internal influence. The organism so changed may respond in an entirely different fashion should it be confronted by the same stress later. However, throughout this book, *Stress* is arbitrarily differentiated as the precipitating factor of the illness.

[3] *Vide* p. 23.　　　　[4] *Vide* p. 39.　　　　[5] *Vide* p. 60.

F. B., aged nineteen years, was referred by her high-school teacher. She complained of being easily irritated, of crying on the slightest provocation, of feeling "sickly," by which she meant being "weak," and "taking everything too seriously." Three years before, she would become "hysterical" at times, and "would breathe heavily and feel half-conscious of what was going on."

Florence had been going "steady" for three years. She was in love at first, and it was when her fiance first kissed her that she developed these "hysterical" spells. They had talked of getting married, but he was only a year older than she and had no prospect of employment. Resenting his inability to support a wife and the necessity of postponing the marriage, he became irritable. As a result, the patient complained, "He doesn't seem to understand me. He's self-centered and isn't nice to me the way he used to be. I don't seem to be able to get along with him; and I can't seem to be able to get along without him."

In the therapy, the patient was informed of the probable reasons for her fiance's actions. Much emphasis was laid upon the possibility that his action might be the result of his irritation at not being able to support her and that at the bottom there might be an intense loyalty. However, the possibility was also pointed out that both were young and that it was likely that neither knew what love was and what it involved. It was then suggested that for a period of six months they go out with others as often as possible. At the end of that time they would be in a better position to know their own feelings, and having tested them by being with others, if they decided on marriage then it should be consummated quickly. In any case, they should evaluate the pro's and con's of the situation as unemotionally as possible. A week later she wrote, in part: "After leaving your office, I was the light-hearted girl I hoped to be. . . . I didn't let my emotion get the best of me, and we face the situation sensibly. . . . I am out to conquer that funny thing called 'life,' not to let it conquer me."

In this instance, one interview was sufficient to set a fairly normal girl on the right path wherein her own common sense could then work out the solution. The therapy in this case was simple advice about how to deal with existing stress. Analysis of the general reaction patterns was not needed for a satisfactory recovery, since there was no indication of a basic instability.

Mrs. B. M., aged thirty-four years, complained of intense nausea, vomiting, insomnia, and great fatigue. Four years before she had tuberculosis and was in bed for a year. At the present time, she had no lung pathology but she was fearful not only of a recurrence but of many other illnesses.

She was the only daughter of maladjusted parents: a dominating mother and an aggressive-on-the-outside, but meek-at-home father. She grew up with marked feelings of inferiority, never relied on herself, was moody, and feared while she resented doing anything without first consulting her mother.

Her psychotherapy consisted of evaluating objectively why she had developed her emotional instability, of pointing out her dependence on her mother and her imitations of some of her mother's conduct. She was instructed to visit her mother less often, to engage in more of her own activities, to learn to make her own decisions, etc. At first, she "intellectually" understood what was said but was unable to make it part of her reaction pattern. With repeated reassurance and guidance in specific problems, she gradually made these tenets and others along the same line, automatic. Finally she was able to deal with her parents and with her own feelings of inadequacy without perturbation; but this condition came about only after a period of a year, with visits twice a week for the first six months, the number gradually decreasing until at the end she came only once a month.

DIRECT DISCUSSION

Direct discussion is probably the simplest and most efficacious means of obtaining the desired information. The technique consists of: (a) a spontaneous history given by the patient of the onset of the illness, and his background, and (b) a directed examination, with specific questions being put toward possible etiologic factors. In some instances, such direction is not possible, as the patient may go into involved discussions about some trivial fact that has little bearing on the symptoms or essential history. It is therefore desirable at the outset to inquire as to just what symptoms the patient has. It is important to record what the patient has to say in his early visits, for later one can refer to these early notes to determine the patient's progress. It is well to inquire "whether there are any other symptoms," or if any doubt exists, to ask, "Would you be perfectly well if you did not have these symptoms?" Such inquiry often brings forth many other complaints which were in the background, and which may throw light on the condition.

Having elicited the complaints, the physician can then evaluate the history in relation to them. It is necessary to determine the date of onset of these symptoms.[1] Here it is important to detect the patient's evasion. Many will reply, "It has been bad for the last six months," or "It really began to bother me some weeks ago." Such a vague onset should be investigated further, and it is then necessary to ask whether the patient was perfectly well prior to "six months ago." Usually one will receive some such answer as "I guess I have been nervous since I was thirteen," or "I've been nervous most of my life." The very beginnings of the illness are important, for in many instances the original stress or irritating factor made its impact at that time, and the patient's adjustment to it was never wholly satisfactory. Starting then as far back in

---

[1] *Vide* p. 265 *ff.*

the patient's history as it pertains to the onset of symptoms, the physician asks that subsequent events be described.

It is often necessary to ask patients about their emotional and intellectual growth and changes as well as about the history of their physical complaints. In the first interview these discussions may be difficult, for the patient does not realize the value or importance of these emotional forces. Moreover, there tends to be a shyness which needs to be overcome; and as the physician develops a technique for putting patients at ease, he may greatly facilitate the production of the needed information. On the other hand, some patients will skip over even the bare outlines of their history and reiterate such complaints as "If only my heart would not beat so fast, I'd be well." With such patients, it is necessary to take firm hold of the examination and direct it along constructive channels.

The factor of time is important. As much time as possible (averaging one-half to one hour) should be allowed for each interview. Otherwise, the patient feels "rushed," and omits mentioning many details which he considers irrelevant, but which may provide important clues to his illness. The patient is given an appointment and by a casual phrase from the physician learns how long the interview will last. The patient should, as many do, not feel that he is "taking up" too much time and so curtail his information. On the other hand, patients who talk endlessly and to no purpose, are encouraged by a definite appointment to "cut short" their saga. If a patient is shy and timid, it is well to inform him that the hour is allotted to him and that no other patients will be seen during that time. It is unfortunate that the busy general practitioner often cannot spare so much time for each patient. This unfortunate time pressure can be compensated for only by increased ability to obtain information, increased insight into the patient's problems, and sufficient rapport[1] with the patient to get him to carry out at least the more fundamental rules of mental hygiene. The less serious psychoneurotic patients may obtain relief in these short-term sessions[2]; and although there may not be a cure, they may be stabilized sufficiently so that they can live more maturely, more efficiently, more happily.

There is a technique and art in interviewing patients. If this technique and art are properly exercised, the physician may not only facilitate the getting of information, but obtain material that was held back consciously or unconsciously. Thus, patients

[1] *Vide* p. 129.   [2] *Vide* p. 257.

not infrequently remark, "I didn't intend to tell you this when I first came, because you'd think it was silly," or, as on one occasion during an analysis of a dream, the patient remarked, "I didn't remember these parts of the dream; they just seemed to come out as I talked to you." The keynote of this technique is an obvious interest on the part of the physician in the patient's story. Human beings respond to interest in themselves more than to almost any other stimulus. Then too, it must be apparent to the patient that the physician listens to the story not to gratify his own curiosity, but in an objective, non-judging manner to determine what in the patient's reaction is unhealthful and needs correction. Psychoneurotic patients so often have feelings of inferiority and self-condemnation that pietistic criticism[1] by others merely deepens the feelings of guilt instead of either removing them or finding their cause. Then too, the tone of voice, the expectant air, the facial expressions of the physician all tend to confirm or nullify his objectivity. Each physician needs to cultivate his own technique, learning by his mistakes and his successes.

On many occasions it is advisable to reassure the patient that what he says is held in strictest confidence, that no one will know of his problems or attitudes.[2] In keeping with this establishment of confidence it is best to ask the patient for permission to speak to the relative; and to the relative, even if he be a doting parent, it should be made clear, that what the patient has said was strictly in confidence and can not be divulged.

Since many symptoms are the psychologic expression of underlying emotional states, it is necessary to watch the patient closely for signs of emotion when certain topics are mentioned; for the feeling or idea behind that emotion may be one of the etiologic forces in the symptom. Thus, if a patient begins to cry while telling of a relatively innocuous experience, it is important to inquire into the reasons therefor. Crying is an obvious form of expressing internal conflict; scrutiny of the patient's expression often reveals a grimace, a frown, a tightened jaw, compressed lips, not congruous with the story being told. The patient, for example, may for no apparent reason pause unduly in his conversation. Here again, investigation may lead to valuable clues.

Mrs. T. H., aged forty-nine years, was brought to the sanitarium laboring under delusions of persecution, and having hallucinations characterized mainly by hearing voices of her children on the floor above pleading not to be

---

[1] *Vide* p. 363   [2] *Vide* p. 152.

killed. She was given several metrazol convulsions and her depressions and delusions seemed to clear up entirely. She was afraid of the treatment, however. While speaking with her about returning home, I asked whether the ideas she had about her children's being killed were gone. She smiled and received the suggestion as "foolish": but at that moment she heard a slight noise in the room above her, and her face assumed a frightened look. A moment later her face was all smiles. Her momentary expression of fright meant one thing—her delusions had not entirely disappeared; and her children visiting her that evening confirmed this view. With three more treatments, however, she became perfectly well and remained so.

In the examination of the patient, there is no substitute for observation. Just as in clinical medicine the physician can often observe many signs which do not appear in the laboratory, so is it even more true in dealing with human personalities. There is something highly contradictory in the finding of a catatonic, mute, apparently emotion-less schizophrenic patient, with finger-nails bitten to the quick: such a patient is in a state of turmoil in spite of his apparent apathy. Or the patient lying in bed calmly and in a smooth, even voice discussing her illness, may express her underlying tension by the way she constantly picks at the bed clothes or by the ischemic whiteness showing at her knuckles because of her clenched fist. Many a person has trained himself to wear a mask over his voice as well as face; and it is this mask which may mislead the observer and cause him to state, "That person doesn't look like a neurotic to me."[1] However, it is often possible to observe tension on the part of the subject; for the total organism tends to be in harmony with the inner emotional state, except where conscious effort attempts to mask it; and even here some part of the organism manifests the lie of the mask.

A spontaneously related history told in the patient's own words will often yield much information which otherwise would be repressed. Consequently, the physician should use a minimum of questions and suggestions during the first interviews. The additional time needed for such spontaneous giving of a history is amply repaid, for the innuendos, shades of meaning, emotional tones may throw revealing light on the reason for certain actions, whereas concise answers to pointed questions may distort rather than clear up the facts.

However, after having heard the spontaneous story, the physician may supplement his information by direct questions on the more common problems which might have a perturbing effect on

[1] *Vide* p. 245.

the patient. The financial status,[1] for example, often is of concern, and the extent to which it plays a role and the extent to which attitudes and desires play a role must be determined. Questions in regard to the marital state may reveal much pertinent information.[2] The ideals of what a marriage partner should be like, the attitudes toward sex before and after marriage, the amount of responsibility, the mutuality of interests—all may be significant. Similarly, it is of value to inquire into the role of relatives, of children, of religion, of ambitions, and any other problems which may seem to have special significance.

In simpler cases, all this information may be irrelevant; or from the point of view of the average physician, unnecessary to obtain relief of the symptoms. Often the handling of some of the outstanding difficulties will remove the "stress," and the basic personality may adjust itself to its former state.[3] But to remove all bases for future breakdowns in the more severe psychoneuroses superficial information is insufficient. One may get results by scratching the surface soil, and the seeds of mental hygiene may grow with little cultivation; but intense cultivation, with plowing and preparing of the soil, hoeing and watering, weeding and care of the ensuing growth, is much more likely to produce the type of crop desired.

FREE ASSOCIATION

With many patients the physician comes to a point where no more information is obtainable by direct questioning. This deadlock occurs when the patient falls into a *rut of thinking*, or is emotionally blocked,[4] and can conceive of no other possible causes; or where the repressions are so strong that the patient cannot consciously bring the irritating emotions to the fore. One must then turn to the technique called *free association*. This method was first systematically utilized by Freud in getting information from neurotic patients. It is an excellent method of bringing to light many experiences which seem otherwise to be forgotten.

Our conscious thinking process is based on the principle of selection of associations. Our thinking is not made up of a sequence of words but of thought-pictures which we try to describe (usually inadequately) in words. These thought-pictures may be vague, shadowy, and indefinite, or they may be sharp and clearly-defined.

---

[1] *Vide* p. 166 *ff.*   [2] *Vide* p. 161 *ff.*   [3] *Vide* p. 155 (Case B. E.).

[4] Often persons cannot bring painful memories to consciousness. Such memories are said to be "emotionally blocked" and to exist in the unconscious.

They occur not in random fashion, but because of some associative attachment to the thought-picture which has preceded it or because of the advent of new stimuli; and this association may be tenuous or it may be strong; just as the new stimuli may be mild organ sensations or severe environmental disturbances. These ideas flit through consciousness much more quickly than they can be expressed, and any single thought-picture may bring up several associated ideas before one of them can be vocalized. Our training at thinking forces us, because of the exigencies of living, to select from these numerous concomitant ideas the ones which lead toward the goal-idea which we have originally selected. The man, for example, who has had an accident[1] and describes how it began, selects those thought pictures for description which eventually will end in a description of his trip to the hospital. This goal is the guiding force present before the beginning of a sentence and ordinarily dictates the choice of the fitting thought-pictures and the elimination of those which have little relation to the goal. This selection of a goal-idea is a cortical process and is facilitated by training and the needs of civilized life. The more one needs to think, even if only in school work, the better trained is the person to think, other things of course being equal. However, the working world is frequently far better than are our schools in teaching persons "how to think." The technique of thinking must not be confused with so-called "education." The cortex is really the "thinking" part of the brain, by which psychologic processes are mediated. Injury to the physical structure of the cortex as in senility, alcoholism, or toxic psychoses,[2] results in impairment of the function, and in "rambling" speech, because the power to select the correct thought processes, or to remember the goal-idea, is diminished. As a consequence, these patients talk endlessly without finishing their story, even forgetting the end. The same is true in manic attacks. On the other hand, in paranoid patients the thought process is disturbed so that certain associations are selected to the exclusion of all others—hence the old term "monomania." In "normal" thinking, the occurrence of several word images at the same time may lead to an occasional digression but usually leads to a goal. Furthermore, the selection of the particular thought image is a flexible process, as distinguished from the inflexibility of psychotic reasoning. Thoughts come so quickly that often we are conscious of only major parts, and miss the

[1] *Cf.* p. 143 (Case X. F.).   [2] *Vide* p. 347.

intervening reasoning process.   When strong emotions exist within
the person, however, there is a constant vacillation[1] between the
two poles of action present in the conflict.   The deeper the conflict
and the stronger the emotional tone the greater will be the vacillation.   As a result, the organism does not progress in a stable fashion
along its course but is markedly unstable.   There is no feeling of
certainty, of security, so long as the emotionally charged ideas are
strong enough to irradiate their indecisiveness to all actions and
thoughts.   The strength of the emotionally-toned ideas is sufficient
to cause emotionalism to protrude into almost every thought and
to influence the direction of the thought.

Mr. S. D., aged forty-seven years, was diagnosed as having an anxiety
depression.   He had constant and severe headaches, was greatly fatigued, so
much so indeed that he did not have strength to eat a full meal, and lost
considerable weight.   He slept sixteen hours of the day and awakened as
tired as on going to sleep.   The slightest effort exhausted him.

He was married at the age of thirty.   He was deeply in love with his wife
and she with him.   They found most of their enjoyment in quiet pastimes
and rarely sought the company of friends.   Soon after marriage it was discovered that she had nephritis, and her systolic blood pressure was over 200.
She became invalided, and he her slave.   He begrudged himself the time to go
to work and spent day and night tending to her.   His grief over her suffering
was great.   He cried frequently and could not bear the "cruel way" nurses
treated her.   He made her bed, cooked her food, and flew into a terrific rage
if he thought she wanted something which the nurse did not get quickly
enough.   He became thin, weak, unable to concentrate, and despondent.
When after a prolonged period of uremic coma she died, the patient was beside himself with grief.

Everywhere he went, something reminded him of his wife.   Jewelry
brought tears to his eyes, houses shaped like the one he had lived in made
him shudder, children playing on the street reminded him of the children he
did not have, the sickness of one of his friends recalled "her" suffering, and
the emotional outbreaks of some of his friends reminded him of the way he
felt.   When he spoke of her three years later, he sobbed like a child.
He remained a chronic invalid until his attitudes toward his wife were reoriented.

Most of the thought processes of this man revolved about the
emotional concern in his background.   All ideas were in some way
tinged by his primary concern.   If this man were to talk at random,
to "free associate," that is to speak of whatever came into his mind,
he would constantly turn to the subject of his wife, even though he
might have started talking about the structural factors of a modern
bridge.   His associations, if released from conscious (and indeed

[1] *Vide* p. 76.

habitual) control would inevitably drift to the topic of constant concern.

In many psychoneurotic patients, the concern is so painful that the patient dislikes thinking of it. The painful memory is pushed into the background and "repressed," although its emotional tone is still active.[1] To ask such a patient whether he is troubled often results in the reply, "Nothing troubles me—only my heart trouble (or other symptom)." The patient has refused to face the emotionally-toned conflict at the basis of his symptoms and even denies the existence of the conflict. Direct questioning may not elicit the causes; free association, however, is effective.

In free association, one trains the patient to let his thoughts associate freely without any conscious direction, while consciously making an effort to verbalize every thought that passes through one's "mind." No effort is to be made "to tell a story"; any interrupting thought is to be mentioned; one is to let one's thoughts wander. Often much training is necessary to teach the patient this technique.

The purpose of this free association is to permit all associative ideas (that do not flit by before they can be mentioned) to be brought to light. Where conflict or emotionally-toned ideas exist they will intrude themselves into some of the associations; and although they would usually be repressed,[2] under this technique they will be expressed. In such a way, one may unearth many etiologic irritants which have been "dynamically forgotten."

In some patients, the repressed ideas are not far below the surface and may be easily elicited by this technique.

Mr. X. F., aged fifty-four years, complained of severe pains across his chest. They were intermittent in character but were severe. They were worse when he was sitting quietly and radiated across the whole chest, but had no focal point, or constancy. Physical examination was negative. X-ray of the chest and an E.K.G. were also without evidence of pathology. There were no complaints referable to the gastrointestinal tract. These pains had been present for three years.

He denied having any worry or concerns. He lived with a son, his wife and daughter being dead. He made a fair salary, played golf once a week, and denied any possible stress. "Only trouble is these pains in my chest."

He was asked to "free associate." The following is a condensation rather than a verbatim account of what he said. "I don't know what to say. I've had these pains now for three years. They're awful at times. I can't stand them. When I'm working hard I don't seem to notice them so much. The pains are as bad as those of my wife. She had cancer of the breast four years

[1] *Vide* p. 63 *ff.*   [2] *Cf.* Dream Analysis p. 150 *ff.*

ago and it spread under her arm and pinched on some nerve. We had to keep giving her morphine. And did I have the tough luck. One after another, my daughter got sick with pneumonia and passed out on me, and my son had a smash-up in a car and broke his ribs. He still has some sore spots over his chest."

This man had had an unusual and severe shock, or rather a series of shocks, all occurring just before the onset of his condition, and the suggestive effects of these emotionally-toned illnesses was one of the bases of his psychoneurotic illness. One can easily follow the trend of his ideas and the manner in which the idea of his pain soon associated and brought to light his wife's pains, his daughter's pains, and his son's pains. Yet consciously he could not see how these occurrences had any relation to his own illness, and so he did not think of them when he was asked to tell about his concerns or anxieties.

In most cases such clear evidence so quickly given is unusual. One will find that much of the conversation, or rather monologue, is not contributory to the problem. Moreover, only small bits of information may be obtained at any given time. The observer must train himself not only to watch for these subtle pieces of evidence, but to follow them up as clues and to investigate them by the method of direct questioning. Such investigation will have the tremendous advantage of dealing with evidence presented by the patient as it is instead of trying to get the patient to fit into some theoretical dogma. The general practitioner often does not have the time to search so systematically into the personality background and must then substitute his "impression" and "guess" for factual basis. Even so the physician who has the capacity really to understand human nature, may often obtain excellent results.[1]

The following is an example of the free association taken from the history of a girl of twenty-three who suffered greatly from fears of being alone. She could advance no reason for her ideas and denied any other topic of concern.

"I've been terrible. I cry a lot—always have. I look at myself in the mirror and I'll be gosh darned if I know who I am—I try to convince myself that everything is all right and I can't—I don't know what to do—I have some silly answer for whatever I say—A silly idea came into my head that I should call my friends together and say good-bye—I know I'm going to die— then I think I won't recognize any of them. So many things running through my head—If I could only be sure that they are not insane thoughts—

[1] *Vide* p. 129.

Sometimes I wonder if I'm just pretending, but I can't do anything about it. I've been receiving a lot of attention but I don't want it now. If I could die I'd be happy, yet I'm afraid of death. Don't tell me I'm not insane—I am. I'm conscious of everything. I'm conscious of being Miss L. L. Tell me what's wrong with me even if it won't do me any good. Boy, I'll bet you never had a patient like me. Wait, something is dawning on me—an idea— I had to choose between two fellows last Wednesday—I've been trying to stall them off—I don't know which one to choose—Both Al and Sam are nice boys. I go to the mirror and ask myself what is there to be afraid of— and I get no answer—I cause everyone I come in contact with to suffer—I can't visualize anything—It seems like a play and I can't visualize the audience. I'll never be able to do anything as long as I have this bowel trouble (a diagnosis of spastic colitis had been made). It always has worried me. I've had this trouble for five years, and I know I'll never be able to get married—I'll never be able to have sex relations."

This stream of speech was not continuous. There were pauses from time to time, and the patient would then be asked, "What are you thinking of now?" Most of what she has said is non-contributory, and the only fact of major importance brought out, just before the end of the interview was her fear that she would be prevented from marrying because she had somehow acquired the notion that "bowel trouble" interfered with sex relations. Through-out her speech, one can see the indecision, the fears, the lack of self-confidence, and the unreality of the world about her. It then became necessary to determine just what she had in mind about her spastic colitis, and just what role it played in her illness. On further discussion, it developed that her unhappy and neurotic aunt was divorced because she had "bowel trouble" which pre-vented normal conjugal relations. The patient "just knew" she too would be unable to live a normal life because she had the same trouble as her aunt. She had developed a neurosis which was in part an exaggeration of her aunt's complaints.

It had never occurred to the patient to mention these thoughts; she was much too concerned about her state of mind. Only when she let herself "ramble," and spoke whatever came to her, was it possible to get at the disturbing forces.

In teaching a patient to "free associate," one needs much pa-tience. The patient will at first say, "It's silly," and "Nothing comes to me," or "My mind is a blank." One needs to reassure the patient that thoughts will come, that it is but a matter of train-ing one's self to speak. It is better to have the patient recline on a couch, but he may be trained to free associate while sitting in a chair. As the patient lies quietly, it is often well to stimulate by

10

asking, "What are you thinking of now?" Some patients will attempt to draw the physician into simple reassurances and not really progress in bringing forth information. With these patients it is necessary at times to state specifically that there will be no conversation for, say, half-an-hour, and the patient must learn to continue speaking. Above all, it is necessary to have facts brought out by the subject before specific corrections can be made. What the patient may regard as inconsequential and unimportant may be the clues that lead to important causes, and this fact must be impressed on him. This method has the marked disadvantage of requiring a great amount of time to obtain small bits of information: its advantages lie in the fact that it is a most reliable method of getting at deeply repressed experiences.

DREAMS

The analysis of dreams is another method of determining basic and hidden memories. Dreams are a function of the cerebral activity during sleep, but they are closely allied to day-dreams. The basis of analysis is the principle that *dreams are thought processes occurring in a non-waking state;* it is our purpose here to give only a brief outline of the subject.

Dream ideas differ from waking ideas in several ways. Dream ideas occur while the activity of the brain is decreased, while there is relatively more anabolism than catabolism. As a result, the training and inhibitions[1] learned during conscious life are in relative abeyance, and the basic; *i. e.*, the more primitive methods of thinking[2] occur without the check or influence of "logical" and learned techniques. The amount of dreaming a person does, however, cannot be determined by what he remembers, for much of dream material is forgotten.

Fundamentally, dreams as well as waking thoughts are activated by emotional tone, by wishes and fears. In dreams, these desires and animosities are far more forcibly expressed than in waking states. In the dream, a wish becomes satisfied and intensified; so, for example, an animosity results in the complete destruction of the disliked one. The primitive method of reasoning by laws of similarity and association is in full operation during sleep; and ideas which have only a thread of similarity, or are only remotely associated to each other, may follow each other in sequence in a dream.

[1] *Vide* p. 40.   [2] *Vide* p. 43.

The dream is primarily visual in nature, and the actions are associated with an unformulated but potent feeling tone.

As primitive thinking is unlogical, so is the dream. Relationships have no rational basis or sequence. The dreamer's emotional attitudes tend to appear in the dream according to their number and intensity. Thus, on analysis of a dream, one finds many different wishes or fears rather than one coherent pattern. Each dream is composed of many symbols, and consequently there are many wishes and fears represented, and the dreams appear to be jumbled. Those wishes or animosities which are deep-seated and present for many years may repeat themselves frequently in the same or in various dreams. On the other hand, incidents of the day, trivial in themselves when viewed sometime later, may carry sufficient emotional tone to permit them to intrude themselves into the dream.

Rationalization[1] plays a role occasionally in the "logicality" that is present in a dream. This fact can be better understood if one refers to hypnosis situations. Actions which these patients have suggested to them are often rationalized. Thus, one young woman hypnotized before a group of students was told to wash her hands when she awakened. When the patient was awakened from the hypnosis, she paused, looked at her hands, and then said, "Excuse me please. My hands feel dirty. Can I wash them?", and saying this went to the sink to do so. This experiment can be repeated in many different ways. In other words, the action which was suggested and which the patient felt bound to carry out without knowing why had to be rationalized. Similarly in dreams, when the dream thoughts are consciously presented there is a tendency (by no means the dominating one) to confabulate[2] and rationalize in order to give the dream a connected sequence. This process is an unconscious one.

The *factors of the dream* may be discussed under three headings: (1) the cortical activity which permits dreams to be produced; (2) the contents, or the wishes, fears, and emotional elements which the dream represents; and (3) the form or symbolic expression of the dream. Cortical activity is greatly decreased during sleep, and if there is no stimulation of the brain there may be no activity to permit thought process. Cortical stimulation may be produced

---

[1] *Vide* p. 71.

[2] Confabulation (making-up stories) is seen for example in the alcoholic dementia patient, who not remembering the past, will invent and believe some wild story about his actions during the period of amnesia. Confabulation is an unconscious process.

by physiologic disturbances such as is common in over-eating before bedtime (by disturbed cerebral circulation), or during menstrual periods; it may be toxic and present in conditions of bodily illness; it may be the result of physical stimulation during sleep; or it may come from the emotional tone and pressure associated with psychologic problems during the day. In other words, whatever stimulates the cortex increases the possibility of dreams. On hearing the alarm clock in the morning, a person may dream of being on top of a church with many people waving at him, and suddenly the church bell may increase in intensity, followed by a collapse of the entire steeple. The brain was stimulated by the insistent ringing of the clock to produce a dream just before cortical activity was aroused into consciousness, although the content and form of the dream were colored by the dreamer's own attitudes and experience.

The *content of the dream*, or that which is dreamed about, is ordinarily determined by the existing "frame of mind." If the stimulus (that which increases the activity of the cortex) is external to the brain, that is, comes in from the outside, or even from the circulating blood, then those wishes and fears and attitudes already present will become formulated into dream thoughts. If the stimulus is internal in the sense that the actual wishes and fears are the disturbing element, then they act both to stimulate and to form the elements of the dream. One might say that dreaming is thinking during sleep—primitive and emotional thinking, but still thinking. As a consequence, the dream is composed of those elements involved in the strivings of the individual, and the intensity of their expression is proportionate to the intensity of underlying desires. They may be incidents long past, the memories of which are continuous, or they may be emotionally-toned incidents of the preceding few hours. It is this content which we try to get at in analysis.

The *form of the dream* is dependent upon the manner in which symbols are used to express an entire concept and emotional attitude. The dream symbol is arrived at in the usual primitive manner; that is, some idea vaguely or partially associated with the existing wishes or fears acts as a condensed[1] symbol. Since each person has a host of wishes at the same time, his symbols are "lumped" together, and the dream appears as a senseless combination. However, the dream may form a pattern when each symbol

[1] *Vide* p. 44.

is influenced to some extent by the preceding symbol, and when the main set of wishes is symbolized in various forms. The pattern which runs through the dream is conditioned in this way and later by rationalization and confabulation. The form the dream takes is thus a variable phenomenon and is significant not in itself but in what it represents.

It can be understood, therefore, that the symbols which appear in the dream have meaning only to the subject, for the associations which are formed are individual. However, there are some associations which are more or less common simply because most persons are subject to similar stimuli in social life, and these may result occasionally in symbols in dreams which have the same meaning. In general though, even here there are individual connotations. Thus, a girl dreaming of being pursued by animals is commonly dreaming (wishing or fearing) of sex relations. This association occurs so often in analysis of dreams that it is possible to make such a relationship. However, it must be emphasized that such general meanings are uncommon.

Sex expressions are common in the content of the dreams, though the form in which they are expressed disguises these ideas. Sex symbolism in dreams is so common in civilized communities because of the necessity of curbing sex expression during conscious life. Moreover, in many persons there is an overly-intense inhibition of these sex drives, and the emotional tones about them find expression in dreams. Again, since sex drives are one of the fundamental orientations of the subject, they are bound to be expressed in some form or other. The presence of sex in dreams, however, does not mean that it is the all-important element in the particular person's life; it may be only one small aspect of it. To trace sex desires from every dream is to over-emphasize what is present in various intensities in all persons. In situations wherein the person's life is imperiled, then the dreams are primarily concerned with his existence. Yet one might conceivably by primitive association on the part of analyst or patient find some sex drives even in such a dream which would be present without any real significance as to what is disturbing that person. When sex is said to be at the bases of all dreams, it may be because of the personal bias of the analyst who finds what he seeks; or because the subject is analyzed in an atmosphere where sex ideas are prevalent and consequently he dreams what he is expected to dream and "free associates" with this connection always before him.

TECHNIQUE OF ANALYSIS OF DREAMS

First of all, it should be stated that the purpose of dream analysis is identical with that of free association: to find clues which may be followed by direct discussion with the patient. Consequently, one should not hope to find too much.

Secondly, since dreams represent groups of many wishes, each dream symbol should be isolated and its particular significance determined. Any portion of the dream may or may not be correlated with the whole dream.

It is then necessary to have the subject "free associate" to each one of the dream symbols. This associative process often leads back to the main content behind the dream, almost in the same fashion as the particular symbol came to represent the dream. However, the thread that leads out of the content to form the dream symbol is often only one of the threads which connect the two, and it is hoped in free association to find that thread (association). Here, more than in ordinary free association, there is a great deal of repression, and the threads of association leading back to the original content may not be found.

By this technique, one can often arrive at the meaning of the dream, and the real significance in this laborious procedure lies in having the subject discuss the meaning brought forth. For example, a young woman brought in the following dream:

"I was walking in party clothes through a gaily decorated village. There were lots of small bears climbing around me and they were very annoying; but I didn't pay much attention to them. Suddenly a large bear rushed out and began to attack me, to tear off my clothes, and it frightened me so much that I woke up screaming."

To the thought-picture "walking through a gaily decorated village in party clothes," she replied in essence as follows: "It was all decorated up as if for a party. I often go out to parties and they're lots of fun." To the phrase, "many small bears annoying you," she replied, "There were five or six of them scratching and tearing my stockings, but I didn't seem to mind them. They're just like a lot of fellows I know, just pestering around. They go out with you, and you are cute, but after while they get on your nerves." To the phrase, "a large bear began to attack you" she could find no association at first. She repeated the phrase several times, and insisted, "No other ideas come to my mind." Finally, she broke out with the statement, "Jack is just like that. He's the fellow I'm engaged to. He's always trying to get me to sleep with him, and I have to fight him off."

The various ideas playing a role in the above dream are clear. The disturbing emotion present in the girl was the conflict between the desires aroused and urged by her friend Jack, and her moral scruples. The great concern she had over that problem and an indication of the relative strength of both elements was revealed by the fact that the fear was so great as to awaken her. Moreover, this clue led to the discovery that there was great conflict within the patient about her affection for Jack in other aspects than sex. (As proof of this lack of affection is the fact that to this present time five years after the dream, she has refused to marry Jack.)

Such a simple dream is not common. It is more difficult to understand the following. Mrs. K., a childless woman of forty-nine, told this to her husband:

"I dreamed that I had a baby, and you said you didn't like her because she spread her feet apart in peasant fashion. The baby said, 'I'll shoot you'; and small golden feathers began to shoot from her eyebrows. Instead of hurting you, they formed a halo about your head; and you said 'I'm God, and they can't hurt me.'"

On analysis, it was revealed that the woman had always yearned for a child—hence, the desire expressed in the dream. The morning before the dream her husband had told her of a woman on the street-car who, on sitting down, looked most awkward, because she had spread her feet in peasant fashion—the picture apparently had remained vividly enough in her mind to show itself in the dream. Mrs. K. had the day before seen a friend's little daughter who had the "cutest golden eyebrows"—and this experience too manifested itself. Finally, her husband had often jokingly insisted that he could never do wrong because he "was as infallible as God," and this memory too came out. It was easily apparent that this woman's dream was a conglomeration of many wishes and inci-dents. Some schools of thought might insist that this dream could be analyzed more deeply as to its meaning and would eventually lead to the Oedipus situation;[1] but such analysis would then resolve itself into analysis of any "emotional thought"[2] and in that in-stance "all roads lead to Rome."

[1] *Vide* p. 421.

[2] All "emotional thoughts" are traceable to fundamental wishes, and all these wishes and fears are so interrelated that if one traces back far enough one can always find sex.

JUNG'S ASSOCIATION TEST

Still another but more cumbersome method of getting at these repressed and unexpressed memories is the written association test as devised by Jung. This test consists of some fifty to one hundred words, most of which are of no special significance, and intermingled with which is a list of words which the physician feels may represent a special role in the patient's life, but which the patient is unable "consciously" to remember. The patient is asked to give the first word that enters his mind the moment he hears the test word. The type of answer, and the time taken to respond, are noted, and if the patient is "blocked" and cannot think of a word quickly, or if the response is peculiar, then all associations connected with that word should be investigated. Thus, if he responds "devil" to the stimulus word, "wife," or cannot think of a word on hearing the word "poverty," he leaves the physician with significant clues.

HYPNOCATHARSIS[1]

Hypnocatharsis is another method of obtaining these unconscious experiences. Essentially, this method consists of hypnotizing the patient and having the patient free associate while in this state. Often memories will flow more easily under such circumstances. The difficulties, however, lie in the facts that all patients are not hypnotizable and that hypnosis casts a shroud of mystery about the process, making a "mystic" affair of that which one desires the patient to be very clear about. The same difficulty applies to the therapeutic side of hypnosis.

INFORMATION FROM RELATIVES

Finally, it is often of value to discuss the patient's problem with a near relative. Two important points must be remembered. First, the patient must have full knowledge of the consultation so that he cannot feel that he is being conspired against; and, secondly, the physician should not divulge to anyone, not even the parents, the personal "secrets" of the patient.[2] This silence is important, for once the relatives know of the several forces behind the patient's actions, they often are unable to suppress their knowledge, and the patient becomes resentful and guarded in what he says later.

[1] *Vide* p. 227 *ff.*   [2] *Vide* p. 138.

CHAPTER VIII

STRESS AS A DETERMINING FACTOR

To TREAT the psychoneuroses it is necessary to deal with both: (1) the stress or precipitating factor, and (2) the personality attitudes[1] (constitutional orientation) toward past, present, and future stress. The technique of determining these factors; *i. e.*, stress and attitudes, was given in Chapter VII. The next step, resynthesis of the personality, involves both factors; and though they are interrelated and mutually determining, they need separate discussion.

It is impossible categorically to state what constitutes stress, insomuch as stress is a relative and not an absolute term. Its effect on the patient is the result not only of its intrinsic nature but also of the patient's attitude toward it.[2] What is a heavy load for one may be light for another; what is a luxurious life for one may be abject poverty for another. Some persons adjust themselves to situations which to the spectator seem unbearable; while others break under what appears to the outsider to be a relatively slight pressure.

One very wealthy man was approached for a contribution to a charity agency. He had always given freely; and although the depression of 1932 had affected him, as it did others, he still was considerably better off than most. He refused the request point blank. He was intensely worried about the future. He spoke as if ruin were not far off. "How can you even think of asking me for a contribution?" he stormed. "My income dropped from five million last year to one million this year."

Contrast this situation with that of the young man of 22.

John had been in love with Sally for a number of years. They had made repeated plans for marriage but were prevented because neither of them could find work. His wet palms, dilated pupils, tachycardia, and other symptoms of anxiety were directly traceable to this apparently unsolvable condition. Yet one day, he rushed into the office with gleaming eyes, and bubbling with joy. He had finally landed "a steady job" on W.P.A. and was going to get married.

The wealthy man was under stress only because of his own attitude; John, however, considered that stress was removed when he procured a precarious position. The difference in what each man "felt" lay not in the actual stress but what each considered stress.

[1] *Vide* p. 121.   [2] *Vide* p. 120.

To say that there are only two categories of stress in which the role of attitude is relatively slight; namely, actual physical want and physical handicaps such as illness, deformity, and restraint does not simplify the problem, insomuch as stress is no less real and devastating in its effects because it has its origins in attitudes rather than in actual situations.

The complexity of modern civilization has greatly multiplied both the demands put upon man, and also the number of directions in which stress may be felt. The primitive conception of security and satisfaction, measured in terms of sufficient protection and food to maintain existence, plus gratification of the sexual desires, has been so greatly expanded that instead of being the primary object of life, it is for the vast majority rather "taken for granted," so that man spends relatively little of his energy in the pursuit of material food to satisfy his immediate appetite. He seeks, in addition, security (food) for the future, recognition, luxuries, response, status, self-expression, etc. Each one of these words is a generic word with an infinite variety of specific meanings and connotations.

In general, it may be said that stress produces tension in proportion to the person's attitude toward it; that is, stress tends to be as bad as he feels it to be. Moreover, if the attitude toward actual physical stress is met with objective determination, then the detrimental effects will be primarily physical and not emotionally disturbing.

Therapy may follow one of two lines: (1) removal of the stress, or the patient from the situation wherein stress exists or (2) reorientation of the patient's attitude so that much of the emotional force involved will thus be removed, and the patient may then be trained to bear the stress with little difficulty.[1] The latter method is not only more practical and feasible but also more universally necessary, because as in most instances among the psychoneuroses, there is a definite lack of ability to bear stress which is normally borne by others.[2] Chapter IX will deal with the treatment of the attitudes; and if the physician will keep in mind that stress and attitudes are inextricably bound together, it will be possible in this chapter to deal with the first method of therapy, that of "removal of the stress, or of the patient from the situation wherein stress exists."

---

[1] Provided of course that there is no actual existing physical illness or need.
[2] *Vide* p. 205 *ff.*

If one meets with patients suffering from malnutrition, as the result of a lack of money, and at the same time suffering from a neurosis, there is no other treatment so effective as the provision of food and the relative assurance of food in the future. If a mother manifests emotional instability because her husband cannot earn enough to provide food and clothes for the children, one can do much to remove the emotional instability by supplementing the family income. If a man develops anxiety attacks, and one finds that he is concerned over his inability to secure adequate funds to care for his tubercular child, psychotherapy is only a sop which may be as false as are the delusions of grandeur in the general paretic. The purpose of psychotherapy is not to relieve empty stomachs by filling the mind, nor is it common sense to try to do so. The purpose of psychotherapy is rather to train men to face their problems objectively and courageously, and not to deceive themselves by the use of various psychologic mechanisms.

Consequently, in the clinics and elsewhere, it is important to ascertain just what the financial status of the patient is; and if there is actual want (and such *need* must be differentiated from *artificial desires*), financial help will be the best psychotherapeutic procedure.

Mrs. B. E., aged thirty-seven years, came to the clinic complaining of marked fatigue. She had headaches, various neuromuscular pains, and had lost much weight. The first tentative diagnosis was that of Addison's disease, but this was ruled out and the diagnosis of neurasthenia substituted. Her early life revealed a distinctly unhappy childhood based on a decided lack of harmony between the parents.

It was quickly learned, however, that this patient, the mother of four, was living on reduced relief allowance. She was unable to feed her children properly, and rather than eat herself, gave most of her food to the children. In addition to this lack of nutrition, she had to take care of her home, do all the washing, and make clothes over and over.

A social worker was able to arrange for a better food allowance. The weakness and fatigue cleared up after a few day's rest in the hospital, on a high caloric diet. There were no symptoms of neurosis left after she heard of the arrangements made by the social worker.

It need hardly be said that in physical ailments the removal of the causative factor is of primary importance.[1] In cases of general paresis, for example, the etiology of the illness is syphilis, although the symptoms may be manic-depressive, schizophrenic,[2] psychoneurotic, etc.; and accordingly, despite the personality reaction pattern, all treatment must be primarily directed toward the cure

[1] *Vide* p. 126.   [2] *Cf.* Ch. XV.

of the syphilis. Disturbing physical ailments in chronic form may often constitute a stress sufficient to cause a neurosis. Strabismus frequently leads to feelings of inferiority; a long-hooked nose may make one overly-self-conscious; a hare-lip, a large mole, a deformed limb, etc., all may lead to emotional disturbance. Modern surgical techniques, and cosmetic aids produce not only a remarkable change in the appearance but in the personality. Whenever possible this procedure should be encouraged.

Miss O. N., aged twenty-three years, was shy, avoided people, and was termed unsociable and introvert by her friends. She was unhappy, cried a good deal, and became very irritable. She admitted having an intense feeling of inferiority, which she said was at the bottom of all her actions. The reason for the inferiority was a marked internal strabismus of the left eye. An operation was arranged for, and the shortening of the external rectus gave her a normal appearance, even though vision was poor in the left eye. The entire personality of the girl underwent a metamorphosis. She became sociable, gay, and as she expressed it, "I can now look anyone in the eye and not be ashamed."

Mr. K. L., aged thirty-four years, was an active and aggressive business man. He was, however, known as a restless and irritable person. He was full of energy, but snapped and fought with almost everyone who came his way. He could not keep stenographic help because of his constant fault-finding and criticism of the way in which the work was done, even when apparently the mistakes were his own.

He complained of pain in the pit of the stomach, especially after eating. He had to avoid highly seasoned foods. He took baking soda after every meal. In the middle of the night he would awaken with pain, and after meals he was excessively irritated. A medical examination revealed a definite peptic ulcer, and when this was adequately treated, much of his emotional difficulty was removed.

It has become increasingly well-known that an essential part of the cure for peptic ulcer[1] is teaching the patient how to relax, how to live more calmly; but it is equally true that such treatment is futile unless the physiologic pathology is also cared for.

Just as psychoneurotic symptoms may disappear with the removal of stress; e. g., treating the parents of a spoiled child or removing a strabismus so also may the same results be achieved if the patient is removed from the situation in which stress exists.

Mrs. N. H., aged twenty-nine years, was a nurse companion of an elderly and irritable woman. She had to be in constant attendance; and while the work was not physically difficult, she was confined to the house except for a short period in the afternoon when very slowly her employer took an "after-

[1] *Vide* p. 302.

noon constitutional." Mrs. N. H. acted in this capacity for six months, having only an occasional afternoon off, which did not afford her much pleasure, insomuch as her work was far removed from her friends. Mrs. N. H. became irritable, short-tempered, and developed dizzy headaches. She felt obliged to continue in the employ of this woman, because the work was easy and the salary better than she could otherwise make. Moreover, she was the sole support of an aged mother. Her symptoms became worse, but disappeared almost immediately when she resigned her position and procured another which, while it paid less, was in the city and near her friends.

Mrs. L. S., aged twenty-six years, had many symptoms of anxiety. She would awaken with a pounding heart, couldn't catch her breath, and was constantly oppressed by the fear of death. She had married some years ago while at a party. A young man with whom she had gone to several parties was constantly proposing to her and she was constantly rejecting him. At one party three years earlier, she became slightly intoxicated, and the man persuaded her to "elope." She consented, and awoke from her alcoholic state to find herself married. Her anger and resentment were great, but she continued to live with him. He, sensing her lack of affection, became increasingly jealous. He began to accuse her of liking her family more than him; of being antagonistic. He flew into violent rages at her, but at the same time refused to grant her request for divorce. Her own family was on relief, and she felt she could not return to them and be a burden. She felt "trapped," and developed the anxiety symptoms described. She hated and feared her husband.

Finally, she decided to separate, regardless of the consequences. She saw a lawyer and arranged for a divorce. She persisted in her suit, in spite of the fact that her husband first threatened suicide and then held a loaded revolver against her side in an effort to change her. She secured the divorce, went to live with her mother, and after a few weeks procured a position. Her symptoms disappeared soon thereafter.

In this situation, the patient removed the stress from her life. This removal was almost essential for a cure. The impossibility of sharply distinguishing, however, between treatment of stress by its removal and the reorientation of the patient toward it becomes vivid when one realizes that often the only way to remove the stress is by changing the attitudes of those persons who constitute the precipitating factor or stress to the patient. In childhood, for example, the emotional tone in the environment and the insistence on certain types of behavior may operate to force the child into a neurotic illness which is called "a behavior problem." Therapy in these instances is directed toward the parental behavior which constitutes the precipitating and determining factor. In many of these young children, discussion with them is relatively unimportant, while a change of parental behavior is essential. The parents must learn that the child will behave and react unstably in proportion to the instability of the parents. The child will be what the parents are. External calm is insufficient; for the child will sense the underlying emotional tone, regardless of the passive mask which may be worn. The atmosphere of tension is the most irritating of all atmospheres and permeates widely. Indeed, neurosis is one of the most contagious diseases known to man.

Mrs. M. P. was suffering from multiple sclerosis. It was incipient and manifested itself primarily by her "knees suddenly giving way" under her. There were no physical pains or disturbances. The positive Babinski was the only organic sign that could be found. The patient, however, was quite unstable. She had emotional outbursts and felt incapacitated because of her walking difficulty. She was afraid to go anywhere, and worried constantly about her "diagnosis" and the paralysis and helplessness that so often occur. She cried frequently, was nagging and demanding, slept poorly, and gave up such interests as playing the piano and memberships in bridge clubs. These symptoms were the result not of her multiple sclerosis but of her personality reaction to the *idea* of her illness and incapacity.

Her five year old daughter was a great problem. The child did not obey, was always into mischief, cried at not getting her own way, fought with her playmates, was finicky about food, was restless in bed, and in her sleep "ground her teeth."

The entire situation was discussed with the patient. Her attitudes toward her illness were revised. This change was accomplished by discussing with her just what happens in multiple sclerosis, with an emphasis on the fact that remissions may occur frequently and may last twenty to thirty years. The absence of pain and discomfort was a boon not to be treated lightly. Paralysis and death might come, but to anticipate them was not only valueless but harmful. Death is inevitable, and yet one does not ordinarily go about feeling concerned. It is important to postpone thinking about the future. She was urged, when symptoms occurred, to see a physician immediately and to abide by his treatment; but once having placed herself in his care she should deliberately and consciously turn her thoughts to something else. Moreover, she was persuaded that while she did live she had to learn to live as happily as possible; that existence with constant foreboding is illogical and impractical as well as depressing. She could still do many things. She could play the piano, engage in the activities of her bridge club, attend theatres, etc. She could learn to occupy herself with these things and not anticipate a dark future which in some cases is not dark. She was told that these attitudes can not be acquired by merely wishing or by intellectually assenting, but only if one consistently and persistently "practices" these attitudes.

The patient was seen twice a week for two months, and once a week for another month. Under the constant urging and with the constant encouragement of the physician she adopted the attitudes suggested above. She developed the attitude, "So what of it?" and this without bitterness. Most of her neurotic traits disappeared.

At the end of the second month she reported that her child had spontaneously changed and was becoming more likeable. "Margery minds me now and doesn't seem to fight so much." Practically the entire behavior problem of the child cleared up, seemingly without any effort on the part of the mother.

This patient was laboring under the stress of a physical disease. She had reacted to it with an emotional outburst which had become chronic and was on the way to becoming a permanent part of her personality. By changing her attitudes toward this illness and its possible future she was able to be more relaxed and tolerant of her difficulties and to enjoy herself. This change was accomplished by constant direction from the physician and persistent self-training by the patient.

At the same time, the child was suffering from the stress of her mother's irritability, and her behavior was the result of her mother's tension. When the mother's emotional strife was removed the stress was relieved and the child's behavior changed accordingly. Whenever a child is brought for therapy of his behavior, the physician usually needs to call in the stress (mother) and deal with it in order to "cure" the child.

Children who are somewhat retarded mentally are even less immune from environmental stress. The stress comes in the form of excessive (for them) demands from the parents and school.

N. L., aged six and a half years, "did not have neuromuscular co-ordination," according to the teacher, sulked a lot, did not study as she should, played pranks, and was a disturbing influence in the classroom. The mother tried to persuade her to study; but she refused, sulked, and had temper tantrums.

A Binet-Simon intelligence test showed the child to have a mental age of only five years, probably the result of a measles encephalitis at the age of three. She could not do those problems done by the usual six and a half year old. Further questioning revealed that she never played with children of her own age but always associated with those four and a half to five and a half years of age. Otherwise she was a normal, healthy, even jovial youngster.

This child had the body of a six and a half and the mind of a five year old child, yet she was expected to do the "mental" work of others her own physical age. She was entirely incapable of so doing. However, under pressure from those who accused her of laziness, and expected more of her than she *could* do, she developed defensive behavior which was called a "behavior problem." Discussion with her parents and teacher, and informing them of the child's ability, reduced the demands made on her, and her problem disappeared.

In this situation, the stress which precipitated the child's problem was dependent on intellectual deficiency and could be alleviated by discussion with the persons involved. The same is often true in situations involving adults; discussion with interested relatives and associates may go a long way toward removing the stress.

Removal of stress of persons suffering from senility or brain injury is also made possible by consultation with relatives. In many instances, actual psychotic reactions may be cleared up if the proper steps are employed. The keynote of therapy is adjusting the environmental demands so that a minimum requirement is made upon the patient.

Mr. L. M., aged fifty-six years, was well thought of in his community. He was an usher in his church, and had a small but successful business. A year before admission to the psychopathic hospital he was involved in an accident wherein he was thrown through the windshield of the automobile, and suffered from a basal skull fracture. When he left the hospital, a decided change in his behavior was noted. He became slovenly in his appearance, was irritable, his memory was impaired, he began to swear and curse, ceased attending church altogether, demanded frequent sex relations with his wife, and soon began to have hallucinations and delusions, accusing his wife of going out with another man, and insisting that the children were putting poison into his food. He finally had to be brought to the psychopathic ward. Investigation revealed that the patient had always been regarded as the head of the family, and respect and consideration had always been his. Following the accident and the failing memory, his actions and words were so childish that he was disregarded. His appetite was uncontrolled; and failure to gain attention from his wife and children angered him. His reasoning ability was too impaired to permit him to vent this anger effectively, and the result was a general irritability which ended in "mean" accusations against his family.

The family were greatly distressed and promised to cooperate. They were told that the patient could not be expected to act as a man of fifty-seven normally does, because his brain cells were too damaged. They must deal with him with much consideration. His children thereafter consulted him frequently on minor matters, asked his advice, listened when he spoke, and did whatever they could to make him feel "important." The wife took him for long walks, and she too listened "with attention" to what he said. The patient was told that sex relations could occur on only two nights a week; and his wife, having been presented with a definite plan, consented. As a matter of fact, being able to have sex relations and being able to secure assent for definite periods tended actually to result in diminished sex drive. The patient changed greatly, as far as behavior was concerned. He became agreeable, quiet, and seemed content. His failing memory did not improve, but his amenability to suggestion did result in vastly improved personality reaction.

In this case, the stress of trying to live up to his former self so that he could obtain the desired respect and solicitude was too great for him. It should always be remembered that the ego, no matter how low the intelligence may be, demands satisfaction and recognizes lack of attention and lack of ability to accomplish what is expected. Such stress, may be altered by changing the attitude of the relatives.

In many patients suffering from senility the same factors hold true. Dealing with the relatives in a way similar to that described above often releases the tension. Where the situation is such as to prevent adequate cooperation, then removal to a rest home frequently clears up markedly abnormal behavior.[1] Senile persons often will be happy and content at a rest home where the routine of life is not demanding and where the environment does not expect of them greater cooperation than they can give. In other words, the existing stress is thus removed and they can adjust on the lower level which their injured brain permits.

Matrimonial stress is often a major factor in the production of the neuroses.

In a recent survey in the psychiatric clinic of the University of Illinois, I found that more patients complained of matrimonial disturbance than of financial difficulty, this condition being true in spite of the fact that patients are admitted to the clinic only if they are unable to afford a private physician. Matrimonial difficulties, however, are based on many different factors, including financial deprivation, and only a few can be relieved by dealing with environmental forces alone.[2] Those forces which involve a change in attitudes will be discussed more fully in the next chapter, but it must be remembered that here as well as in any other human reaction, the stress and the attitude are inseparable; and in practice must be dealt with together.

As has been discussed elsewhere,[3] marital difficulties may be based on general early attitudes toward the opposite sex; selfishness and habits of petulance and wishing to have one's own way; standards for a mate set up by one's parents or other admired persons; temperamental and philosophical differences; differences in cultural background; sexual maladjustment; financial stress; interference by relatives; etc. In many instances, the stress implicit in these differences may be relieved by discussion with the husband and wife, if both persons are willing. An analysis of the

[1] *Vide* p. 277.   [2] *Vide* p. 167 (Case S. O.),   [3] *Vide* p. 101 *ff.*

11

factors involved, with an explanation of them, and urging that allowances be made are also helpful. There are many persons who really do care for each other but who will persist in being irritable if they do not receive certain attentions. While the patient is trying to change his attitudes, the simultaneous adoption of these desired attitudes by the mate will often facilitate harmony. Often this attempt to deal with such stress directly resolves itself into dealing with the attitudes of the mate. Nevertheless, with intelligent persons who care for each other and wish to cooperate, much can be accomplished by a few discussions.[1]

Mr. B. K. worked hard at his manufacturing plant. Its operations involved much concentration and energy. He frequently worked late into the evening arranging, calculating, planning. When he returned home he was tired, disturbed because of the infinite number of irritating details at work, and desirous of sympathy and attention. He wanted to be pleased instead of irritated, and he wanted an appreciation for his efforts.

His wife, a few years younger, was absorbed in her household duties. She cooked, planned good meals, and kept an excellent home. She helped her married daughter and married son take care of their children and even busied herself with visiting and helping some of his relatives. She was occupied all day with these minor tasks; and shopping for clothes, for food, for gifts represented the expenditure of much energy. She desired appreciation and admiration from her husband. When he returned home she dressed well and waited to be complimented and made love to.

The result was to be expected. He sulked because of lack of attention for his hard work, and she felt hurt because she wasn't admired; each wanted attention and sympathy from the other. The resentment grew apace, and finally he would leave the house in anger, and she would refuse to prepare the meals he liked.

In this case, discussion with each of the partners was remedial. The reasons for the other's actions were explained. Since each professed much affection for the other, this affection was constantly emphasized in the discussion. Each was urged to give the other the attention desired; and since doing so required just a little more consideration, the tension was relieved. However, it was necessary for the physician to see these persons several times, for minor incidents came up and threatened to start the conflagration all over. Under the constant urging of the physician, these situations were faced and surmounted with little friction.

The stress which results from maladjustments of sex relations, similarly, may often be removed by discussion frank and specific. The causes of sexual difficulty must first be determined[2] and then

---

[1] *Vide* p. 126.   [2] *Vide* Ch. VI.

the difficulty removed where possible. Here again, though much of the stress is dependent upon the attitudes involved, talking to the mate often is productive of good results.

Thus, for example, the male often approaches the woman sexually without adequate preparation;[1] and advice on this subject is helpful. The husband may need to be advised to pet and caress for some time before actually beginning coitus, in order to bring his wife to the same state of excitement that he is in. To many women even this technique is insufficient.

"I haven't ever had an orgasm, even though I'm married for five years. I want sex relations, and my husband pets me, but he never says anything to me. I tell him to make love to me, to say nice things and to be romantic, but he says there is nothing to say."

Discussion with the husband was very helpful. He loved his wife, and learned easily to make his affection articulate. Usually if cooperation exists, the difficulties can be overcome.

In those maladjustments resulting from primary disturbances in sex tempo and not dependent upon the attitudes and personality troubles of the partners, the use of proper contraceptives is of help. Many men have orgasms quickly because of the extreme stimulability of the penis, and thus leave their wives in a state of tension and frustration which may begin a chain of domestic disharmony. In such instances, the use of a condom may decrease the stimulability without interfering with the male satisfaction, and thus permits a longer period of time for female orgasm to occur. In other situations, the use of a condom is irritating to both persons, and if contraceptive measures are desired, a pessary and spermatolytic jelly are advocated. Contraception by the method of withdrawal of the penis before ejaculation is decidedly unsatisfactory, for not only is the possibility of conception great, but the orgasm is interfered with in both the male and female, and the attendant fear of conception acts both as an irritant and to produce tension.

The fear of pregnancy often leads to difficulties,[3] for not only does the woman fail to obtain her orgasm, but the male, missing the excitability of the mate and sensing her anxiety, may have ejaculation, but be dissatisfied because of the lack of response. Advice on how to use contraceptive methods, even if it be only the "free period" technique will make for much greater matrimonial happiness. Such instructions to the husband and wife relieve the psychological tension regarding the matter also.

[1] *Vide* p. 108 (Case T. V.).   [2] *Vide* p. 108 (Cases D. I., and I. C.).

Mrs. H. I., aged fifty-four years, had had three children before she was twenty-one, within three years after her marriage. She had difficult labor each time and feared conception thereafter.

Her husband came for advice one day. He was sixty-one, seven years older than she. For some weeks his wife had been acting queerly. She quarrelled with him frequently, and one day said that some one had telephoned and told her to watch out for her husband. He promptly had a watch put on his phone service by the telephone company so that each incoming call was checked. Several days later his wife flew into a great rage when he came home; some one had called, she said, to tell her that her husband was going out with another woman. He called the telephone company only to be told that no one had made a call to his home at the hour his wife had mentioned. This accusation was repeated several times and could not be verified by the telephone company. The delusional character of her accusations became more apparent when she said one day that she had seen him across the street from their home walking with a colored woman who was wearing a big red hat. The wife became more and more depressed, and finally was found in the kitchen with the gas jets turned on. She was revived, but still insisted on accusing her husband of infidelity.

He told of the fears she had of pregnancy. All through their subsequent life (from the first pregnancy to the present) she had avoided sex contact as much as possible. The menopause came at forty-five, and when she was completely over it, she remarked that now they could have sex contact without fear. Mr. H. I., however, was approaching his declining years and unable to have sex contact very often. At the time of the interview, he stated that once a month was the limit of his capacity. At first his wife tried all manner of means of arousing him, and felt frustrated constantly. She began to accuse him of being too much with other women and so unable to satisfy her. These accusations hardened and crystallized into the delusions expressed above.

The stress which precipitated this woman's illness was the strong sex desire which was not satisfied. All her pent-up desires which were restrained by the fear of pregnancy were released after the menopause, but could not be satisfied. She refused to face the fact of her desire, and her interests were too circumscribed; it became necessary to make her aware of the psychologic basis for her delusions, and teach her how to meet reality more concretely and practically. Her husband arranged to spend most of the day and night with her so as to create a greater sense of security. In addition, he became more attentive and pursued a continuous round of pleasure trips, parties, sight-seeing, and the like with her. In the third place, she was brought to the psychiatrist on the pretext of a neurologic examination, and was told after she was persuaded to tell of her life history and desires, that her strong sex desires were normal, but needed to be: (a) restrained to satisfaction at only monthly intervals, and (*b*) sublimated by her taking part in other interests.[1] Under this guidance, she was entirely cured of her delusional symptoms. The stress of her desires which produced her illness was relieved by increased attention from her husband, by new diverting interests, and by understanding and changing her attitude toward her desires.

In many patients there is an awareness of the sex difficulty but a lack of knowledge of what to do about it. As one husband remarked, "We have been told many times to have 'normal sex relations,' but this is the first time anyone has discussed specifically and in detail what procedure we should use in this case." His wife had dyspareunia, and he and his wife were instructed to avoid actual coitus for several weeks, although he should massage and dilate the vaginal orifice nightly, first inserting one finger, then several until sufficient relaxation occurred. Dilation by the physician, in a busy office, is generally unsatisfactory, because the dyspareunia results from spasticity of the genital musculature which can be relaxed only voluntarily, and this relaxation is best done by the husband, with the associated emotional tone acting as a releasing mechanism.

In persons in whom the sex desire is overly-strong, the use of sedatives, suggestions, or hypnosis[2] is often of help. Likewise, much can be accomplished by cultivating outside interests.[3] However, if any permanent "cure" is to be accomplished there must be a change in attitude, brought about through discussion.[4]

Before entering upon the discussion of attitudes as such, it will be valuable to examine one or two cases which indicate both the relative nature of stress and the fact that even if stress cannot be removed, it can be alleviated.

Mrs. F. S., aged twenty-four years, suffered from severe headaches. They had been present for five years and were of such intensity that she had to go to bed. They increased in severity, and she was rarely free from them. She had all sorts of examinations, spinal punctures, X-rays of the head, and took "almost pounds of pills and quarts of medicine." No physical reason for the headaches could be discovered.

She had three children. Marriage had taken place seven years before her visit and had been with a man whom she loved, but to whom her family objected as being below their standards. She lived happily with him for awhile, but two years later found that he had gambled away all his life's savings, and even had borrowed all that was possible on his life insurance. She quarrelled bitterly, not only over the lost funds, but because he had lost

[1] *Vide* pp. 249.   [2] *Vide* Ch. XI.   [3] *Vide* p. 249.   [4] *Vide* p. 121.

his position and had to work as a milk driver for a relatively small wage. He would leave the house about 3 A.M. and not return till noon. When he came home he was tired and would go to sleep about 7 P.M. She had to stay home all day to take care of her children, and in the evening when she wished to go out, could not persuade her husband to go with her. If she went out alone, he rebuked her and became very jealous. She became secluded from all her friends, and saw only her own relatives. They invariably would bring up the subject of her husband's delinquency. She was ordinarily a very sociable person who had many friends, who liked being among people, and who wished to do other things beside stay home. She was practically incarcerated in her home. Her headaches developed on this background, and were the expression of the emotional tension she felt over her unhappiness and inactivity.

The stress of being bound to her home, and her resentment over her husband's actions were the important forces in the etiology of her neurotic headaches. She was persuaded to change her attitude toward her husband. She was taught to regard the loss of the funds as an unpleasant occurrence which could nevertheless be forgotten as one of the many unpleasant experiences in life. She was then urged to go out among persons she liked, to attend the bridge parties she loved, to go to affairs with her friends, to attend club meetings; in other words, she was urged to enter into as much activity as her housework would allow. If her husband objected too strenuously, she was then to insist that she too was an independent human creature who was entitled to fun out of life; and that though she would rather appear with him, if he did not go she would go alone. She was taught to pursue this conduct without being upset. After a short period, her husband was seen by the physician and the same thing told to him. He did not like the new state of affairs but accepted it in part. The headaches diminished in intensity little by little, until four months later she had headaches only during her menses, and was not incapacitated thereby.

In this case, the situation precluded the possibility of separation from her husband, but a new adjustment was necessary before she could achieve any modicum of emotional release. She needed this emotional release in order to rid herself of the neurotic headache. She could not change her husband very much, but she could change her attitude toward the way she lived, and toward what he did. It was this change that brought about the cure.

No other aspect of life indicates more clearly the relative nature of stress than does the economic. Sufficient food and sufficient protection are basic;[1] but as soon as they are achieved, new desires and needs arise to disturb the balance.

Clothes that are presentable, recreational facilities, adequate care of children, provision for education may be considered almost essentials. Lack of them may make for ill-tempered parents, for

[1] *Vide* p. 39 *ff.*

chronic dissatisfactions, for emotional outbreaks, for anti-social and psychoneurotic reactions. Matrimonial disharmony and a home life that is fraught with frustrations and maladjustments may, in turn, be the direct result of the lack of adequate funds. Tolerance is much more possible on a full stomach than an empty one; and the feeling of insecurity at being far below the level of the community in material possessions reflects itself in a general feeling of inferiority.

Mr. S. O., aged twenty-nine years, complained of impotence and a peculiar weakness of his legs. These symptoms had been present for two years. In addition, when he tried to work, he was able to carry out his duties for only a few days after beginning his position, and then would become so weak that he would have to leave.

He had been married for five years. Two children were born. He had cared for his wife, and although she was of a different religion, and although there were many protests from their respective families, they had felt they could get along. Actually, during the last few years, the topic of religion never entered their arguments. He was earning $18 a week; and notwithstanding the fact that they lived poorly, at first they were content. After the first child came, however, the financial pinch began to be felt. They had to cut out many of their recreations, and so could not go with certain of their friends who liked various amusements. When the second child came, the expenses incurred drained them of all their resources. Their clothes became shabbier, and even the quality of food deteriorated. Tempers grew short, and quarrels became frequent. His wife changed from a helpful and encouraging person to one who nagged and complained of what she didn't have, and what she and the babies needed.

The patient became discouraged. He could find no outlets for his own emotion. He began to drink to forget his difficulties. His drinking created a vicious cycle by causing more nagging, which in turn caused more drinking; his two children had to be sent to his wife's parents in the country; he felt shaky and insecure with his wife; the guilty feelings over his drinking expressed themselves by weakness and later by his impotence.

This patient would perhaps never have developed these complaints had it not been for poverty staring him in the face. His basic inadequacy was precipitated by the financial stress; and secondary to the financial stress, there developed marital difficulty. When the moral support given by his wife was removed, the patient sought refuge in alcohol. The entire chain of events was predicated on an inadequate personality, but precipitated by his economic strain. Psychotherapy, here, consisted not in dealing primarily with the alcohol, but with the basic causes: he was urged to go back to work so that he could contribute to the support of his children, thereby to regain some of his self-respect. Since he did not drink constantly, the physician's moral support was sufficient to enable him to work steadily. He was an intelligent man; and possibilities for his future were discussed and the hopes for an adequate salary in the future were raised, provided he worked diligently and consistently. At the same time, his basic emotional problems, his dependency and need for the moral backing of his wife or someone else, the ability to bear responsibility without allowing it to become overwhelming were pointed out; and he was made conscious of his personality defects whenever they occurred. Simultaneously, he consciously forced himself to think in more constructive and independent ways. As time went by, the physician was able to remove his moral support;[1] the wife agreed to cooperate, her life being made less dull by joining the local bridge clubs and recreational groups;[2] and the patient learned to accept life as it is, trying to change it, but not allowing it to be too irritating.

In this situation, the primary problem was the precipitating factor of financial stress; and the therapy was primarily directed toward getting the patient to change that situation in part by working. The next problem was to change his attitudes, his hopes, and his goals, so that he could maintain his position and strive for greater self-sufficiency. His personality inadequacies were brought to light, the patient was made aware of them, and consciously made to retrain his feelings of insecurity and to change them. The alcoholism was but a symptom which disappeared readily.

There are situations labelled "financial embarrassment," occurring in those homes wherein the income is sufficient for ordinary needs, but where the desires are far beyond the capacity of the pocketbook. These situations are more productive of neuroses than the former. In general it may be said that the more one must do something about pressing and actual problems, whether they be financial, physical, social, or otherwise, the less one tends to be concerned about one's self.

During a recent flood in the Ohio River valley, the city was inundated. The medical dispensary of its large hospital closed until after the high waters had receded. When the dispensary was opened, for some weeks the number of patients who attended was very small compared with the usual attendance. A social worker was sent out to investigate. She found the average patient working about the debris and mud-covered homes. "We ain't got time to go down to the hospital till we clean up this here mess." Their aches and pains receded into the background, while there were problems that needed immediate attention.

[1] *Vide* p. 218.   [2] *Vide* p. 249.

Mrs. O. K. was a "high-strung" person, according to her friends. She herself was constantly troubled by vague and fleeting aches and pains, was subject to headaches, and visited one physician after another for her weakness and troubled sleep.

She lived in her own home with two children. Her husband earned a comfortable living, and they had sufficient for the usual recreations and a small life insurance policy. However, she complained constantly to her husband about the lack of funds. Mrs. Smith had a maid; Mrs. Jones had a new car; Mrs. Clark purchased a new dining room set; Mrs. Johnson sent her daughter to a very expensive summer camp. The patient enumerated her desires quickly and unthinkingly. She was never satisfied. Every effort her husband made to please was met by grumbling because of its insufficiency. He worked overtime to increase his earnings, but to no avail. The patient's constant tension and desire could not be satisfied, and her symptoms were the direct result.

The complaint given here and the apparent etiologic force in her neurotic illness was financial stress. This, however, was again based on a more fundamental inadequacy; for even if this patient could have had as much money as anyone in the town, she would still have been chronically unhappy and neurotic.

Stress thus results from extremely variable forces, varying with the time, place, person, what has gone before, and what will come after. Such stresses as lack of food and shelter, physical disability or restraint, are relatively independent of the person's attitude; while such unsatisfied desires as special clothes, housing, education, money for vacations, recreations, etc. depend more upon the attitude than upon actual danger to the person's existence. Nevertheless, the advance of civilization has enabled man to shift the emphasis from the mere getting of food and protection to more sublimated and pleasure-giving forms of energy. What the man "feels" has become in many instances more important than what he as a physical organism "needs." Men will die for "freedom"; and it is generally conceded at present that man prefers to be able to go about as he pleases and obtain sustenance with difficulty to being placed in jail and having food and shelter provided. Man has as yet failed in spite of his intellect to solve the problem of preventing starvation and deprivation, irrespective of the fact that more than sufficient food and clothing is already existent. Some of the solutions have come into conflict with the attitudes which man has valued most (e. g., living in a modern dictatorship with all its restrictions). Stress has, therefore, come to mean infringement on ideals as well as organic disturbance. When men become objective and tolerant, when they become determined to carry out, without bias and clear sightedly, those changes necessary for the greatest individual good compatible with the greatest social good, then will much of the needless stress and suffering, many of the distorted and psychoneurotic personalities disappear.

Since man has not adequately learned to make and balance these sublimated pleasures and pleasure goals called ideals, many disturbances appear in his goals, and consequently artificial stresses are created, simply because of what he has said he must have before he is satisfied. It is this tendency which is often present in the psychoneuroses. It is this tendency which must be evaluated before one attempts to remove the existing stress.

CHAPTER IX

RETRAINING ATTITUDES AND REACTION PATTERNS

THE medical care of physiologic factors, and the social care of environmental stress need to be accompanied by the change in the psychologic states or attitudes.[1] The terms "psychologic states" and "attitudes" are used for convenience and not because they are strictly correct. What the physician wishes to do is to change the person in such a manner that he will no longer respond to stresses with symptoms of neuroses. However, psychoneurotic symptoms result in large part from unhealthy and immature reaction patterns, and reaction patterns are interpreted psychologically as attitudes. The cure of the neurotic symptom is brought about by the changing of the person's unhygienic patterns of reaction; and this change, in turn, is accomplished by retraining attitudes. The changed attitude which is first a conscious and directed reorientation, will, if persisted in, result in a similar reorientation of the organsim as reflected in the lowering of blood pressure, the decrease in muscle spasms, etc.

Attitudes may be arbitrarily divided into two groups: general attitudes and specific attitudes. The *general attitudes*, or orientations, are the *fundamental* general patterns of reaction by which many situations are met. They are the techniques of thinking, feeling, and responding to life's forces.[2] These patterns of reaction are laid down early in youth, and having been inculcated continue to be self perpetuating. They are broad principles of action which apply to many specific situations. Certain nationalities, for example, are characterized by over-attention to the "manner and form" of acting in every day life; others are known for their stoicism in situations of great joy or of great sorrow; still others are trained early to work arduously and apply themselves continuously; others habitually give intense, immediate expression of their feelings. These attitudes are cultural patterns absorbed in early childhood by precept and example.[3] They form patterns of response which continue even though the person is transferred to an entirely different cultural group. All persons are subject to the formation of such general attitudes which color to a large extent their future activity.

[1] *Cf.* Attitude formation, p. 42. [2] *Vide* p. 55. [3] *Vide* p. 46.

Similarly, individual persons develop characteristic responses to situational stresses in individual ways. Normally, these patterns include attitudes of sociability, of emotional control, of a definite pursuit of some form of education or training, etc. In the psychoneurotic patient, the reaction patterns tend to consist of irritable, egoistic, and over-emotional responses to almost every situation. The patient is trained so continuously, usually by the instability of the environmental forces, that such general reaction patterns become automatic. This instability is usually inculcated unconsciously by the very emotional instability of the parents, by their relationships with each other and their attitude toward the child.[1] Under such circumstances the child may become fearful of making any decision by himself because of a frequent tendency of the parents to criticize every action; and this fearfulness will extend itself into adult life, giving rise to what is called an inferiority complex.[2] Or the parents may be continually bickering; and the child identifying himself with one of them, and "taking the part of one of them," will yet feel guilty because of the social pressure to "love both one's parents." The vaccillation[3] between such conflictual points of view may turn the child into a vacilating adult full of conflict over opposite wishes and fears. Or the tense attitudes of the parents, and their tense and emotional ways of meeting ordinary life situations may be imitated by the child, who after all does not know instinctively how to meet life, and so follows the example of those about him. The child may withdraw under such pressures and become seclusive and asocial;[4] or he may overcompensate for the pressures and become aggressive and driving. If the child is dominated by an over-solicitous mother, he may remain dependent all his life,[5] seeking out some one to lean on long after his mother has passed away. If the father is tyrannical the child may react by meekness,[6] or by a similar tyranny towards others, both instances often being associated with a tendency toward masochistic and sadistic behavior.

In these few examples, one may see that patterns of behavior are developed because of external pressures and because of the constitutional factors in meeting such pressures. *These general patterns of behavior, once established continue to perpetuate themselves; and even when the original irritations and forces have long ceased to be disturbing to the adult person, the habit factor will keep these general*

---

[1] *Vide* p. 46 (Case B.).   [2] *Vide* p. 48 (Case M.).   [3] *Vide* p. 76 (Case N. D.).
[4] *Vide* p. 68 *ff*.   [5] *Vide* p. 197 (Case N. T.). [6] *Vide* p. 209 (Case G. F.).

reaction patterns in action so that all life will be reacted to accordingly. When (and if) the adult person begins to think for himself, and understands the immaturity of his responses, he finds that it is an almost insuperable problem to over-come these early formed traits. However, with the aid of the physician, who acts as a catalyst, and the persistent efforts of the patient, many of these reaction patterns *can* be altered.

While it appears quite clearly to the author, that environmental forces are the essential molding forces of each particular constitution, the psychoanalysts on the other hand insist that there are "deeper" reasons for adult neuroses. They insist that these general patterns and the fundamental causes of the neuroses lie in the unsolved *Oedipus situation*.[1] Freud (and his school of psychoanalysis) postulates an Oedipus situation in early life, where from the ages of two to five, the boy has incestuous desires for his mother; and he states further that the boy gives up these desires when he develops the castration complex; that is, when the boy unconsciously fears that his father will find out his incestuous desires and may castrate him for having them. Rather than be castrated, says Freud, the boy, still less than five years old, gives up his incestuous thoughts. Should such a solution fail, the child will then develop a neurosis in later life. The only effective therapy of the neurosis, according to the analysts, is to solve this Oedipus complex. The general attitudes present in adult life are, according to the psychoanalysts, governed by this Oedipus complex and its sequelæ.

Regardless of their origin, however, *general attitudes* become ingrained into the personality pattern so that they are habitual and automatic in nature. Often the emotional factors which first conditioned the person are lost to memory, and no longer exist as an irritating force, even though the results of these first emotional factors continue to influence the later life. Consequently, in the therapy of these general reaction patterns, the most important factor is that of retraining. There is no royal road to changing these patterns without consistent and persistent effort. Occasionally, however, the emotional irritations which first brought the reaction patterns into being, may still continue to operate unconsciously, so that the person reacts continuously to the memory of this irritation as if the actual irritation were still present. When such memory or "residual irritation" is present then the therapy

[1] *Vide* p. 421.

consists not only in retraining the patient as to his habitual responses, but in altering his attitude toward this initial irritation so that he faces it objectively and unemotionally.

Superimposed upon these general attitudes, and indeed usually dependent upon them, are the *specific attitudes*. The separation between general and specific attitudes is arbitrary; for although the specific attitude is designed to meet a specific situation, the attitude will become general in character if it exists for a long period of time or if it is very intense.   Specific attitudes are often the more *immediate etiologic factors* in the neurosis. The number of specific attitudes may be as numerous as the various situations one meets in daily life.   Specific attitudes tend to differ from the early childhood reaction patterns (though there are many exceptions) in that the memory of the original irritation is more likely to continue to irritate the person as if it still existed in reality.   Mr. A.[1] who lost his executive position a year before he came to the psychiatrist to be treated for hysterical aphonia, continued to have a "sickening feeling in the pit of his stomach" every time he thought of the loss of his position.   Mrs. F.[2] had violent blushing spells every time she "thought" (unconsciously) of her husband's infidelity.   Mr. I.[3] became irritable and sadistic towards girls every time he (unconsciously) "thought" of his amputated leg.   Such specific attitudes exist often as a background of specific irritability and color many conscious actions without themselves being in the center of attention at the moment.   Within all broad orientations or attitudes there are countless specific ones, some of which may even run in contrary direction to the main one.[4]   A political reactionary may treat his servants in the most considerate and liberal fashion; while an ardent liberal, politically speaking, may be a tyrant to his maid. Some societies boast of great love for animals while still being opposed to the abolishment of child slavery in mills and factories. Contradictions in attitudes are more common than not, each attitude being formed by the interaction of environmental pressure and existing wishes and fears.   These attitudes are many and may be specific to innumerable situations.   For example, there may be attitudes toward food, toward certain kinds of food, toward certain kinds of food on certain days, towards certain kinds of food in certain situations.   These attitudes which may be multiplied indefinitely are specific orientations, but emerge from and have some

---

[1] *Vide* p. 120.　　　　　　　　[2] *Vide* p. 64.
[3] *Cf.* p. 63.　　　　　　　　　[4] *Vide* p. 41.

relation to the general orientations. The treatment of specific neurotic responses consists in changing the person's attitude towards the original cause, and therapy of such cause is usually the most important factor in removing the irradiation[1] of harmful emotion which tends to produce further neurotic symptoms. However, if these specific attitudes have been in operation for a long period of time, or are extremely intense, it will be necessary to treat the habit factor (*cf.* general attitude) as well as the "intellectual" attitude.

Thus one may say that every person has a basic foundation consisting of certain general or broad orientations of behavior, which are more or less the guiding principles in his way of meeting life. These general orientations may be hygienic and efficient; or they may be inefficient and symptom producing. Superimposed upon these general attitudes are secondary and more specific ones, often possible only because the soil has been prepared in early life. These specific attitudes tend to deal with more specific situations and problems; and in the neurosis, specific tensions or symbolisms may result from a specific "cause." All psychotherapy is directed at: (1) discovering what specific attitude exists behind the symptom[2] and changing that attitude to a more healthy one, and (2) retraining the person so that he responds automatically and with his total organism, in a hygienic and efficient manner instead of in a symptom producing manner. Broadly speaking, one may say that general attitudes require much greater emphasis on retraining, while specific attitudes of comparatively recent genesis require more emphasis on removing the "unconscious" irritating memory.

TECHNIQUE OF CHANGING ATTITUDES

The principles of this technique have been discussed in Chapter VI. In essence the attitudes and reaction patterns of the organism are changed by: (1) bringing to conscious attention in specific detail the unhygienic attitudes and their attendant irritating memories, (2) removing the emotional tone attached to the memories, by intellectual understanding and by desensitizing the patient through repeated discussion,[3] and (3) retraining the patient so that he will react automatically in a hygienic, efficient, and non-symptom forming manner to the various stresses of life. These changes cannot be brought about simply by the patient's being

[1] *Vide* p. 77.   [2] *Vide* p. 180 *ff.*   [3] *Vide* p. 179.

aware of what he should do; consequently, very few patients are aided by reading books on treatment. A catalyst is usually necessary; and the catalytic process is, in large part, effective in proportion to the physician's skill, and to the amount of positive rapport[1] present. Time and persistence are essential elements in making the changes permanent and automatic.

Preparation of the Patient.—The procedure outlined above lends itself to patients whose symptoms even to the patient are, from the outset, obviously psychogenic in origin. There are many more patients, however, in whom the symptoms appear to be organic even though they are psychogenically determined. These patients, as a rule, cannot be approached immediately with the statement, "Your pains are the result of emotion." It is necessary to prepare the patients first so that there will be no antagonism. Very much depends on the personality of the physician and the way he phrases his diagnosis,[2] as well as on what he says. There must be a sympathetic explanation, and even a yielding occasionally to the patient. Before presenting the psychoneurotic formulation of the illness, the physician should be well convinced, and well fortified in his conviction by having made thorough physical examinations and tests, that there is no fundamental organic pathology, or if there is such a pathology, that it in itself cannot explain all the symptoms. Only then can the physician speak with conviction and certainty and point as proof to these examinations when the patient insists on some organic pathology. Nevertheless, it is not necessary to perform tests which are unessential, simply for the satisfaction of the patient. Thus, x-rays of the skull because of a transient throbbing in the temples, or electrocardiograms for "palpitation of the heart" which shows no other signs of pathology, generally are a waste of the patient's funds and allow the patient to continue in that state of mind which makes him ask for the miraculous x-ray whenever any ache or pain occurs. On the other hand, pain in the epigastrium after meals, a constant hacking cough, persistent pain over the eyes, etc., may well be studied by roentgenograms. However, the judgment of the physician is important. Moreover, practically all these examinations and tests should be done before psychiatric diagnosis is given so that the patient will not be able to counter with suggestions that he wasn't adequately studied.

[1] *Vide* p. 129.   [2] *Vide* p. 219.

Bob H., aged fourteen years, came in complaining of severe headaches which had been present for six months. He complained of their persistence and their severity. He could not go to school, and spent most of his day in bed. His mother was a fond parent who sympathized and mothered the boy a great deal. Neurologic examination was negative, and X-ray of the sella turcica showed no bony pathology. The diagnosis was made of a psychoneurotic headache, and an attempt was made to change the attitude of the mother and the boy. The headaches increased in intensity, and the boy complained of such pain as to make him threaten to commit suicide. His symptoms did not appear to be psychoneurotic and there were no other symptoms of instability. An E.N.T. specialist was consulted, and trans-illumination and X-ray showed sinuses choked with purulent pus. Drainage of this pus resulted in immediate and complete relief.

On the other hand, the reverse situation is frequently found. A physical symptom may be "diagnosed" as being of some obscure organic pathology and treated by "injections," which fail to give any sort of relief because they leave untouched the personality difficulty underneath.

Mrs. O. P., aged thirty-two years, mother of three children, complained of severe headaches for three years. No organic pathology could be found, though the sella turcica appeared slightly larger than "normal." On the strength of this meagre evidence, and for some vague reason suggested by advertising circulars, antuitrin was given twice a week. The headaches were not only unrelieved, but actually continued to increase in intensity. In spite of the fact that no relief was given, the antuitrin was continued, being given some weeks daily and never less than twice a week for the next three years. With two hypnotic treatments, the headaches ceased; and although they tended to recur on the slightest provocation, the ensuing psychotherapy, by relieving the patient of her emotional stress secondary to her husband's infidelity, brought about a complete cessation of the headaches.

Having come to the conclusion that the symptoms are the result of psychogenic factors, the physician broaches the subject to the patient. The general technique of telling these facts to the patient is roughly as follows, although it will be remembered that in this instance as well as in all others cited in this volume, it is understood that there is no *one* way, no hard and fast rule, to do anything. Individual situations call for individual therapies. Generally, the patient is told that no organic pathology of any significance has been found in all the examinations; that if there is any organic basis for the complaint it certainly cannot be serious in nature, though it may be irritating; e. g., in the same manner as is a tooth-ache; that emotional tension is one of the most important forces which may aggravate some actual organic ache or pain which in

12

itself might be easily borne; and that it is important to treat these emotional forces. The physician must then proceed quickly to those symptoms which the patient recognizes as being "emotional," point out how these symptoms are "aggravated" during periods of tension, and outline in simple terms the mechanism of tension and symbol formation.

Often a patient, after such a discussion of the nature of the symptoms, will ask, "Does this mean that I am crazy?" Then the physician explains that emotional disturbances are common; that occasionally these emotional reactions "work inwardly" and affect one's organs without one's being aware of the influence. This situation often occurs in intelligent persons who are far from being "crazy." Moreover, when a person is under tension, any actual physical ache which may be mild in itself is intensified. "But how can tension produce pain in all these parts of my body?" is next asked. The answer to the patient is diagrammatic,[1] analogous, and simple. "The reason one feels pain anywhere is that the brain receives sensations of pain. If the brain is in a state of excitement, any stimulus that comes to it from the periphery is felt more keenly than usual;[2] and if there is a mild 'organic' stimulus causing this pain in you, it would hardly be noticed except for the fact that emotional tension has aroused the irritability of the brain." Such explanations are deliberately diagrammatic and over-simplified, for only by such explanations can the patient grasp the basic truths involved. In general it is well to understand that patients will comprehend better and cooperate better if they have some reasonable explanation for their illness and for what is being done for them. As a rule, the background of the patient is inadequate to enable him to understand the mechanisms in physiologic or psychologic detail; but some simplified statement, while it is not theoretically exact, is adequate to give an understanding of what the physician is trying to do. When patients are suffering from "spastic colitis," where the etiology is some psychologic disorder, one may answer the question of how emotion can cause colitis somewhat as follows: "The term spastic colitis means that the intestinal tract is in a state of spasm so that normal peristalsis is interfered with. Spasm means contraction of muscle, and muscle contracts when there are many nervous impulses coming to it. There are many causes of increased nervous impulses, but in this case the basis is an increased flow of impulses down the nerves from the

_____
[1] *Vide* p. 216.   [2] The reverse may also be true.

brain. This increased flow occurs because the brain is in an increased state of excitability; and this in turn is the result of your emotional state." One may then add, when speaking to patients in whom there are many other symptoms beside "colitis," "That is why you have such a rapid heart at times, and why you get headaches: all parts of the body are connected with the brain, and emotional excitement is transmitted to all parts; some parts such as your head, your heart, and your intestine are more susceptible and hence your symptoms are there. In other patients in whom the skin, or bladder, or other part of the body is most susceptible, symptoms will show up in those parts." Some such explanation couched in the terminology which will be best understood by the patient is very effective. It places the origin of the difficulty where it belongs, in the emotional stress, and at the same time gives the patient an understanding of what needs to be treated when a symptom does occur. It makes him realize the necessity of co-operating in the changing of his attitudes.

Unearthing the precipitating and determining memories has been discussed in Chapter VII. *Desensitizing* the person toward the emotional tones present in an irritating memory is accomplished by having the patient formulate very specifically just what it is that he is irritated over. So many irritations are vague and unclear to the person, so that when they are stated in some definite fashion they tend to lose their force; and their immaturity becomes obvious even to the patient. The discussion of just how the patient should deal with the original irritations and what the mature responses would have been and are, is very effective in removing the emotional unrest, the "bound energy"[1] produced by the memory. The very fact that the patient can discuss the "hurts" of the past in a calm, objective fashion with the physician who is clearly analytical and objective, is therapeutic in removing these emotional tones. Often times, the patient may feel very disturbed "at the very thought" of the irritating memory, but upon insistence, and repeated discussion, the patient will become desensitized to the irritation. Repeated discussion with the patient about the problem is very much the same as the use of pollen vaccines for the hay fever sufferer; desensitization should be done by mild and super-ficial discussion at first; deeper, more pointed, and even more pride wounding discussions may be carried on later, as the patient builds up a tolerance and an ability to withstand the shocks.

[1] *Vide* Ch. XII.

Mr. J. M., a freshman in medical school, wondered whether he should give up the study of medicine, for whenever he went into an operating room, he fainted at the sight of blood. In addition to the analysis of the causes and the changing of the boy's attitude toward his basic problems, *desensitization* was carried out. The student was told to walk into the operating room during an operation and immediately walk out. On the second day he was to walk into the room, count five, and walk out; on the third day he was to stay a full minute and walk out; and each day the length of time he stayed was increased. In two weeks the student reported that on the preceding day he was supposed to remain for ten minutes, "but I got so interested in the operation that I forgot how long I was to stay." In other words this boy was desensitized to his fear by small but increasing doses of that which he feared. He had no trouble thereafter about witnessing blood.[1]

Retraining Attitudes.—The attitudes which the physician attempts to retrain should be as fundamental as possible, and the principles of feeling and acting to be inculcated should be as general as possible. Treating symptoms or secondary attitudes alone is like cutting off the tops of weeds without uprooting them. To say to a person who fears insanity, or anything else, "Train yourself not to be afraid," is dealing with the problem only superficially. The physician needs to know "why" the person is afraid, and change the attitude towards the cause. The "why" can be determined (as seen in Chapter VII) and that "why" must be treated, else failure is bound to occur.

Miss S. G., aged twenty-five years, complained of having "terrible thoughts." When she thought of her boy-friend she wished he were dead; when her mother went down the stairs, she "wished she'd fall and break her neck"; when her sister spoke of going to the beach with her infant daughter, the patient "hoped that they would both drown." These thoughts "make me hysterical. I love them; why should I wish such terrible things to happen. It drives me wild, makes me feel I'm crazy and don't belong in society; maybe it's best for me to end it all than to go on thinking such terrible things about those I love."

To try to train this patient to change her attitude toward these persons by instructing her merely to "think kindly" of them would and did meet with failure. She had tried to do so herself and was encouraged in her efforts by some of her closest friends. Only after getting at the bottom of her trouble and ascertaining the determining mechanisms was it possible to suggest a constructive

---

[1] Many persons have a tendency to faint at the sight of blood. The most common reason for this fainting is that the spilling of blood and its connotations of danger and death arouse an almost reflex fear and excitement; and the emotional tension is associated with vasomotor spasm which produces in the brain a temporary cerebral anemia and, consequently, a fainting spell.

attitude for her to adopt. The first step consisted in inquiring into the *specific* difficulties which existed at the time of the onset of her symptoms.

She was in love with a young man three years her senior. He possessed all those personal qualities which she highly admired. When she was in his presence she was very happy and had a good time. None of the other boys she went out with compared with him in the qualities of gentleness, intelligence, good nature, etc. There was, however, one fly in the ointment. He was short, and he was homely to the point of ugliness. She had always despised short and ugly men.

It might thus appear that the fundamental approach to the treatment was to develop in this girl the attitude that handsomeness in a man is of secondary consideration; for this concern of hers appeared to be at the basis of her particular symptom. The young man had asked her to marry him and she had consented. Then she had begun to think of how persons would point him out, how ugly her children would be, and so forth. Though she spontaneously said to herself that character was more important than appearance, she could not get herself to "feel that way." It becomes necessary to ask the question, "Why does this girl attach such an overwhelming importance to physical appearance; isn't this attitude in itself a symptom based on some more fundamental difficulty?" These ideas about the handsomeness of men, and what others would think about her were unhealthy specific attitudes; and were likely to be based on more fundamental unstable general attitudes.[1] It thus became necessary in the therapy to determine just what her fundamental *general* attitudes were.

Miss S. G. was the oldest daughter. She was about 5′ 1″ tall and was very attractive. She lived in a home which was known for its emotionalism. There was constant quarreling, and at the same time a general air of superiority expressed by each member of the family regarding his own ability and the lack of ability of others. The patient was given her own way in everything and was constantly admired for her cleverness and beauty. She became conceited, and at the same time developed an attitude of inferiority when anyone did anything which gained praise, for she continually contrasted herself with others, and felt slighted if she was not the center of attention.

She worked in an office, and because of her intelligence and enterprise was put in charge of her office force. The salesmen all "raved" about her beauty. The patient boasted of never deigning to consider a fiance who wasn't handsome and financially sound. She was a beauty, she and her

[1] *Vide* p. 172.

family said, who could choose the best of prospective husbands. Her whole philosophy pointed in the direction of overweening self-esteem. She was anxious to obtain the approval of other people, to be able to look and act superior. She wanted her own way, and had a violent temper when thwarted. When she met her "ugly fellow," she was surprised that she cared for him. Her feeling grew into "love," which made her unhappy when she was separated from him. She looked forward constantly to seeing him, to being with him, and to hearing his voice over the telephone. At the same time, however, her entire attitude toward life, and her expectations, and her desire to be able to "show off the catch" she had made in a husband were at war with this "love." A great conflict arose within her; should she sacrifice what she had always wanted, or should she sacrifice her "love"?

It thus became increasingly apparent that the patient's "terrible thoughts" were the result not simply of her desire to marry a handsome man, but of the fact that from earliest childhood, the patient had grown up in an atmosphere of "superiority," lack of consideration of one's fellow man, irritability, and bickering. These general factors expressed themselves not only in her desire for handsome men, but in her manner of speaking to others, in her attempts to be something other than what she was, in her being overbearing at work, and in her feeling of inadequacy at not achieving the heights she had so falsely evaluated. Her general pattern of reaction to many factors in life was essentially the same.

It would thus appear that the fundamental factor had been reached—a basic, inculcated egocentricity. However, if we use the formula that neurotic symptoms are the result of stress acting upon a constitution, which in turn is the result of environmental modification of the inherited constitution,[1] we have ascertained the Stress (the idea of marrying the ugly young man) and the Environmental pressure (the unstable home environment with its spoiling of the patient and the inculcation of unhygienic ideas), but have not determined the constitutional background.

In Miss S. G. the background was very significant as to heredity. Her mother was "very nervous" and high strung; her sister had "something like a breakdown" after puberty but recovered; one maternal aunt was very "nervous" and had a breakdown at the age of forty, when she had to be in the sanitarium; one maternal uncle was brilliant but irresponsible, and even at the age of fifty-five had to be "looked after"; one paternal uncle was "perfectly normal," but had three sons and two daughters all of whom were "peculiar."

[1] Symptom is resultant of S × E × Inh. C. (S = stress; E = environmental pressure; Inh. C. = inherited constitution).

Although it is impossible to separate the influence of family training, such a history is certainly indicative of an inherited predisposition. It thus may be said that the heredity was a "fundamental cause" of the neurosis. In Miss S. G. this inherited predisposition was, however, greatly modified by environmental pressure, so that one may say that there were several fundamental causes.

A fatalistic outlook because of the constitutional factor is not only erroneous, but definitely injurious. These patients can be aided, and aided greatly. In terms of social adjustment and contentment, these patients may even be "cured." A therapeutic approach is not one of bland optimism. From what has been said, it may be seen that the patient is the result not only of the inherited factor but of the environmental forces. Under adequate and intelligent guidance it is not only possible, but likely, in view of the succeeding events, that she would *not* have suffered from such an obsessional neurosis. The molding forces which man can bring to bear on inherited defects are great, and many deficiencies which are "inborn" may well be compensated for by training. Therapy directed at developing the patient's assets to the fullest may often more than compensate for liabilities. In many instances, however, one does not disregard the constitution. For example, a constitutionally feebleminded child[1] may develop psychoneurotic symptoms as the result of situational stress acting upon an inadequate constitution. In the therapy of such a person, one must consider the constitution, and attempt to inculcate only such attitudes as can be absorbed, and treat the environment even more than the patient. Psychopathic personalities must be similarly considered. Even so-called normal persons may be "constitutionally" adequate to meet only the mildest of situational or psychologic stresses; and many of these persons may become psychoneurotic patients.

Having determined and evaluated the fundamental causes, and the possibilities of therapy, physically, socially, and psychologically, the physician should proceed to give *specific suggestions* as to methods of cure.[2] Individual attitudes should be discussed in detail, and the original ideas should be discussed as to their immaturity, their ineffectiveness, their egoistic and asocial character, and the role which they play in the production of tension and symbolism, and of unhappiness. Such "intellectual" understanding carries with it the force of urging the patient to change his

[1] *Vide* p. 159 (Case N. L.)   [2] *Vide* pp. 127; 193.

attitudes. If despite such understanding the patient constantly reiterates as did Miss S. G., "Yes, I know this is true, Doctor, but all I want is to get over my funny ideas," she is to be told again and again, that the ideas are "funny" because her fundamental attitude toward life is "funny," and to cure the "ideas" she has first to remove their basic cause. The physician must be firm, definite, and concrete. He must be specific and give frequent illustrations from the patient's own life, as to what he means. Thus, for example,

Miss S. G. readily agreed that her attitudes were childish and immature. She also quickly agreed that it was more mature to be less egoistic and more objective. She understood that the centering of attention on herself, and the desire to "show off" and be superior in these artificial ways indicated immaturity. She agreed to try to *change these basic attitudes*. When she felt or acted "superior" on *any occasion*, she was consciously to say to herself that superiority is a matter of character and ability and not of social position or of appearance, and that she would evaluate the situation in this light and not permit herself to think in a wish-fulfillment manner. She told, for example, of "putting on airs" before one girl in her office. This habit she was "consciously" to change. She told of refusing to go out to parties with a certain young man she thought well of except that he wasn't "good looking," and she agreed to see him, and while with him "consciously" to change her stream of thought should it revert to his appearance. She told of conversations with her family and certain of her girl-friends in which the general tone of the discussion was to make odious comparisons and comments; and she agreed to try to make the conversation as far as she was concerned less derogatory in nature.

The patient was urged *to think consciously* according to the suggestions given. In effect, the patient was to say to herself, "Those old attitudes were immature; I shall try to believe and feel and act according to these new attitudes." Every opportunity that arises should be made an occasion for the subject to practice his newer way of understanding. The more persistent the patient is in his efforts the more surely will the immature reactions be uprooted and the more surely will the mature ones be grounded. The more the patient wishes to change, the quicker he will change.[1] The fact that he may feel, "I have always been this way," or "This is my nature," makes the changing more difficult but by no means impossible, provided the subject is willing to cooperate.

In other words, this girl was taught consciously to change her attitude toward every action which was a specific manifestation of her general attitude. Specific suggestions were constantly given,

[1] *Vide* p. 192.

and what is most important, were carried out successfully after a few trials. She learned how to put her "intellectualized" concept into action, which in turn soon became so much a part of her as to be basic in a new personality.

The change which occurred was obvious not only to the patient but to observers. Indeed, one of the first signs the author deems important prognostically is the spontaneous comment to the patient by a friend who does not know that psychiatric therapy is being given, on how much more relaxed and calm the patient appears to be. The entire expression of the patient becomes more reposed, and the facial appearance, the manner of speech, the attitudes are indicative of this new quietness of spirit.

In many instances, the most important element in successful therapy is to have the patient willing to change. The very attitude of setting up as a goal a new type of attitude is in itself corrective. Learning, in general, is the result of practice directed toward a certain goal. As long as the goal is there, the number of failures is in itself unimportant.[1] There are bound to be failures in adopting a new attitude, particularly in the beginning. Patients become discouraged and state, "It's no use; I guess I'm not built that way." Yet, if they are willing to change, such failure is soon reversed.

Steady reassurance and encouragement by the physician are important during the early part of this retraining. Belief in the patient's ability, the assurance that many other patients in similar situations have recovered, the understanding that the difficulty has existed for so many years and is not easily overcome, though it will be conquered, are all supporting for the patient. It is important to persist in the training, despite recurrences of symptoms, which as we shall see when we discuss prognosis, tend to recur even during improvement.[2] Too often a physician will attempt to apply these techniques, and not succeeding in one or two visits will try some other remedy. Obviously, a personality trait built up over a period of years will hardly be remedied in so short a time. It is important to carry the training to its logical conclusion.

The physician must be careful to avoid making a moral issue of the subject;[3] for it is not a question of moral issue, and the patient not only resents such an implication, but worse, fails to learn to solve his problems without the fear of guilt or sin. The arguments advanced must carry their own validity and be logically correct;

[1] *Vide* p. 204.   [2] *Cf.* Ch. XIII.   [3] *Vide* pp. 129; 406.

the patient must be persuaded, and not driven, to accept them. It should be pointed out that the psychoneurotic actions are immature responses, those which are present in childhood and adolescence. Maturity is something to be acquired, and can be achieved only after childish attitudes have been abandoned.

Miss S. G. was seen twice a week for one month, and then once a month for a year. Some patients can be well started on the road to a change in much less time; others require more time. At the end of that time, she had lost her obsessional ideas, and was content to go everywhere with her young man. In addition, she stated, "I have many girl friends now, something which I never had; when in a group, I am at ease, and can talk freely without always being aware of what others think of me or what they may say; I am no longer disliked by the girls in the office, and instead of thinking me overbearing and 'stuck-up,' they're very friendly and congenial." The patient changed in a myriad of ways. Her very walk, which when first seen was a stilted, ostentatious, "peacock strut," became a more relaxed normal gait. In other words the entire psychobiologic reaction pattern was influenced "unconsciously" by the changed "attitudes." This patient came to understand the cause of her ideas, and the role of the early general orientations; and she cooperated in a consistent effort to reorient and retrain herself so that the old attitudes were discarded and mental hygiene attitudes became automatic. A long period of time was necessary to obtain a full result, for attitudes acquired over two decades can not be altered in two weeks; and the physician acted as the catalyst, who provided moral support and encouragement, until the patient was able to stand on her own feet.

It is not so important to teach the patient what specific attitudes to have toward specific situations as it is to teach him the technique whereby he will be enabled to develop healthy and efficient attitudes toward whatever situation may arise. Stated more simply: it is more important to teach the patient *how* to think; *i. e.*, to discriminate, evaluate, reason logically, etc., than it is to indoctrinate specific facts and theories, however valid they may be. Facts, knowledge are of value only if the person can use them; and the making of intelligent decisions based on such facts presupposes that the person has developed the ability to think. Moreover, it is not enough to rid the patient of certain harmful or ineffective attitudes and inculcate others; he must formulate his own general attitudes that will make it possible for him to deal with specific situations.

Miss S. I., aged twenty-four years, complained of severe dysmenorrhea. Violent pains assailed her during the entire menstrual period; and for several days before and for several days after the period there was extreme lassitude and irritability. Physical examination revealed no pathology, and the use of ovarian extracts proved of no avail. Further examination revealed that the patient was "nervous," that she startled easily, that she had always been easily excitable, and irritable. The most important "cause" in this girl's case, was the role of the dominant, irritable, demanding, and highly neurotic mother, who by her attempts to control the lives and actions of her children had rendered them unhappy and unstable. One of the important elements of therapy was to train this girl to change her attitude toward the mother, so that she would listen carefully to what the mother had to say, and then, in her own mind, decide what was the right thing to do. She was then to tell her mother, objectively, quietly, and unemotionally what her conclusions were and, where possible, to act on her own conclusions. Her entire attitude toward her mother was to be converted from the emotionally dependent, cringing, unself-reliant type of reaction to that of an independent, reliant person responsible for her own decisions and actions. When the patient learned this procedure, in addition to other changes, she lost her "nervousness," and her dysmenorrhea could be easily relieved by aspirin.

There is no one attitude or set of attitudes that are the *sine qua non* of effective living; it is by no means suggested that all persons should think and act in a prescribed manner. There is no virtue in conformity *per se;* individuality calls for many and varied types of action and reaction. There is only one general statement that can be made: one's attitudes should not make for a disturbed emotional state, and even this statement has exception). In other words, whatever one decides to do he should do without feeling irritable, or needing to express tension in an unhealthy fashion. It is not the physician's purpose to set cut and dried standards for every one to follow but to see to it that those standards which are followed are not unhealthy. Since persons differ so much, standards for one may be inadequate or wrong for another.

Miss K. D., aged thirty-six years, complained of gastrointestinal difficulties. The complaints were vague and non-specific, and the attending physician ordered a complete laboratory and X-ray examination. When these reports returned "without pathology," he inquired more carefully into her other symptoms; and the patient poured out a host of complaints which seemed typically neurotic. During the first psychiatric interview, she stated, "I should have known from the beginning it wasn't my stomach that was ill; I've been worried over a boy friend and that's what affected my stomach." The patient revealed that she had been keeping company with a divorced man, ten years her senior. He was brilliant and kind, and he filled a long felt need in the patient's life. After three years she suddenly discovered that this friend was seeing another woman at the same time; and though she berated him, he refused to give up either of his "girl friends." The patient became extremely jealous, and in the natural sequence of events, the other woman discovered the patient; the mutual jealousies added to the fire. "In the last two months I lost 15 pounds, and menstruated for fourteen days." This extremely frequent "triangle" was the specific cause of the patient's "stomach trouble." Some of the more general reaction patterns included seclusiveness, and the absence of any friends, and an over-dependence on an invalid aged mother with whom she lived and who dominated the patient's every move. The therapy was directed first to changing her attitude toward her "boy friend," and making up her mind that she voluntarily give him up, since the whole situation could not result in anything but unhappiness. She was to understand the futility of jealousy and actions based thereon. She was to avoid seeing this man and to do her best "mentally to give him up." In addition to this specific change, she was urged to cultivate a more extrovert attitude toward friends, to be more sociable, and to break her emotional dependence upon her mother. Her gastrointestinal symptoms cleared up in one week, but it was two months before she could be made sufficiently emotionally stable to prevent a return of symptoms.

It will be further noticed that the advice just given is relatively, not absolutely important. It is good for the person and for society for man to be somewhat dissatisfied with things as they are. Dissatisfaction and irritation call for changes, and changes if well controlled and guided make for a better situation all around. This dissatisfaction should not go to the point of preventing the person from solving his problems in a most efficient manner. Consequently, when a patient asks, "When will I be completely happy and not dissatisfied?" it is well to discuss these points with him.

Just as there is no absolute standard of attitudes, so is there no one method of removal and substitution of attitudes which rigidly followed will always be effective. Each physician must make specific application of the general principles discussed, and the success of the therapy will be determined to a large extent by his ability to meet the particular needs of his patients.

CHAPTER X

CHARACTERISTIC GENERAL ATTITUDES AND THEIR TREATMENT

THE "psychological"[1] attitude, which is but one facet of the total "physiological" and constitutional reactivity, is the conscious or unconscious pattern by which the person reacts to any particular stimulus or circumstance. These general patterns,[2] or orientations to situations, are largely determined by deliberate (or conscious) training and by environmental pressure; and like other responses take on the automatic nature of habits. The problem of therapy is the problem of retraining the patient and is two-fold: (1) breaking down or removing those attitudes which are unhealthful or immature, and (2) substituting and making automatic more efficient and mature orientations. To label certain attitudes as "immature" and laud others as "mature" is not enough.[3] Rather, there must be detailed analysis[4] of each specific attitude so that the patient will realize how it came into existence, and wherein it is inadequate. When the patient realizes that his present attitude fails to give him that which he desires it is possible convincingly to present more mature ways of thinking. As soon as the patient gives his intellectual consent to the desirability of the new attitude, the next step is to show him how consciously to apply the attitude in the specific problems with which he is confronted, and to persist in consciously training him until the desired attitude becomes automatic.

In the following discussion of the more common mature and immature attitudes and techniques of thought, specific suggestions will be made as to how to remove or inculcate them. It is essential to remember, however, that these suggestions are only *some* of the methods by means of which the orientations can be changed. Just as there are innumerable variations in the attitudes and ways of thinking which need correction, so are there in the methods which can be utilized effectively. Individual patients always require individual therapy. However, it may be said, in general, that the *therapy which is most likely to be of permanent value is that which teaches the patient to be self-reliant, to be cognizant at once of his*

---

[1] *Vide* p. 171.   [2] *Vide* p. 171 *ff*.   [3] *Vide* p. 193.   [4] *Vide* p. 128.

limitations and his assets, and to react to situations in terms of an objective perspective of himself in relation to his environment. Further the reader will need constantly to bear in mind that there are relatively few clear cut pictures of single symptoms; so that although the various attitudes are discussed separately for the sake of clarity, in reality the psychoneurotic patient usually presents a symptom complex; and though the physician may focus his attention on a particular attitude that is manifestly immature, the problem is not one of single attitudes but of the total personality of which the particular attitude is but a reflection. The following discussions are perhaps over-simplified, but they have the concrete value of showing how the principles of therapy discussed in the preceding chapter can be practically applied to bring about changes in attitudes and consequent personality reorientation.

EMOTIONAL THINKING[1]

At the basis of most immature attitudes will be found "emotional thinking" which consists primarily of jumping to conclusions because of the undue influence of wishes or fears, or because of the lack of training in the proper way of thinking. The term "emotional thinking" is used advisedly though it is patently paradoxical and self-contradicting and must not be confused either with emotion truly understood, nor with thinking as a logical rational process. Emotion is an integral part of the bodily process, and the expression of the basic drives and energy of the organism. Emotion may be suppressed or emphasized but not removed; nor is it desirable that it should be removed. Just as emotion without the direction and control of the intellect defeats itself by its own excesses, so the intellect without the driving force of emotion remains sterile, incapable of accomplishment. It is man's affections, sympathies, sorrows, antipathies, and aspirations that urge him to effort and achievement. There are many persons who have excellent "minds" but who accomplish little because their ideas are not translated into action, action itself being a form of emotion.

Emotional thinking is the antithesis of logical thinking. Logical thought or reason is direct, clear, influenced only by facts, and based on premises arrived at objectively and understandingly. Reason evaluates facts dispassionately and faces them as they are, without attempting to alter them by either wishes or fears. Emo-

---

[1] *Cf.* Primitive Thinking, p. 43.

tional thinking, on the other hand, is unclear, associated with emotional turmoil, vague in its premises, and subjective to the point where perspective is lost. Every person is more or less subject to this fallacious type of thinking, particularly when confronted by situations in which his ego may be threatened. It is relatively easy to be objective about impersonal matters; and, conversely, difficult to subject to "the cold light of reason" anything which, however remotely, impinges upon one's ego. Accordingly, the greatest progress in civilization has been in technical matters, since they are relatively free from emotional distortion; the least progress has come about in social reorganization because of the intense emotional tone associated with the solutions suggested. Emotional tone blurs the facts, and confuses the logical process in evaluation of the facts. Rational thinking which is basically objective leads to understanding; emotional thinking which is primarily selfish and subjective tends to result in antagonism and anger or in neurotic affections.

Mr. K. lived with his parents, two sisters and one brother. He would leave the house in the morning and come home late at night. On Sundays or holidays he would avoid his home as much as possible. For six years he had not spoken to his brother, and he answered his parents only in the most curt and abrupt manner. He had many neurotic traits. "I'm twenty-eight, and my mother treats me like a baby. I have to give her everything I make, and if I hold out a few dollars, she's mad. When I was out of work, she and my sister didn't speak to me and I didn't to them. They said I was lazy. They are against every new idea. They follow the ideas of the 'old country,' insist that I'll go to hell because I don't believe as they do, and they call me a good-for-nothing. They never think whether a thing is right or not; they like it if it's the same as what they were used to; and they are against it if it's in any way different from what they already think. They are good at heart but they sure can hate."

This man of twenty-eight sulked like a child; but his childish reaction (in this instance a synonym for "emotional") thinking was but the mirror image of the emotional thinking in his environment. He was not spoken to because he did not earn money; and since the parents needed money, they assumed that the patient did not earn it because of "spite." Not only did they take no cognizance of economic conditions, but they also blamed him for their own difficulties. Their actions toward each other were not thought out in any rational or logical manner, but were primitive expressions of distorted personalities, justified by the pseudo-logic called rationization.

The treatment of emotional thinking may be done by direct and conscious training of the patient. The general pattern of responding emotionally must be replaced. This concept should be continuously held up before the patient; and specific examples given constantly. The changed emotional thinking will show itself in many ways. Often the changing of the patient results in a different attitude on the part of the family. Dr. E. X., a medical student, whose home life was very similar to Mr. K.'s, told me one day how the attitudes of the entire family seemed to have undergone a revision with the change of his own personality. Undoubtedly, part of this family change was the result of the altered manner in which the patient viewed their reactions, but much of it was real change. The patient himself must first be persuaded *to wish to change*.[1] It is surprising how many patients will come for treatment and yet insist on doing things the way they wish and not the way the physician prescribes. It is here that the problem of rapport[2] comes into play; and the more the patient feels he is "understood" and his difficulties appreciated, the greater will be his cooperation. The first step in removing the emotional thinking is a detailed explanation of what it is. Then specific experiences in the current life of the patient should be analyzed, and both the incorrect and correct (correct because effective) forms of behavior in the specific instances pointed out. For example, Mr. K. was told that not only his family but he also did not think logically. He was asked what logical reason lay behind his not speaking to his brother. He could give no reason other than that his brother and he were angry at each other, and that his brother would probably not reply even if he did speak. "Besides, I won't give him the satisfaction of having me speak first." It was pointed out to him that carrying a grudge was immature behavior; that irritations between persons are common; but that if grudges were generally kept, no two persons could live together. Moreover, it was emphasized that not only was it far more mature to be friendly and tolerant, but also that his constant attempts to bolster his self-respect indicated a basic lack of self-confidence. The emotionalism directed towards his brother was but one aspect of his sense of personal insecurity and of his tendency to self blame. It was necessary to *reason out* how, without the bias of anger, he should act towards his brother, and then to persuade and encourage him to carry out his plan. He was advised not to be obsequious and try

[1] *Vide* p. 184.   [2] *Vide* Ch. VI, p. 129,

to curry favor, but rather to speak pleasantly whenever the occasion would ordinarily require speaking. He should continue to speak even though he received a discourteous answer or even none at all. Moreover he was to realize that the purpose of his changing in regard to his silence was not primarily to be courteous to his brother, but to learn to be without the anger towards himself, which almost invariably accompanies such anger towards another.

It will be observed that merely stating that his attitude was immature was not sufficient; indeed such a statement alone would tend merely to produce a defense reaction.[1] Detailed reasons for its immaturity were given, as well as specific instruction as to what constituted maturity. The patient was shown how, in a more certain and efficient way, to get what he wanted. He could understand that this newer method was not only more logical but would make him happier. Value to the patient is quickly recognized and adds force to the persuasion of the physician. However, since the emotional attitude has usually been existent for many years, it can rarely be removed by a single explanation. Intellectual acceptance is insufficient, and the subject must be *trained* into the new habit. Care must be taken lest the physician alienate patients, for irritation, impatience, or anger will prevent rather than hasten the adoption of the principles laid down; and failure immediately to apply the principles is not so much an indication of unwillingness or lack of cooperation as it is a sign of the pervasive strength of the emotional orientation.

WORRY

One of the most common forms of emotional thinking is "worry." To worry is to be in a state of anxiety about some particular problem. It is interesting to note that "worry" comes from the Middle English word "worowen," meaning "to strangle." Worry is never effectual, and persons *can* be trained *to think instead of to worry*. Worry is an emotional phenomenon wherein a problem is evaluated in the light of wishes and fears instead of objectively on the basis of the facts as they are. Anxiety is the prevailing state in worry, and is frequently associated with such physiologic evidences of muscle tension, as hypertension, hyperchlorhydria, spastic colitis, tachycardia, etc. Persons who worry are presumably confronted with some difficult problem which they are trying to solve. How-

[1] *Vide* pp. 63; 406.

ever, instead of reasoning out the problem, they "think about it emotionally" which is to say, they see the difficulties magnified through the eyes of fear, and what they see is vague, without perspective, distorted. Sometimes the problem is seen clearly, but there is overconcern, *worry*, about the solution. To be worried generally means to be overcome by distressing emotion instead of reasoning out and working for the best solution.

It must again be stressed that the human inclination to worry is common. Even the making of practical decisions is "upsetting." We resent having to "make up our mind" when we are tired or absorbed in a task. Any situation which affects us adversely is disturbing, and naturally so; but the point which the patient must keep in mind is that the less effort he expends in fruitless worry, the more energy will he have for working out an adequate solution of his problem.

There are two types of worry, each of which needs different treatment. One type is that of the more or less "normal" person confronted by a difficult situation; the other and more common among the psychoneuroses, is that of the chronic worrier, to whom each event in life is a subject for "fretting and stewing," and who when he has no problems of his own of major importance, will grieve over the catastrophes in the home of a neighbor or friend.[1] In the first instance, the reasoning process is temporarily overcome by the emotional tone of the problem; in the chronic worrier's type, there are both a basic sense of insecurity and feelings of inferiority which need to be overcome before he can practice the "logical" process of thought.

It is well to outline arbitrarily several steps in reasoning out a problem. These steps are not sharply divided in real life, and they may be greatly modified by each person. Nevertheless, they form a concrete plan which the "worrier" can follow in overcoming his tendency to emotional thinking. *Primarily*, the subject must be taught that difficulties are best solved by reason (it seems almost too obvious to be said, yet it is a fact overlooked by these patients) and that the facts of the situation must be evaluated as they are and not obscured by possible dangers. Where dangers are real, it is not easy or even at times possible to remove all apprehension; but in the usual case, most of the apprehension is unnecessary. The subject must train himself *to state his problem clearly and*

[1] *Cf.* p. 73 (Identification).

definitely; to put aside his fears and observe the situation objectively. What one desires may form the goal toward which one strives, but the actual working out of a solution must be impartial. Secondly, after the facts have been ascertained and weighed, *an analysis should be made of the possible solutions.* Some of these solutions are more desirable than others, but all the possibilities must be faced as unemotionally as possible. The best solution available should then be followed with an understanding of its values and inadequacies. In the third place, it is most important from the point of view of avoiding worry to *resign one's self* to the difficulties of the "best solution," *until one can work out a better one.* The fact that a course of action has been planned and a decision taken leaves the person infinitely more stable and generally enables him eventually to bring about the most efficient solution of the pressing problem. Should the problem not require immediate solution, then one can continue to analyze it over a long period of time; but in such cases, continuous thought on the problem must be avoided, for continuous thought usually leads to a "rut formation" and the person overlooks possible answers because of an accustomed pattern of thinking. One should therefore consciously allow himself only a certain portion of time in which to examine the problem, and at other times deliberately occupy himself with unrelated interests so that the problem may not intrude. This free period with its "natural" and logical relationships, tends to make for a *general reorientation* which continues to apply when the pertinent matter is again taken up, and may bring about a more effective orientation there also. The absence of emotion leads to a clearer and more logical result.

Having determined his course of action, the patient must, in the fourth place, proceed to *carry it through even if it is distasteful.* The difficulties must be accepted unemotionally; that is, recognized as being distasteful and to be changed as soon as possible, but not permitted to be too disturbing. This is perhaps too ideal a condition to be more than approximated, but the combination of doing all that can be done while avoiding tension can, by self training, be brought to a fairly high degree of success. It is far better to carry out that which is planned than to drift aimlessly in the sea of indecision. The physician needs to give much moral support to enable the patient to do that which is distasteful, until the patient learns the principle of doing the necessary but unpleasant things himself.

D. G., aged forty-two years, complained of dizziness, nausea and light-headedness. His company physician treated him but could find no organic pathology. Questioning brought out the information that two months prior to the onset of his symptoms the firm for which he had worked for twenty-two years had been amalgamated with a national institution. Less help was needed after the union of the firms and many of this man's associates had been discharged after long terms of employment. They were stranded without positions and untrained for any other kind of work. The patient believed that it would not be long before his discharge would occur. He felt that his work was not altogether essential to the firm and one salary reduction had already been made. This man had saved very little, most of his earnings having gone into life insurance policies and for the education of his children. He was greatly worried over the future.

After an analysis of the situation, it developed that this man had his home paid for, and no outstanding debts. He was not at all certain that he would be discharged from his position. He had investigated a small road stand near his home which he believed might be profitably developed as a gasoline station as well as a restaurant. The possible solutions then to this man's problem seemed to be: first, to keep on with his work as long as he could and see whether he might not make himself more valuable to, and thus more secure in the firm; second, should there be any real evidence of being removed, to take over this road side stand, and see whether it could be developed. In the meantime he was (1) consciously to change the subject of his thoughts should they concern the difficulties in the office, and (2) at the same time, further investigate the new way of earning a living so that he could take it over if his office situation became bad, or if the prospects seemed brighter; third, he was to view the situation as objectively as possible; and fourth, stick to his decision. Finally, he was to develop new interests and hobbies both for the negative value of removing his thoughts from his problem, and for the positive worth of obtaining pleasure.

The patient, an intelligent executive, saw the value of the procedure, and put it into effect. When he understood the relationship between his symptoms and his worry, the symptoms cleared up almost immediately. He was given $\frac{1}{2}$ grain of phenobarbital to use whenever he felt tense, realizing of course that it was a "crutch" which he should discard as soon as he could stand on his own feet. A month later, he was still working at his position but had decided to make the best of it, since worry did no good. He had arranged for fewer expenditures so that he could save more, and he had "made a deal" to take over the "stand" at the end of several months.

This man under guidance had analyzed his situation and found it not so bad in fact as his fears had led him to believe. He made his plan of action, logically; decided which was the best course to pursue; and consciously learned not to think of the situation until he had some definite plan. He learned to "forget" his troubles. He did not thereby neglect his problem; but he "reasoned it out" instead of worrying. His new attitude did not mean that his situation was any less precarious, but it did mean that he dealt more efficiently with his situation. By following this procedure he rid himself of the emotional disturbance which had caused neurotic symptoms and which was both incapacitating and depressing.

The substitution of such a reasoning process for worry is not always so simple. Moreover, the type of reason suggested above did not emanate entirely from the physician. Rather the patient brought forth all the facts and suggestions, and under guidance synthesized his own ideas into a plan of action. Further, and this fact is exceedingly important, the very making of a decision in itself relieved emotional tension. Many persons would welcome having a decision made for them, an unhealthful dependent attitude, if thereby they could for the time being be relieved of the responsibility of decision. The mere making of a decision is of great importance in removing emotional stress; and where possible, the patient should be taught how to think logically and come to his own decisions. In the beginning it may be necessary to coach the patient and often even to suggest solutions; but if the patient is at all intelligent and willing he will soon learn the technique himself.

Most psychoneurotic patients dread carrying out a line of action or thought, no matter how convinced they may be intellectually. The general attitude of emotional thinking makes for avoidance and fear of facts as they are. In strange contradiction to this timidity, these patients will often perform acts of martyr-like courage.[1] Closer analysis, however, will show that to the patient, the "courageous" act was less to be feared than are the imagined dangers of his conflicts.

Where the tendency to worry is chronic, however, there is need, in addition, to change the basic difficulty, which often lies in a basic emotional instability which must be corrected in the fashion outlined previously; that is, by determining the etiology, the existing stresses, and by treating the specific attitudes concerned. Often, persons who are chronic worriers have not learned to think rationally, and have always been emotional in the making of their decisions. In some instances there is a lack of emotional emancipation[2] from the home, and a feeling of dependence which has prevented thinking of an independent and logical nature. Whatever may be the basis of the *chronic worry, it must be primarily treated as one treats a neurosis* in order to bring about a readjustment.

N. T., aged twenty-two years, complained of nervousness, faintness, dizzy spells, heavy breathing, a pain up and down the breast bone, pounding of the heart at the least excitement, difficulty in breathing, and difficulty in swallowing. These symptoms had been present for six months, and continued

---

[1] *Vide* p. 276.   [2] *Vide* p. 209 (Case G. J.).

unabated. "On December 26th, the night before leaving for a vacation, I was driving the car home. Suddenly I was seized by a terrible pounding of the heart, and I couldn't catch my breath. I felt I was going to die. These other symptoms have come on me since. I have taken all sorts of pills and some 'red medicine' but it made me dopey for a while and didn't stop my trouble." After several interviews, I learned that the boy, before leaving for his vacation, had been gambling and owed some money which he was to pay by borrowing from a loan company, the matter to be taken care of by a friend of his in whom he did not have much confidence. Although this chain of events seemed to be the cause of his troubles it was difficult to believe that a full-grown young man could develop such a lasting neurosis from one difficulty of this kind. Closer analysis, together with interviewing the parents, brought to light the following. The father told of the boy's being a "mama's boy" and of his never having been allowed by the mother to "be on his own." In addition, the father told of always insisting that the "boy make something of himself" instead of going to school and playing football, which the father insisted was too dangerous a sport. The father was short tempered and irritable. He wanted his son, who worked in his store, to display more initiative and energy. The mother vehemently denied keeping the boy "tied to her apron strings" and insisted that he could go where he wished and do what he wished. "Of course, he is the kind of boy who always tells me just where he goes and what he does. He always wants me to buy his clothes for him, and he asks my advice whenever anything comes up that he's worried about." The boy's version (he was 6 feet tall and weighed 190 lbs. of solid muscle and bone) was somewhat different. "I guess I was always babied and spoiled. My father is high strung, and my mother always gets her own way. They always were afraid I'd make mistakes, and they'd tell me what to do and even what to say. They were afraid to let me play football because I'd be hurt, and I didn't want to be called a 'sissy.' If I go to buy a suit of clothes, Mother comes with me and she selects the color and the style, and talks about the price. At the store, Father watches me like a hawk. I guess he wants me to take his place eventually; but he's so anxious about everything I do, that I'm afraid to do anything. When I come into the store now, it is as if a cloud settles over me and I can't breathe. I want to do my own thinking for a change. That's why I started to 'play the ponies'; I got a thrill out of it at first; but now every time I think of it and what my parents would do to me if they found out, I shudder and my heart begins to pound. I guess it's because I've always been a worrier. I can't stand to owe anyone money, and I worry until it's paid. Every small thing which wasn't just right annoyed me and I worried about it. If a customer wasn't quite pleased, if I promised to do something and failed, if I had to hand in a theme in college and had little time to prepare it, if anything occurred in which I *might* not do the *right* thing, I worried."

This boy's symptoms, it becomes apparent, were the result of a life-long personality molding by an over-expectant father and a domineering mother who never permitted the boy to develop any security or any emotional satisfaction over his own decisions.

His chronic worrying tendencies were the result of this life-long lack of emotional independence. A cure in this instance could be brought about only by changing the emotional independence of the boy on his parents.[1]

First the situation as outlined above, was discussed with him, but in much greater detail; so that he had a thorough understanding of the mechanisms behind the formation of his symptoms. The next step was to outline a course of action whereby he could retrain himself. In this plan, he had to consider the facts that he still cared for his parents; that he owed them consideration and respect; but that he need not be obsequious or subservient to their wishes and demands. Moreover, he should proceed about this emancipation without rudeness or brusqueness; and there should be every courtesy and consideration. When he was given advice by his parents (or by anyone) he should evaluate the advice in the light of his own knowledge and experience, and with due consideration of the experience of the person giving the advice. Simply because advice is given is no reason that it must or should be accepted. But he must be sure that reasoning, and not just thinking emotionally determined the conclusion as to whether to accept the advice. Further, if he agreed with his parent, he should be courageous enough to say, "You're right" and follow the suggestion. Should he reason to a different conclusion, his response should be something of this sort, "I follow your reasoning, Mother; but it seems to me that my particular reason is more applicable to the situation, and I will therefore do it thus and so." In this particular case, the patient had further to be told that he should not attempt to carry out his point by being emotional nor, on the other hand, should he feel it necessary to do what they said, merely because it was his parent's advice. He was shown that *extremes even in reasoning are dangerous,* for often what at the time appears to be a good reason, may at another time seem foolish. Moreover, the quality of emotional tone must be considered, and due weight given to parental desire. It was a question of learning just when to be firm and when not to be, that it is just as bad to have too much salt in food as to have none at all. The principle, however, underlying the making of all decisions was to be that of unemotional and logical thinking, which the boy was to do for himself.

In addition, all the ordinary tasks which the usual man of twenty-two years does for himself and which this boy's mother had done

[1] *Cf.* p. 300 (Case N. T.).

for him, were to be his sole responsibility. He was to buy his own clothes, make his own decisions, avoid asking for advice on the trivia of his life, avoid telling his parents every little difficulty that arose, etc. In other words, he was to learn to be self-reliant, but without discourtesy to or disregard of his parents. His father and mother were spoken to and they too saw the value of letting the boy make his own mistakes in order that he might develop self-reliance. At first this new order was irritating to them but soon their son seemed actually more affectionate to them since his affection was the understanding one of an adult and not the neurotic one of a dependent child. The chronic worry tendency disappeared as the boy learned to make his decisions and to carry them out without being upset.

EMOTIONAL EMANCIPATION

One especial kind of emotional thinking, of immature attitude, is found in those patients whose major difficulties appear to stem from their over-dependence upon or attachment to their families.

Attachment to members of the family is "normal" and desirable. The constant association breeds a community of interests and a common bond of affection which "makes blood thicker than water." Many times, however, among psychoneurotic patients, this family dependence is excessive. As a matter of fact, *most of the psychoneurotic actions do not appear as generically different from what is average, but as an over-intensification of the average reaction.*

Many young men and women have psychoneurotic problems, the basis of which is an excessive attachment to their parents. This attachment is in the form of a neurotic love, differing from the normal in that it is so excessive that it calls forth the other extreme (see ambivalent)[1] of dislike for the same parent, and develops in the child a feeling of inadequacy which is compensated for by an attempt to find all satisfactions in terms of this "neurotic love," which from its very nature inevitably must yield more disturbance than it does pleasure.

Every growing thing once reaching maturity desires to be independent. When the child is young much maternal attention may definitely be overwhelming, but especially after puberty such excess of attention makes the child feel increasingly irritable. On the one hand, he "feels" that he owes allegiance and love to recompense

[1] *Vide* p. 76.

the mother and father for all their effort; and on the other, he feels resentment at not being able to do things completely as he wishes. If the child has managed to preserve his "will to be independent," then even though his actions may be self-determined, there often lurks in his feelings a sense of being an ingrate or of being disloyal. If there is no conflict between the desire for independence and parental domination, then psychoneurotic symptoms rarely occur unless by some fortuitous chance the child (he may be chronologically an adult) is bereft of the parent, or other member of the family on whom he has learned to lean for support. Even if there is no conflict with resultant neuroses, the person so smothered with affection, so trained in over-dependence, never can reach full maturity, never can become a self-reliant, integrated personality.

In such situations the parent is usually at fault. He wishes the undivided attention and devotion of the child as recompense for all the "sacrifice" made in rearing the child; or, equally often, the child becomes a substitute for direct emotional satisfaction which the parent has missed in his own personal life.

The problem of teaching parents to be "normal" in their attitude toward their children is a delicate one, insomuch as success is dependent upon the parent's having not only a genuine love for the child, and respect for him as a personality with certain "inalienable rights" but at the same time a sense of proportion which will prevent him from going to the other extreme of expecting too much self-reliance, too much independence from the child. If too much attention leads to lack of self-reliance, too little may equally lead to emotional insecurity. Rarely is a child spoiled by being loved "too much" if at the same time he is taught to be self-reliant, come to his own conclusions, make his own mistakes and profit by them, etc.

In the individual case where the psychoneurotic symptoms are clearly based on this over-attachment,[1] the patient must be urged to follow a "golden mean" course of action. Even though he is urged to think for himself, he is cautioned to listen carefully to parental advice and to weigh it on its soundness and applicability. To refuse to follow a certain course merely because it is recommended by a particular person is as indicative of lack of maturity and independence as is the opposite extreme. Parents, on the other hand, should be urged not to be overly concerned when their children disagree with them, for as long as a child is reasoning his way

[1] *Vide* p. 186 (Case S. I.).

to a conclusion, he will learn far more from a single experience of his own than he would from any amount of verbal instruction.[1] One very wise mother commented, "I wonder why my boys are so good about listening to and accepting my decisions, when so often their judgment about their own affairs is better than mine."

When children grow up they must assume the responsibilities of independent human beings living their own lives, suffering their own sorrows, experiencing their own joys. To expect the child to be constantly or even primarily interested in the parents is expecting the abnormal. When children reach maturity (a state which is reached gradually and through training and experience; not automatically by attaining a certain chronological age), parents should turn much of their attention to interests and pleasures which they personally derive from life and which they should have been cultivating all along. Not only are the parents themselves happier, but thereby they both set an example of happiness and permit their children the freedom which is essential for the development of self-reliance.

Among the attitudes most essential for the development of a mature and integrated personality are: (1) self-tolerance, (2) the ability objectively to evaluate one's liabilities and assets, and (3) the will honestly and intellectually to face difficulties. One realizes at once upon reading such an enumeration that *these attitudes are not separate entities*[2] but rather different aspects of the same quality —the ability to face reality objectively, dispassionately, unemotionally.

SELF TOLERANCE

It is a common experience for "normals" (*i. e.*, persons who have infrequent psychoneurotic disturbances) to find satisfaction with what they themselves do, and dissatisfaction with what others do. However, most psychoneurotic patients are intolerant alike of their own and others' inadequacies and manifest their feelings by compensatory mechanisms, rationalization, emotional thinking, irritability, or by an admitted sense of inferiority.

The difficulty with such persons lies in the fact that they fail adequately to understand and therefore to make allowances for "human nature." The French proverb, "Tout comprendre, c'est, tout pardonner" is applicable in this connection.

---

[1] *Vide* p. 204.

[2] For example Case N. T. (p. 197) which illustrates the tendency to worry may well illustrate, also, the lack of emotional emancipation.

These patients have standards (usually inculcated by the environment) which tend to condemn as "sinful" all "normal" wishes and desires and which demand a level of behavior impossible of attainment. Their fears and wishes are based not on facts as they exist but, rather, are an outgrowth of a distorted sense of their abilities and values. These persons feel they are not so "smart" as others, they are not so "good" as others, that the particular task they are engaged in is not being so efficiently done as others would do it, etc. Any desire for sex satisfaction, for money, for fame, is looked upon by the patient as being "sinful," forbidden, "untouchable," reprehensible, and is surrounded by emotions connoting dread. When they perform some task and fail, they berate themselves; and if they accomplish something well, they find reasons for feeling that they might have done it better.

These persons who are intolerant of themselves often develop a compensatory attitude of intolerance of others. It is very common to find that persons who are over-bearing, over-certain, almost offensive in manner, are underneath shy, sensitive, and fearful of their own inadequacies. Frequently they will criticise harshly in others the very faults which they themselves display.[1]

Mr. T. C. stopped by the office one day. "I just noticed you talking to K. T. Is he a friend of yours? I can't stand him; he has the crudest manners and is rude and impolite. He has no social sense and his clothes are atrocious."

It was somewhat amazing to hear Mr. T. C. make this statement insomuch as K. T. had, a few minutes earlier, used almost the exact words to describe Mr. T. C.'s behavior!

This attitude of intolerance of themselves and intolerance of others (the second is generally the result of the first) can disappear only when the patient learns to *understand*. "Understanding" for the psychoneurotic patients suffering from this difficulty means recognizing that the body and bodily desires are normal; that ambitions and desires are in themselves not wrong; that to desire sex contacts, to wish to be wealthy and powerful, to aspire for recognition is neither abnormal nor "wrong." In anger, for example, it is not "wrong" to wish to destroy one's enemy.

Children in a momentary heat of rage say: "I wish he were dead"; and many of the early folk songs give similar direct expressions of hatred—primitive expression of a primitive emotion. In

---

[1] One might suggest the rule that he who denounces vehemently some trait in another, frequently suffers from that same trait himself.

like fashion, the adult who wishes to destroy his enemy is neither a
"sinner" nor a "criminal"; he is merely a partially civilized person
(as are all others of the human race) who has momentarily slipped
back to a more primitive level of thinking. The psychoneurotic
patient who is troubled by his guilty conscience and a fear of killing, needs to be reassured that his feelings while not mature are not
wicked; and more particularly he needs to be trained to raise his
whole pattern of reactions from a childish and immature level.
Similarly the person who has violated the sex code and consequently suffers from a sense of sin or guilt needs to be taught both
that his desires and impulses are part of his basic nature, and that
the code has value for society as a whole, of which he is a member
with certain obligations and responsibilities. It is interesting to
notice that patients suffer as much from what they wish, from their
"wicked thoughts and desires" as they do from any overt acts
which they may have committed.

We need to recognize that our social order demands that we
discipline ourselves so that our desires are controlled.[1] The specific
manner which is decreed by society varies in different lands and in
different ages, and as a consequence what is wrong at one time or
place is right in another. If the patient can learn to understand
this fact and realize that *though the desire is not wrong, the action
may be*, much suffering will be alleviated. In the usual situation,
comprehension of this fact results in the disappearance of the
desire; whereas the guilt feelings attached to having the desire
make the desire continue. Once a patient understands, for example, that it is neither harmful nor sinful to masturbate, and that
most men and even animals practice masturbation, the drive and
practice actually decreases. It is a common rule: *repression makes
for increased intensity of that which is repressed*. It is necessary to
be tolerant not only of the impulses and desires so characteristic
of the human race but of individual limitations as well. When one
understands what he is capable of at a given time, he will cease his
bitter self reproaches for not achieving more and will turn his
hitherto wasted energy toward increasing his capacities, improving
his skill, developing his abilities. Mistakes and failures are not
sins; they are indeed essential in life's learning process, training
being largely a matter of making a series of mistakes until one can
become skillful enough to overcome them. The very fact that a
person makes mistakes may indicate that he is directing his efforts
toward a goal.

[1] *Vide* p. 117.

LIABILITIES AND ASSETS

It is well for the person to know (realistically not fatalistically)[1] what are his special abilities and his particular limitations. In the psychoneuroses there is too great a tendency to desire aimlessly and widely, with consequent feelings of constant depression and irritation at not obtaining these unformulated desires, or of equally constant dissatisfaction if they are obtained. Conversely and as a corollary, these same persons expect of themselves that which is manifestly impossible either because of lack of training or because of native inability. If one wishes to achieve a particular goal and at the same time escape the disintegrating effect of indecisiveness, it is essential that he formulate in concrete form just what it is that he wishes,[2] and then evaluate accurately and objectively his limitations and his positive potentialities. The futility of attempting or wishing the impossible is no more tragic than the conscious or unconscious failure to achieve the possible. Happiness and efficiency are achieved not by resignation to a typically Oriental fatalism, on the one hand; or on the other, by grim adherence to the ultra aggressiveness so characteristic of the West.

Understanding one's limitations does not mean a passive acceptance of them. Rather, it means recognition of the problem, such recognition to be followed by working out a technique of temporary resignation and compensation.

The physician need not be too concerned with what the individual patient desires, for that is entirely in his own realm. He may wish to become President or to be the greatest scientist in the world, or to be the richest potentate in existence. If he has healthy ways of thinking, understands what his desires are, and plans to overcome his limitations, he has desirable mental hygiene. If, on the other hand, he has vague day dreams and struggles aimlessly, wishing beyond what is possible at the moment, and making no effort to accomplish what he wishes, then he would generally tend to remain an inadequate personality, and potentially if not actually, a psychoneurotic patient.

FACING DIFFICULTIES

In a world so constituted as ours is, both physically and socially, there is no possibility of a person's escaping all difficulties. If, "One takes the trouble to be born," it is into a world wherein there

---

[1] *Vide* p. 183.   [2] *Vide* p. 242.

are many barriers, stumbling blocks and hurdles, not all of which can be managed with ease and success. It is a "mixed world" and must be so accepted; and more important, dealt with. Rarely does one find a person overwhelmed by his joy, seeking an explanation of his good fortune. One of the most difficult tasks man must perform is to learn "to see life and see it whole"; face difficulties as they arise; deal with them as adequately as the limitations of his ability and the nature of the situation permit; and adjust himself to those conditions which he is powerless to change. Two dangers which are equally to be avoided are: on the one hand, the easy fatalism which adopts the attitude of "What's the use? This is the way it is and there is no use in trying to change it," and on the other, a refusal to face irritating and disturbing facts, which refusal brings in its train the host of psychoneurotic symptoms so commonly observed. It must then be remembered that the insistence on the necessity of resolutely "facing difficulties" means neither a blind nor a martyr-like acceptance of them as inescapable, but rather an honest and objective evaluation of specific problems, a calm, unemotional, a "thought-out" not a "felt-about" plan as to what can be done. In actuality there are relatively few situations which cannot be at least ameliorated, if thus "intellectually" handled.

Even in those instances where "nothing can be done," the person can be trained deliberately to refuse to be disturbed by that which he is powerless to change. He must learn not only to understand the cause of his troubles but consciously and consistently to practice the attitude of refusing to be emotionally "wrought up" by truly inescapable and irremedial circumstances. Here, as elsewhere, the element of time is important, for rarely can attitudes be successfully applied the first few times they are called into play. Habits are formed only by repetition, and the habit of objectively facing difficulties is no exception to the rule. On occasion the patient can find great relief by some recreational outlet which releases the tension built up by his acceptance of the difficulty.[1]

Mrs. C. O., aged forty-three years, who had detachment of the retina in both eyes, had very little vision, and saw only large objects in the light. She was referred by her nephew, because of her paranoid ideas. She felt that her sister with whom she lived was playing tricks on her, that her vision was poor but not bad, and that she was being taken advantage of. She was

---

[1] *Vide* p 250.

sure that her food was poisoned, and that everyone was intent on taking advantage of her. Her paranoid ideas became systematized into a regular delusional system.

When she was spoken to she vehemently denied that she was practically blind, or that her poor vision interfered with her activity (she could hardly move about the house without feeling her way). She was ready to "flounce" out of the office the moment it was suggested that she learn Braille. "I'm not blind. What are you trying to do to me?" She refused to admit to herself how severe her ailment was and she tried to go about the house by memorizing the position of the furniture. Her paranoid ideas continued, and it was finally decided to hospitalize her for therapy. Through a friend she became acquainted with a totally blind man five years her senior; and she immediately took charge of him, tended to his wants, leading him about gropingly but surely. Almost immediately her paranoid ideas disappeared, and for the past few years she has been quite happy, going with him "as a companion" to the home for the blind.

This woman found an outlet for her emotions by "proving" she could lead the blind and not need to be led. The torture caused by doubts of her adequacy was relieved, and there was no necessity for such compensatory explanations to herself as had been expressed in the paranoid ideas. Her compensation was, however, a precarious one, since there remained the basic refusal to recognize her inadequacy and make the best of it. Should the new balance which she established break down in some way, her symptoms would recur. The psychotherapeutic formulation should have been directed toward persuading the woman to understand her condition, face it directly, and do what was best under the circumstances.

The frequency with which psychoneurotic patients avoid facing the issue is an indication of the basic attitude of trying to avoid danger by denying its existence. This attempt proves a boomerang however, for the memory of the danger continues to exist "subconsciously," and then assumes a shroud of imagined danger in addition to the real danger, so that the situation has greater fear producing potency than it would if examined consciously and frankly. In general, that which is not clearly defined tends to carry with it a halo of vague wishes if it is pleasant, and a shadow of disconcerting fears if it is unpleasant. Situations which are anticipated[1] often are not so pleasant nor so bad in actuality; for the imagination surrounds the situation with qualities and emotional tones that do not actually exist. Music[2] is so powerful and moving, because it permits each person to clothe the harmonious tones with his own connotations, associations, and emotional tones,

[1] *Vide* p. 78.   [2] *Vide* p. 250.

thus enhancing the effects. This fact accounts for the various meanings a single musical composition may have, depending on the "hearer." Similarly, if one anticipates some irritation or danger, the more the anticipation and the more the tendency to avoid meeting up with the actual circumstances, the more will the danger be clothed with a fog of fears and disconcerting possibilities. Accordingly, it is most important for the patient to face the facts as they are, see clearly the outlines of the undesired irritations, and understand *without disturbed feelings* how much actual harm can be produced. Such understanding in itself often removes fear. It is common experience to be at a swimming pool and stand on the edge, hesitant about diving in, because the water looks so cold; only to find it pleasant when one has taken the plunge. Miss C. O. denied any suggestion of blindness because of its dreaded connotations; and had to develop some sort of "reasoning" (paranoid) to justify her failure to adjust. Persons who are deaf, and particularly those who are partially deaf, frequently develop paranoid symptoms because they refuse to accept the fact of their deafness,[1] and insist that when they cannot hear what is said, it must be because people are whispering something, and that they are whispering because what is said is detrimental to the patient. Such cases are so frequent as to warrant the term "psychosis of the deaf," and the therapy lies in early training of the subject to face this deafness and to resign himself to it when he cannot hear what he wishes. The use of hearing aids and lip reading is to be greatly encouraged, but equally important is it for the person to cultivate the attitude of understanding and being patient with his disability.

In many instances, however, the stress or precipitating factor lies not in obvious difficulties such as physical or financial disability, but in more subtle ones which concern one's pride and ego and which may cause far more intense suffering than does actual physical distress.[2] Social estrangement, ostracism, contempt, lack of appreciation, even the difference of being unusually thin or fat or short or tall may exert a pressure which will result in the warping of the personality. These differences need to be faced, understood, and dealt with unemotionally, else there will be improper orientation which may lead to neuroses. Ambitions which are unsatisfied, desires which cannot be obtained, fears which cannot be eradicated form a more potent disturbing force than the cruder and more

---

[1] *Vide* pp. 93; 321.   [2] *Vide* p. 155.

obvious physical or financial forces. Cure of the neuroses caused by these subtler forces is often more difficult to achieve than is a remedy for actual stress.

Mr. K. M.,[1] aged thirty-four years, entered the most violent of physical encounters and most dangerous of physical enterprises. He was afraid, very afraid of all these physical encounters, but he forced himself into them because as a child he had been called "yellow" and he could never overcome the fear that he really was a coward. He could not face the fact that fear is a natural human quality and that to be ashamed of it is unnecessary. He tried to compensate by proving to himself that he could do anything that he feared. He had to learn that courage means the overcoming of fear, and not the absence of it. He learned to tolerate and face this fact, knowing that if a situation arose in which courage was necessary, he would not fail. Constantly trying to prove an absence of fear merely emphasized its presence. His nightmares were so bad that he did not go to sleep till late, in an effort to have so little sleep that there would be little time for nightmares. As he grew more tolerant of himself and, in an objective manner, faced his inadequacies as well as his capacities, these terrifying dreams lost their major causative factor, and in time ceased to trouble him.

Similarly there are innumerable persons suffering tortures, self-produced because the intensity of their inhibitions, and their failure to tolerate the inadequacies of ther human nature cause an intense feeling of inferiority.

Miss G. J., aged twenty-seven years, who earned her livelihood as a legal stenographer, experienced intense fear whenever she had to leave the security of her own home, and could not "take dictation" from an employer without bursting into tears. She suffered from sudden attacks of diarrhea, from sudden and impelling desire to urinate, from spells of suffocation. If she left the house and walked down the street, such intense fear would seize her that she would have to sit down on the curb, straining herself with all her power to prevent a bowel evacuation. Psoriasis had been particularly bad for many years. Physical examination revealed nothing. The intestinal tract and bladder examinations were negative, bacteriologically, roentgenologically, and cystoscopically.

This patient lived with her elder sister, and contributed to her support. Nevertheless this elder sister took it upon herself to nag, belittle, and generally make life miserable for the patient (probably as a compensatory mechanism for having to accept financial support). When the patient was asked why she continued to live with her sister, she unfolded a long story of family domination. From early childhood she had been restrained and restricted. She was not allowed to go out evenings because her father "would have no child of his running loose on the street." She was not permitted to go to the motion pictures because they were "lewd" and "sinful." She had to follow without question the commands given by her father who even when everything was done as he had ordered, would scold and berate her. He prided himself on being a good disciplinarian, and felt virtuous and

---

[1] *Vide* p. 260.

14

"progressive" for having sent the patient through high school. In his own way he felt that he cared for his daughter, and she in turn believed she owed allegiance to him. Her entire attitude toward life was one of fear, of trying to please the members of the family, of fear of what other persons might think of her, in a word, intense insecurity. She was inhibited in every way, inhibited because the constant undercurrent of fear prevented her from doing anything. She was constantly unhappy, having few girl friends and fewer boy friends. She was inadequate, felt inferior, "knew she was worthless," and in general tortured herself with doubts and self-reproach. She was sure she did her work poorly, that the neighboring girl was more efficient, that she was "dumb and ignorant," and that she never could amount to much.

In the office where she worked, there was a woman's lavatory adjacent to the office manager's desk, and when she would pass by his desk, she felt that he looked at her with a leering and insulting expression. As a result she restrained herself constantly from going to the lavatory. One day this man came to her desk to dictate to her, and she was seized with an intense desire to urinate; and felt so intensely ashamed that she left the office immediately. Soon thereafter the other symptoms developed.

To treat her fear of crowds, of streets, and her spastic contractions of smooth musculature, it was necessary to modify her fundamental fears and inhibitions. It was important to get the patient to face the actual facts as they occurred and teach her not to be afraid. Her early life was discussed in detail, and the development of her fearful condition carefully analyzed. She came to realize for herself that her family attachment was more one of fear than of love, and she learned to trace to its original source each item involving intense fear or failure to do what she wished. Very gradually her attitude began to change. Each day she went out a little from her house, going until she felt fearful and then returning; she invited persons to her home with increasing frequency. Very gradually she improved until she could take a bus downtown, but it took several trips before she could alight from it. She secured a position and worked as a file clerk, and at the end of the second year of treatment she was able to resume her position as a legal stenographer. At the end of treatment she had few fears left; looked at life with relative objectivity and with the philosophy that she could always take care of herself financially, that she was not dependent upon her family in any way, and need not be disturbed by what they thought or said, that her limitations were in no sense peculiar to her alone; in other words, she had learned to have self tolerance and understanding of others. Her psychoneurotic symptoms disappeared completely; and, coincidentally, the psoriasis also cleared up.

Mrs. S. O., aged twenty-nine years, complained of irritability, emotional instability, insomnia, temper outbursts, and depression.

"Inside I boil. When new problems arise, I flare up like a fire cracker and shoot off my big mouth. I get upset over the least little thing. I guess I mind everyone else's business. I've always worried over everyone since I was a kid. My mother was very cold natured and she never showed any affection to us kids; and I guess I'm trying to be different from her.

"I'm always in a hurry. Just can't sit still. I'm not satisfied with anything. I've always wanted an education but never got past fifth grade, when I had to go out and help support the family.

"As a child I was always sickly, but I never got any attention, or any of the things I wanted. I was always nervous, and felt I wasn't as good as other persons, I was so nervous that I was kept out of school and then when Pat was a couple of grades ahead of me I was jealous. When I grew older I wouldn't let a fellow touch me—I was afraid of what people would say. As a child I saw a fellow grab Eloise and try to make her sit on his lap. She refused and I thought it was wonderful to be like her."

This girl's life was one full of frustration.[1] One can readily understand how such a background can contribute to such a personality. However, in adulthood, this girl continued to live and feel as she had in childhood, but unnecessarily so. She could be trained to face her past and present experiences in an objective and unemotional manner. She was told that unquestionably her past was unfortunate, and difficult, and that she should try to avoid the same mistakes in rearing her own child. Nevertheless, since she could not "unlive" the past she had to accept it as it was and admit its reality without "bringing herself to a boil" every time she thought of it. Then she needed to list her assets and liabilities. She felt on the one hand, that she was uncultured and uneducated. She was emotional and envious and expressed herself loudly whenever she was displeased (which was most of the time). On the other hand she had insight into her condition, knew how it developed, and understood her own peculiarities. It was time to put aside all "feelings" about the wrongs in the situation and do something about them. She finished her housework early and had spare time. She was to write to a public school extension course and start studying to finish her grammar school education. In addition, she was to cultivate the acquaintance of several of her neighbors who she knew often went on educational excursions to the museums, to lectures, etc. She was to watch her conduct in specific detail (and her actions were specifically discussed) and make deliberate efforts to follow another pattern of behavior. In short,

[1] *Vide* p. 40.

by conscious effort she learned to understand and not be emotional about the unfortunate past and to do something constructive about the present. This patient was seen twice a week for a month and then once a month for six visits. At the end of that time her brother remarked that his sister "had a new personality." There was nothing seriously wrong with this woman that could not be corrected with patience and consistent effort.

Among the immature attitudes which make difficult the attainment of self-tolerance, true self-evaluation, and the ability objectively to face difficulties are those of: (1) rigidity; (2) resentment; and (3) over-emphasis on the opinions of others.

RIGIDITY OF PERSONALITY

Rigidity in personality is manifested by the tendency to be intensely disturbed by any deviation from accustomed routine. Persons so characterized have either accepted from their environment or have laid out for themselves a fixed pattern of reaction and ideas, a pattern so crystallized that any break or modification forced on it by the environment is met with more or less violent resistance and emotional upset. Here, as elsewhere, the physician is concerned not with "absolutes" but with matters of relative degree. As was pointed out in Chapter II,[1] it is desirable that much of life be routinized for the conservation of energy; but it is equally important to remember that any virtue carried to excess takes on the nature of a vice. Whether the habits of a person are a help or a hindrance will be determined largely by his attitude toward them. If he finds it more convenient to do things in a particular fashion, more efficient to follow a specific routine, well and good; if, however, he becomes explosive, irritable, excessively disturbed when his routine is disturbed, then obviously the end—effectual living— is being sacrificed for the means. Habits, if they are to be valuable, must be flexible.

Indeed, the essential difference between a human being and a highly complicated Robot lies in this very flexibility. At a recent exhibit, there was a mechanical contrivance that could play and win at checkers, *if* the right counter moves were always made, but which failed when unexpected moves were made. Although the nervous system has been likened to a central switchboard with many telephone extensions, the human differs radically in that it is

[1] *Vide* pp. 42; 272.

flexible and adaptable. When persons become rigid, their response becomes as predictable as the telephone system, and furnishing certain combination of stimuli will produce a predictable response. Such a person, in spite of the efficiency or ingenuity he may display in his vocation, having become an automaton in effect, has, to that degree, adjusted on an inferior level.

Patients who are overly automatic and irritated when this automaticity is disturbed should be educated to increase their plasticity. Some patients on hearing such advice tend to go to the opposite extreme and deliberately do everything in a vacillating manner, thereby indicating that they have failed to realize that the goal is to avoid extremes in anything.

Mr. D. I., aged fifty-three years, a successful business man, complained of intense fatigue and dizzy spells. No physical basis for his condition could be found. He was sent on a Caribbean cruise for six months, but came back worse than ever. He perspired freely and when he went into a restaurant grew so hot and short of breath that he had to get up and leave quickly. He was depressed and suffered from insomnia.

Mr. I. was normally a pleasant person who got along well with others. However, his entire life was carefully routinized even to the most minute detail. He was married and had three children, who, when they grew into adulthood, revolted against the systematic way he attempted to routinize them. When his wife died, his manner of living, of necessity, had to change; and gradually he went into this depression, and became increasingly irritable with no specific precipitating factor other than the fact that he could not endure living in a world different from one routinized in a certain way. In addition to this severe neurosis, he developed many hatreds for persons who differed from him. Psychotherapy consisted of discussing his problems with him; and since he was an intelligent man, he could understand the paralyzing quality of his rigidity. He was trained to be more plastic, to consider other and apparently alien points of view, to avoid doing the same things in the same manner day in and day out. This man who had not worked for two years, went back in his office after two weeks, and with the aid of persistent training, underwent enough of a change of personality to make his friends remark on his new manners of living. It took many weeks of discussions and urging however, to get him to change his life-long habit patterns.

The deleterious effects of an iron clad code are even greater if the rigidity is of ideas or ethical theories rather than of the minutiæ of daily life. In the first place, other persons will "give in" more easily on scores which they consider unimportant; i. e., they will indulge the whims of the rigid personality. On the other hand, most of our concepts which we like to label "ideas and ideals" are not intellectually arrived at and scientifically held convictions, but rather inherited and emotionally retained "certainties." The very "taken for granted to be true" quality of codes makes them resistant to displacement or modification.

ATTITUDE OF RESENTMENT

When persons are frustrated, when an endeavor does not succeed, when a desire is not fulfilled, there tend to result anger and irritability. This attitude is natural and "normal." In the average "healthy" person, such anger and irritability disappear shortly, forgotten in the activity of new events and problems. In many psychoneurotic patients, however, the failure to obtain that which is desired leads to the establishment of grudges and continuous anger. This attitude may be a general one and assumed toward all frustrations, with the result, since daily life is far from being continuously flattering or wholly satisfactory to the average person, that myriads of animosities remain within the person rendering him and all those about him unhappy, creating that chilled anger and fear called hate, or that self-abuse termed "feelings of inferiority," which, in turn, result in hypertension, insomnia, digestive disturbances, etc.

It is necessary, accordingly, to teach most of these patients not only the deleterious effects of resentment, but also a technique for overcoming it. The subject must be discussed in detail so that the patient can see the rationale and logic thereof. Then the patient must be told that whenever he is disappointed he must consciously force himself to think the situation over objectively and understand it dispassionately. This attitude can be adopted, but it takes time. It is a common experience in the psychiatrist's office to hear some such statement as, "I'm not so easily bothered when things go wrong, anymore." At first, the patient will be able to apply this attitude only partially; but later on *if conscious training by the patient persists*, this attitude will become automatic.

Understanding a situation and being dispassionate about one's failure to achieve a desired goal, do not mean that the patient should assume an attitude of "That's the way it is, and nothing can be done about it."[1] Such an attitude would in the end make for a smug, unprogressive, and ultimately self-injurious condition. On the contrary, the patient should plan and work as much as possible to change the irritating situation, but always in an understanding manner and with a minimum expenditure of emotion,

---

[1] *Vide* p. 205 *ff.*

since emotion tends to interfere with the reasoning process,[1] hinders success, and makes for an unhealthy condition. The very fact that the patient is assuming the *active* role of *doing* something to change the situation, rather than the passive one of accepting the status quo, helps him remove his disturbing and neurosis producing memory of past injuries and disappointments.

There are some patients who are "born lazy" and it would be better for them if irritations were added rather than removed. The physician must use his judgment[2] in each individual case. In few situations, however, should emotion be permitted to interfere with the thinking process, as it does in worry, resentment, etc.

WHAT OTHERS THINK

Social pressure results from the influence of the prevailing ideas in the community on its members. This factor of social control is one of the most important in keeping a social order stable, and makes for community of interests. A certain percentage of the human race always will tend to have the opposite opinions to those prevailing in the group; and such *differences are necessary and healthy for the homeostasis*[3] *of civilization.* However, in the psycho-neuroses there is a tendency to be too much influenced by this "community" ideal. Many such persons will vacillate and hesitate in their decisions which may be entirely correct both from a personal and social point of view, merely because they feel that others may not think well of them. Miss S. G.[4] did not wish to be seen with the man for whom she cared greatly, because she was ashamed of what others would think of his "ugliness" and his short stature. One "southern lady" told me that as a young woman, if she ever had occasion to launder some small article, she would hang it in the attic to dry, because the neighbors would be shocked if they saw her doing anything so "unladylike" as washing clothes.

In these instances, there is an over-evaluation of what others think and an insufficient courage to carry out what the person thinks. Such a lack of belief in the validity of one's own opinions often connotes a feeling of inferiority and a lack of balance. Also in many instances it is the result of lack of emotional emancipation and the consequent lack of training in self-reliance.[5] Again, this

---

[1] *Vide* p. 194 *ff.*   [2] *Vide* p. 129.

[3] Homeostasis is a word coined by Dr. Cannon to signify the constant play of opposite forces within the human body, in such a way as to maintain a healthy and functioning balance between the constantly present extremes.

[4] *Vide* p. 181.   [5] *Vide* p. 202.

fear of the opinion of others may be directed in a single direction, the person being overly conscious, for example, of what his "hero" or "ideal" would like him to do.[1] Here, once more, the task is to bring the person back to the normal line of doing that which he considers right, as long as he does not violate too strongly the existing social code. There is no sharp boundary that can be drawn, and only common sense can decide the correct attitude in any given situation.

WISHING TO REMAIN ILL

It is a strange paradox to find many patients suffering from psychoneurotic difficulties who seemingly wish to remain ill, despite the fact that they come for treatment. Patients frequently come to a physician and after complaining of some ailment, make their own diagnoses, and even tell what they wish prescribed. These persons come merely to obtain official sanction for one or more of their vague emotional wishes. They tend to refuse to admit the trouble lies where the physician indicates, and insist that it is somewhere else. Particularly is this attitude true in the psychoneuroses, the patient refusing to recognize his personality difficulties, or if he does recognize them, seemingly preferring to remain ill rather than try to do something about them.

One of the most important points in psychotherapy is to make the patient not only see his problems but *wish* to change.[2] Patient after patient will in one breath admit that he has been too concerned about some incident or some method of living, and then in the next breath insist that he wishes to continue to act and feel the same way. Once the patient has changed his attitude so that he is willing to try to correct his difficulty, the rest is a matter of time and practice.

It has been a matter of personal amusement to have patients come in after several psychotherapeutic discussions with the statement "I'm *afraid* I'm better, Doctor."

UNDERSTANDING SYMPTOMS[3]

Very early in the therapy the patient should learn the real significance of his symptoms and the consequent necessity of treating not the symptoms but the causes lying behind them. It must be pointed out that whatever may be the organic basis for the symptoms it is so slight as to be incapable of producing the symptoms described by the patient. The patient is told that although

[1] *Vide* p. 73.   [2] *Vide* p. 184.   [3] *Vide* p. 178.

the symptoms are real, the basis for them lies in the spastic condition of the blood vessels, in the heightened irritability of nerve centers, etc. Such an explanation[1] while not wholly accurate, scientifically speaking, serves to give the patient a better comprehension of his pain or complaint. Patients dread being told there is no cause for their symptoms; and lacking understanding of how emotion could possibly mediate pain or physical aches, they often refuse to accept medical ex cathedra statements. When the physician diagrammatically puts forth a possible connection between the way the patient feels and the symptom, acceptance is far easier both because "it makes sense" and because it is less wounding to the false pride built up by so many persons.

Subsequent to such an explanation, when the symptom reappears, as it inevitably will until the fundamental cause is dealt with, the patient must be trained to think to himself: "I know I feel this pain; but this pain in turn is caused by this and this problem of mine and is in itself an indication that the problem is getting the better of me. I must shift my thoughts from this pain, and think again about the problem in such a way that I can solve it." Patients do learn to think in this way; and the understanding implicit in such thinking makes for disappearance of the pain.

MORAL SUPPORT AND ABILITY TO CARRY RESPONSIBILITY

Though no human being is wholly self-sufficient, the need for self-reliance stressed in these chapters is essential for the optimum operation of the human personality under changing conditions of existence. The number of restrictions to which we as civilized persons must assent in order to have the rewards of a civilization are not always easy to accept; and so society arrogates the right to discipline the individual man. Such discipline presupposes that man cannot control and guide himself and needs always the fear of punishment from without. This assumption is true as long as the person has not learned a *self-discipline*[2] *which avoids both capricious self-indulgence and rigid self-intolerance.* Only when this self-discipline is reached can man govern himself, singly or collectively; otherwise he needs external governing. Care must be taken, however, that self-discipline be not confused with asceticism, but rather be based on a tolerant understanding of the basic drives of all living organisms, and a reasoned control of such drives.

---

[1] *Vide* p. 176.　　　　　　　　[2] *Vide* p. 117.

Complete self-reliance is rarely possible, man being so constituted that some moral support is necessary. This moral support is found by many in religion, in idealisms, in the approval of their fellow men. However, under conditions of stress the ordinary supports may be insufficient; and the person, particularly if he is so disturbed as to develop psychoneurotic symptoms, needs help which is direct and personal. Marriage, for example, can sustain a person through stress which would ordinarily "crack" him. When the wife and husband "understand" each other, their mutual aid is not only sustaining, but energizing.

The physician who listens to the patient's difficulties and is directly interested and encouraging, can provide the moral support which the patient needs to enable him to clear the hurdles before him. The physician by his sympathetic manner and understanding, offers the patient something to rely on, some backing and orientation, so that the daily difficulties lose their frightening aspect and his certainty in dealing with them is surer and more definite.

It is insufficient, however, for the physician merely to provide moral support; he needs to train the patient to have as much as possible of his own moral support, of self-reliance—and this, as has been stated before depends upon a tolerant understanding of what one is and can do together with a working technique for changing undesirable habits and attitudes to mature and satisfying ones.

The ability to bear responsibility is proportionate to the amount of self-reliance present. There are many persons who cannot endure responsibility and develop emotional difficulties under responsibilities. Many of these persons can perform the most difficult of tasks, and exercise the greatest amount of ingenuity, but only if the final responsibility for success or failure rests on someone else's shoulders. These persons, too, need moral support. Schizophrenic patients, in their pre-psychotic life history, show this dislike or inability to carry responsibility. They have this weakness primarily because there is excessive emotional tone about the possible failure of the task for which they are responsible, and because they have not learned to face failure without fear. The moral support which the physician supplies is not equivalent to "carrying" the patient over rough places in the road, but rather offering a strong arm on which the patient may lean for security and steadiness, until he can walk unaided.

CHAPTER XI

ADJUVANT THERAPY—SUGGESTION, HYPNOSIS, AND DRUGS

SUGGESTION

SUGGESTION is one of the most important measures in the physician's armamentarium. True, suggestion is usually temporary in effect, and it does not attack the basic etiologic factors; but it is nevertheless an invaluable aid until the physician is able to inculcate the more important changes in the personality structure.

At the outset it is well to keep in mind that suggestion may be grossly misused. As has been stated previously[1] suggestion is the keystone of many healing cults, and the secret of the success of many charlatans. When suggestive therapy involves some mysterious or supernatural agent, the results are not only temporary, but eventually harmful. Not only is such a dishonest technique of procedure ethically "wrong," but pragmatically it is harmful because it provides the patient with a false belief, a temporary crutch, which prevents him from facing and adjusting to the basic difficulty which initially produced his symptoms. When such a false support collapses, as it almost inevitably does, the patient is left more helpless than he was and either despairs or becomes prey to a succession of mirage faiths, the promises of which are never redeemed.

Many physicians practice destructive suggestion, without being aware thereof. So many patients are over-sensitive to the physician's opinions and place such emphasis on each word that may have frightening connotations (misunderstood or unexplained gravity of manner or silence can be equally devastating for the patient) that they leave the office perturbed and convinced that their illness is more dangerous than it really is. These patients are affected destructively instead of constructively so that instead of feeling sustained and encouraged by the physician they have rather a sense of increased anxiety which often aggravates their symptoms. It is difficult for the physician to balance between a false cheerfulness and an overly serious and frightening presentation of facts; yet it is important to be able so to state the nature of

[1] *Vide* p. 130.

the illness that *the patient will go away with both a sober awareness of what he is confronted with and the knowledge and comforting assurance that his illness can and will be properly dealt with.* In certain diseases, for example a metastatic carcinomatosis, an added burden is placed on the physician, to convey the information to the patient, and at the same time help and train the patient to accept the diagnosis with a non-depressing fatalism and without becoming an emotional wreck. Adequate suggestion can, in these cases, emphasize the boon of pain relieving drugs and the value of a sustaining philosophy of life. It is surprising how patients, if they have the proper outlook and perspective, can learn to face with equanimity approaching death. One physician who suffered a coronary attack, and was told by competent authorities that the slightest over-work might result in a sudden stoppage of the heart, settled his affairs and calmly went back to his usual routine of life, resigned to the inevitable, and preferring a short, active existence to a more prolonged passive one. When he suddenly dropped dead at an autopsy table, his friends had the impression that his choice of actions and his emotional response had been the wisest and most courageous of all possibilities. One patient who was brought into the county hospital and who was suffering from metastatic carcinoma, pleaded tearfully to be informed of his true diagnosis. He suspected cancer, but every one answered his questions vaguely and evasively. He could not sleep at night and had a typical anxiety syndrome.[1] After thorough investigation confirmed the entrance diagnosis, the patient was told the exact nature of his illness, and the probable duration of his existence. He was reassured that he would have no pain, and that whatever requests he had would be granted within the limits of the existing possibilities. It was surprising that the patient became calm instead of excited, and the definite diagnosis of the illness together with the knowledge that he would have no pain, relieved instead of disturbed him. For the first night in many weeks he slept, and his natural cheerfulness returned, for he knew what he had to face, he resigned himself thereto, and forgot about it as much as possible.

In the second case, the patient was, at first, in a constant atmosphere of destructive suggestion. He had been told he had some vague inflammatory condition of the bowel. The hospital atmosphere was most kind in that it had attended to the physical wants of the patient; and although he was grateful for and impressed by

[1] *Vide* p. 27.

the implicit wisdom of the nursing care and of the medication, as well as the cordial consideration of the attending physician, nevertheless he was haunted by the fear that he had some grave and "awful" disease; and the silent, all-knowing, highly dignified actions of those about him convinced him that his fear was true. The less that was said, the more the patient feared. To the patient in this state of anxiety, bland, "Polyanna" statements were far more damning than an outright admission of the feared facts. His active mind conjectured possibilities,[1] particularly as he did not improve; and his anxiety state resulted in many additional emotional symptoms.

Lack of definite knowledge in relation to an illness, permits the patient's imagination to enlarge on the possibilities. A disease which "may" exist is more liable to be shrouded by a fog of fears and premonitions, than a disease which one knows exists and is able to face directly. When in the face of an obvious intensification of symptoms and suffering, the "Polyanna" atmosphere is maintained, most patients are intelligent enough to understand that "something is being hidden." *Fancy is far more to be feared than fact;* and where fancy is permitted free play, the patient too often develops emotional symptoms in addition to his physical ones.

On the other hand, the extreme reverse attitude of the physician may also carry destructive suggestion. A brusque and untactful announcement, "You have cancer and will probably die within six months," carries with it the virtues of truth, but it also has the realistic effect of being struck with a club. The average patient's understanding of the "incurable" diseases is warped by the wild tales and the gruesome stories of his friends. The idea of death does not as a rule hold so many terrors as does suffering, and it is this latter idea which overwhelms most patients. Here again, it is fear and the lack of exact knowledge that prove so disturbing. A patient suddenly confronted with a poor prognosis tends to enlarge on it far beyond its real significance. To deal with this difficulty demands that the physician spend *time and patience, exercise all his tact and consideration,* and present not the gloomy side of the picture but the actual facts in the least disturbing manner possible. Above all he must convince the patient that courage and a calm philosophical outlook are more than ever important, and that control of one's attitude can make the remaining time pleasant.

[1] *Vide* p. 207.

The physician should try to leave the patient determined and confident that he can face his death without either self-pity or the heroics and wailing of a pseudomartyr.

The personality of the patient will, to a great extent, determine just how he should be told of his illness. There is no formula which can take the place of the physician's common sense judgment,[1] his understanding of the nature of a particular patient. Those who have always tended to be hypochondriacal need a far more gentle approach, and much more positive suggestion in the revelation of an incurable malady than do their more stoical, matter of fact, courageous brethren. Only with much experience can the physician learn just how much to say, and how much not to say. There is no hard and fast rule to be followed, and in some cases, it is even more advisable to avoid telling the patient of the exact nature of his illness, than to have him suffer excessively. Flexibility and adjustability must always characterize the physician's therapeutic attitudes; even when "the rule" is hard and fast.

Positive or constructive suggestion (all suggestion is positive though its effect may be negative or destructive) produces its effects: (1) by increasing the patient's confidence that his illness can be cured or adequately dealt with, and increased confidence is associated with increased ability to carry out the physician's treatment; (2) by directing his thoughts and attention towards pleasant possibilities and away from unpleasant ones; (3) by reorienting his psychobiologic attitude so that the decrease in emotional tone is associated with decreases in smooth muscle spasm, decrease in hypersecretion, etc., and (4) by raising the threshold of pain and discomfort (probably by diversion of attention) so that he is better able to withstand his own symptoms.

When a patient is adequately reassured that he will recover, and the suggestion of good health and happiness is strong enough, he will leave the office with a feeling of confidence in his recuperative powers; he will avoid dwelling on the depressing aspects of his illness, and think more in terms of what he will do and how he will feel; he will change the direction of his thought away from his body and his illness toward outward activities and accomplishments; and he will be better able to disregard minor discomforts, because he will pay less attention to them and understand that the symptoms are not significant.[2] The value of *suggestion* is thus seen to be far more significant than simply as it concerns the effect on symptoms;

---

[1] *Vide* pp. 119; 215.   [2] *Vide* p. 180 (Case S. G.).

and its worth is, therefore, *to be measured in proportion to its effect on general reorientation and change in attitude, rather than in terms of symptom disappearance.* The patient is improved not only in relation to the specific complaint, but in relation to his underlying emotional problem.

Suggestion may be *direct* or *implied.* Direct suggestion consists in telling the patient that he will be cured. Implied suggestion, directed toward the same end, may emanate from the optimistic and confident attitude of the physician, the atmosphere of competence in the hospital, the effect of medication, the contact with other patients who have been successfully treated, etc. Both methods should be used as much as possible as aids in the retraining of the patient's attitudes.

The personality of the physician[1] is one of the most important elements in the art of producing desired effects through suggestion; and of all his traits, the physician's sincerity is, in this connection, the most important. His sincerity can be expressed in many ways: his demeanor, a self-confidence which lacks arrogance, a definiteness of procedure which rules out indecisiveness, an interested and sympathetic manner, a frank statement of difficulties with an optimistic attitude as to their solution; all these are expressions of sincerity. After all, the doctor wishes to impress the patient that when he says, "You will get well," he is expressing a real conviction. Obviously a cold, impersonal statement lacks the dynamic assurance that a more earnest personal statement has. The suggestion of "getting well" must not only be intellectually understood by the patient, but to be effective, must be believed "emotionally."[2] Suggestions for recovery can rarely be totally objective; in some way there must be sufficient emotional over-tone to the verbal statement, so that the patient is "won over." Accordingly, it is essential that the patient be impressed by the fact that the physician really believes what he says. The encouraging smile, the sureness of manner, the forcefulness of expression (which must avoid a dogmatic tone), the warmth of tone, vitalize the reassuring words, so as to give the patient not only confidence in what is said but also the moral support which he needs to enable him to face his difficulties.

Direct suggestion that the patient will get well should be accompanied by qualifying remarks. For suggestion to have its desired effect, it should be as truthfully and convincingly stated as is pos-

[1] *Vide* p. 130.   [2] *Vide* p. 126.

sible. To make a suggestion which ignores the facts of the situation, or is contrary to that which the patient understands cannot be conducive to good results. The physician should be completely honest; and the difficulties should be stated clearly, so that the patient will not fear that "something is being hidden from him." Where possible, this statement of the difficulties should be accompanied by a diagrammatic and not too scientific statement of how these difficulties came into being,[1] and what role the patient's emotions have played. There should follow an explanation of how, by proper control of his emotions, the patient can facilitate his recovery. After this explanation, and the presenting of a formulation which the patient can understand as reasonable, the suggestion can then be put strongly, "If you follow these principles, you will unquestionably get well."

Such a direct suggestion is made all the more forceful, because it is reasonable; and in addition, it places upon the patient the full responsibility to do what can be done to alter his emotional state. It appeals to both the reason and the spirit. The results of this type of suggestion are likely to be relatively more permanent because the patient both understands, and is called on to cooperate in achieving the desired goal. He has an active rather than a passive role to play.[2] It is well to warn the patient that the miracle of an over-night cure is not to be expected, for a symptom which has existed for many years cannot be removed in a few days; but, at the same time emphasize that the symptom can be removed, and will be removed, the length of time necessary to obtain complete and permanent relief depending largely upon how much the patient will cooperate. In any case, the patient should be told that though the symptom may be annoying, it is not fatal or dangerous, and that there is no need for more concern over its outcome than there would be for a toothache or a sprain. "And it will not take long to overcome the annoying features of the ailment."

The effect of suggestion varies with the patient. Some persons are extremely susceptible and others extremely resistant. That many persons are susceptible to suggestions of illness, is exemplified by the assiduous readers of the health columns of the daily newspapers.[3] These persons will quickly skim over the statements concerning the possibility of cure or the mildness of the ailment discussed, will pessimistically insist that they will surely be the one in a thousand to develop the unusual symptoms described, and,

---

[1] *Vide* pp. 178; 216.   [2] *Vide* p. 215.   [3] *Vide* p. 73 (Identification).

ignoring all optimistic expressions, will in some manner manage to find dire and dark prophesy for themselves. These patients are oriented toward a philosophy and outlook of gloom. Their general existence, exclusive of their physical complaints, is an unhappy one. Their emotional thinking is such as actually to oppose any pleasant feelings. These persons "glory in their misery,"[1] and are almost masochistic in the manner in which they appropriate and cherish any suggestion of unhappiness.

The treatment of this group, must be directly aimed toward their fundamental attitudes, since "suggestion" avails little for patients who are cynically skeptical and "know" they can never recover. These patients, however, are easily led by dramatic prophets of "a new vision of life."

There are many patients, however, who are not very susceptible to suggestion in its direct and open form. These persons "think too much," in the sense that they over-emphasize the importance of every possible obstacle and are checkmated in their recovery before they start. Such persons also are better approached with the "rational" method than with the suggestion technique. There are many who, having been presented with and having accepted a logical and rational formulation, can then be greatly influenced by the suggestion that the results predicted by the physician are the inevitable conclusion of the matter. How much suggestion should be used in any of these instances must be determined by the response of the patient at the time. As has been previously pointed out, the patient's expression, his attitude, his verbal responses should be constantly observed in order that the treatment may be better guided, and that the physician may continue or discontinue in proportion to its effectiveness whatever form of therapy he is using.[2]

Still other patients are overly suggestible; but this over-suggestibility usually proves to be a disadvantage, for the suggestions given them by the physician may be quickly nullified by other suggestions. Such patients may leave the office, fully confident and impressed, only to return dejected and disconsolate because they have heard of some exceptions to their case, or have experienced some pains which, in turn, have started new "suggestions."

One of the commonest ways of giving suggestion is through the use of placebos; i. e., substances which in themselves may have no particular therapeutic value for specific conditions but which

---

[1] *Vide* p. 216. [2] *Vide* p. 139,

15

usually consist of such innocuous agents as bicarbonate of soda, sodium chloride, or bromides. It has been remarked that vitamins in capsule form have come to be one of the most widely used of placebos; and every physician knows that many injections have far greater suggestive than actual value. There are some psychoneurotic patients to whom placebos must be temporarily given, so accustomed are they to regulating their lives by "pill-time," until the physician has established enough personality change so that the patient realizes that he himself and not medication will solve his problems. At best, placebos are temporary in effect, and the patient sooner or later fails to obtain relief.[1] Generally, much better results can be obtained if during the first few interviews the physician spends sufficient time to establish the real basis of emotional disturbances, for then he need not temporize with palliative measures but can direct his suggestions along constructive and curative lines.

The physician's staff may be an invaluable aid and asset. Too much cannot be said for the pleasant, cheerful, and sympathetic nurse or secretary who first meets the patient. Embarrassment, shyness, and even fearfulness can often be relieved by a competent nurse who without being officious calms and reassures the patient before the interview with the physician. In a hospital the effect of suggestion from the nursing force is extremely great, for the nurses constitute the more or less constant environment of the patient. Nurses who are machine-like, irritable, impatient, and demanding may be efficient in giving the exact dosage of phenobarbital prescribed but may at the same time so disturb the patient by insistence and abruptness of manner as to nullify any benefit from the medication. A kind, sympathetic nurse who is patient and pleasant is far more calming than almost any form of medication. In delirious reactions which are so common before sleep, the nurse with a soothing and reassuring tone can procure sleep and eliminate fear where medication would fail.[2] Fears are rarely dispelled by drugs; while courage can be instilled by an understanding nurse.

In a hospital, good effect can also be obtained if the patients are divided into groups, the center of each being a patient who is almost well and who, accordingly, can exercise a cheerful influence. In hospitals or sanitariums for nervous ailments, such an arrangement is most effective. Often a patient who is almost recovered wishes to aid one much sicker than he; and such a patient, having

---

[1] *Vide* p. 132. [2] *Vide* p. 349.

himself experienced the depths of despair, and the torture of doubts and fears, may be a better counselor and a greater comfort than a more highly trained but less understanding person.

It must always be remembered, however, that suggestion is only an aid, and not the essence of therapy.

HYPNOSIS

Hypnotism which has been used for many years is a phenomenon which is not clearly understood, though the concensus seems to be that hypnosis is merely a state of increased suggestibility. Hypnotists, contrary to popular opinion, do not have tremendous or occult powers, nor is the subject weak willed. Intelligent and unintelligent persons can be hypnotized, as well as young and old. Indeed, it may be said that only the very feebleminded, or disturbed psychotic patients are consistently resistant to this form of therapy. Only in unusual circumstances can a person be hypnotized entirely against his will; although skeptics who are willing to undergo the attempt are often the best subjects. On the other hand, not all persons can be hypnotized[1] and it is difficult to foretell those who will be good subjects and those who will not.

The therapeutic effects of hypnotizing a patient are the same as those of suggestion, except in the matter of degree; and hypnosis has the same limitations in that it is only an adjunct and not a substitute for the essential psychotherapeutic removal of the cause of the neurotic illness. If the slower but more lasting psychotherapy is not used, the symptom removed by hypnosis will soon recur, or some other neurotic symptom will occur in its place.[2] It is a common experience to hypnotize a patient in the dispensary and in the most impressive and dramatic fashion remove the torticollis,[3] hysteric paralysis, aphonia, or any one of a host of psychoneurotic symptoms without real organic basis, only to have the patient appear at the next session with a return of his entire symptomatology. However, hypnosis may be used as an aid both in determining the psychologic difficulty[4] and the subsequent removal of this cause.

The technique of hypnosis is relatively simple, and can be practiced by most physicians. In principle, hypnotism is produced by repeating the suggestion over and over that the patient is asleep.

---

[1] *Vide* p. 152. [2] *Vide* p. 230.
[3] *Vide* p. 31. [4] *Vide* p. 152.

If sufficient repetition is used, the suggestion takes effect and the patient goes into a hypnotic sleep. It is advisable to have the patient in a darkened room, which is as quiet as possible. The patient reclines on a table or couch and is told to relax. The physician should speak softly and in a monotone. The patient's attention gradually becomes narrowed and fixed on the thought of sleep. The patient is told that his limbs are becoming heavy, that his whole body is relaxed, and that his eyes are very tired. Then he is told that his eyes are becoming heavier and heavier so that he cannot keep them open. The phrase "Go to sleep, go to sleep," is repeated constantly. After some minutes of such repetition the patient develops a hypnotic trance, which may or may not go on to the state of amnesia.[1] One can test this state by asking the patient to hold his hand in the air until commanded to put it down; the hypnotized patient can without evidence of tiring keep his hand up indefinitely. Or, the physician may brush an area with alcohol and state that the patient cannot feel anything, and then pierce the skin with a needle. Generally, however, if the patient appears asleep, one makes no attempt to determine the depth of the hypnotic state, but proceeds with the therapeutic suggestions. After the patient has awakened, the physician asks how deep the sleep was for this knowledge is useful for the next session. Some therapists awaken the patient after he is hypnotized, ask "how deep he is under," and then send him right back to sleep by the same method, acting on the information thus obtained either to attempt deeper hypnosis or to begin with the suggestions.

Although the above described technique is generally followed there may be many individual variations. Verbal suggestion is sufficient; but some physicians reinforce this suggestion by having the patient focus his eyes on a bright object or glass held about a foot above the eyes, or by stroking the patient's skin, or by staring into the patient's eyes. Some prepare for hypnosis by an elaborate and dramatic admittance of the patient into a darkened room. On some occasions, a narcotic administered one-half an hour before an attempt at hypnosis reduces the patient's resistance; and once the patient responds properly even with the aid of a drug, the subsequent response can be similarly obtained without this aid.

However, all these adjuncts are unnecessary. One may hypnotize a patient sitting up or standing, in a bright noisy room as well as a dark quiet one, alone or in the presence of others. Once the

[1] *Vide* p. 232.

patient has been successfully hypnotized in a reclining position, it is my custom to have him sit in the office chair during the subsequent hypnoses. These details, however, are simply a matter of convenience.

In the therapeutic suggestions, it is not only important to suggest that the symptoms clear up, but to suggest that the basic emotional difficulties be dealt with in a more hygienic manner. Indeed, *far more emphasis should be placed on the underlying factors than on the symptom.*[1] This line of suggestion presupposes that the patient was examined and studied before the hypnotic treatment was begun, and that an analysis was made of the etiologic factors. Hypnosis thus becomes a valuable aid in enabling the patient to carry out the retraining of the personality, as well as "suggesting away the symptom." Hypnosis which deals only with the symptom cannot obtain permanent remission, and the symptoms will recur until the basic cause of the symptoms is removed. The case of Mrs. K. U.[2] is used as an example of such hypnosis and suggestion. The following example is the essence of the technique which the author uses:

"I want you to relax. Relax every part of the body. Now when I pick up your hand I want it to fall as a piece of wood without any help from you. (The examiner then picks up the hand and lets it drop to the couch.) No you helped raise the hand that time; just let it be so relaxed that you have no power over it. (The test is repeated as often as is necessary for the patient to learn to let it drop.) That's the way. Now relax your legs the same way; just let them be limp. Now take a deep breath and let it out slowly. Now concentrate on your toes. A warm sensation starts in the toe and sweeps up your legs, abdomen, chest, into your neck. Now relax your jaws. Relax them more, still more. Now your cheeks; now your eyes. Your eyes are getting heavier and heavier. You can hardly keep them open. Soon they will close. Now smooth out the wrinkles in your forehead. Good. Now make your mind a blank. Allow no thoughts to enter. Just blank. You see a blackness spreading before you. Now sleep. Sleep. Sleep. Sleep. Your entire body and mind are relaxed—sleep, sleep. (This phrase is repeated several times in a soft and persuasive voice.) Your sleep is becoming deeper, still deeper. You are in a deep, deep, sleep."

It must be emphasized that this is only one technique, and that there are innumerable modifications of it. Having thus spoken to the patient, one continues with the therapeutic suggestions. In this case, the girl had a torticollis.

[1] *Vide* p. 180.   [2] *Vide* p. 32.

"Now relax your neck; relax it still more. Your head feels so very good, and all the tension is gone. It relaxes still more and still more. Now the head begins to straighten itself out. It turns to the midline—and your head tips to the opposite side. Good. Now your chin is down and your head is in normal position. It will continue to be normal. It feels so good now. Your head will remain normal. (After these specific suggestions, the emotional bases behind the symptom should be dealt with.) Your aversion to your employer will disappear, and you'll regard him as an old and disagreeable person; but you will not be affected by his manners. You will not be disturbed by your husband's irritability but will just let his anger fall off you—like water off a duck's back. You will learn not to let anything bother you. That's why you will face everything straightforwardly. Your head is straight now and will stay that way. Next time you come here you will go to sleep more easily and quickly, and until then your head will remain in midline. Now gradually wake up, and you feel very well. Wake up completely."

The above procedure may take anywhere from ten to thirty minutes. The patient may awaken easily, or may be permitted to sleep until he awakens spontaneously. If no command to awaken is given, the patient will usually awaken by himself. Only in rare and extremely unstable persons will the hypnotic sleep continue very long. (In intractable cases, a subconvulsive dose of metrazol (2-3 cc. intravenously) will be effective in awakening the patient.) It will be noticed in the above talk to the hypnotic patient that an attempt was made not only to suggest that the torticollis disappear but what was more important, that the underlying attitudes (which had previously been determined) be dealt with. *It is this change of attitude which will cause the head to remain permanently changed.* The patient usually returns after the first visit with a partial or complete recurrence of his symptom; and after a discussion to determine and treat the underlying emotions, the hypnosis is again repeated. In some instances several visits a week for a month or two are necessary; in others, fewer or more may be required. It is generally advisable that the treatment be extensive as well as intensive; *i. e.*, that the patient come back once every two or three weeks over a long period of time until the cure is firmly established. The keynote of maintained improvement in psychotherapy is persistence.

Roughly speaking there are three stages of hypnosis. These stages are arbitrary and are only crudely descriptive of the level the patient is in. Since hypnosis is an increased state of suggestibility, there may be fluctuating degrees of intensity of suggestibility in the patient at one time, differing according to the attitudes of the patient. Moreover the borderline between suggestibility and waking, and between the various stages is so vague and so changeable as to be impermanent. However, in spite of such qualification, one may say that there is first the stage of increased suggestibility during which the patient is fully aware of all that is being said and done. He feels as he ordinarily does when conscious. However, this stage is accompanied by heightened suggestibility, and suggestions may have a powerful effect.

A young man was hypnotized before a group of students. He was told that on awakening he would tug his right ear after the examiner had counted three. At the command to awaken, the subject stood up and spoke very sarcastically. "I wasn't asleep. You didn't have me hypnotized. I just lay there and listened to everything you said but I didn't have to. You told me to pull my ear and I won't. You didn't even get near to hypnotizing me." While this young man was "orating," I kept looking steadily at him and counting 1—2—3. At the count of three, he suddenly stopped his tirade, said "Aw shucks," and tugged at his right ear.

In other words the suggestion had its effect and the boy felt compelled to do what was suggested in spite of his resistance.

An almost similar instance occurred with a young man who was in great difficulties with his wife over some minor problems such as ordinarily occur in married life. He sulked and refused to speak to her and was exceedingly irritable. He had a "nervous stomach" and could not eat; his hands had a "nervous" tremor. His brother-in-law referred him for advice; and after some discussion, the young man was placed on the table and an attempt made to hypnotize him in the manner described above. On awakening, he made the same statement as the boy just discussed. "I wasn't asleep, I just lay there and heard what you said, and it didn't phase me." Three days later the brother-in-law approached saying, "I don't know what you did to him, but yesterday for the first time he went out and acted like a human being again. He had his first big meal last night, was cheerful, and went for a long walk with Sister." Here again it becomes apparent that only a surface depth of hypnosis did not prevent its effectiveness.

The second stage is one characterized by catalepsy and anesthesia. During this period one may place the patient's limbs in any position and they will remain there without fatigue for long periods of time. Anesthesia may be tested by sticking pins through the skin. Even during this stage the patient is aware of all that is going on, but feels sleepy and listens passively to what is said. He may be completely relaxed, and unable to open his eyes but conscious of what is being said.

Mr. K. L. described the sensations accompanying hypnosis as follows: "I was just laying there, hearing everything you said, and feeling all right. But I kept wondering why my hand was up there in the air, and I didn't seem to feel it. It was just like it was floating and I didn't have to hold it at all." (The patient's hand was raised above his head, and he maintained this awkward position holding his arm erect for fifteen minutes with the hands and fingers perfectly relaxed and without any signs of fatigue.)

The third stage has all the characteristics of the other two, plus that of complete amnesia. There is complete loss of memory for the hypnotic event, although the suggestions given may be fully carried out. This stage is the most difficult to obtain, and one should not discontinue giving suggestions simply because this stage has not been reached. Suggestions, however, given in this period tend to have more effect than do those made in the two minor stages. The physician may apparently be using the same technique and yet obtain different stages of hypnosis in different patients. The physician-patient relationship has been different in each case.

Post-hypnotic suggestion consists in giving to the patient during the hypnotic stage suggestions which he is to carry out during his waking period. All manner of tricks can be performed by this method; but the physician interested only in therapy should avoid any suggestions which might make the patient appear ridiculous, for the patient, although hypnotized, may retain some awareness of his surroundings and will resent the situation in which he was placed, and may become a difficult subject later. All therapeutic suggestions are essentially post-hypnotic; insomuch as the aim of hypnosis is to change future performance of the patient.

There are relatively few contraindications to hypnosis. As has been stated, the patient is not made a moral weakling or in any way disturbed as far as his character is concerned. It is not a method to be chosen if the usual psychotherapeutic procedure can be practiced, for it shrouds the technique of cure in a mysterious and "someone else doing this for me" attitude; whereas the physician wishes the patient to develop self-reliance. Moreover, during hypnosis one cannot be made to do that which he basically is opposed to doing. Under hypnosis a man cannot be made to steal, to commit murder, nor can a woman be made to have sex relations or to expose herself. The person during the entire hypnosis still maintains some degree of awareness of what is going on (hypnotic sleep is not true sleep) and so will not permit violations of his moral code.

One experiment was reported as follows: A patient was hypnotized and a rubber knife was placed on the table. He was told to pick up the knife and stab the examiner. He responded immediately, making the stabbing movement. The knife was thought to be too apparently rubber; so it was silvered and made heavier. On command, the patient again stabbed the examiner. Not being satisfied, the examiner donned a metal breastplate underneath his clothes, and laid a real knife on the table; but this time, the patient picked up the knife, and refused to make any stabbing movement. In other words, even under deep hypnosis there was enough awareness present so that he could distinguish the difference between a real and a rubber knife.

Many similar experiments can be cited to demonstrate this general tendency. However, certain hysterical patients may develop hallucinatory experiences, so that they may accuse the hypnotist of improper advances. It is, therefore, always advisable to have a nurse in attendance during hypnosis.

Hypnosis is of value in pregnancy where labor may occur without pain or awareness of delivery.[1] It is also of value in preparing a patient for operation so that the patient may be asleep when brought to the operating room, and be anesthetized without returning to consciousness. It is of great value in the treatment of stuttering, aphonia, and various symbolic symptoms.

MEDICATION

Although the essence of therapy consists in analysis of the emotional background and the resynthesis of the new attitudes, in many patients it is necessary to treat the symptom itself if this is very disturbing. The medical treatment of the symptom in these instances is usually confined to sedatives. If the patient has a pain, or cramp, paresthesia, or twitch which has resulted from emotional difficulty, then the treatment must be directed not at the pain, or twitch, but at the emotional disturbance. However, sedatives may be used effectively. Often they have suggestive power in themselves, but their use is to be restricted; for practically, if one tells a patient, "This medicine will cure you," the patient may be relieved for a week or two, and then will come back with the statement that he is no longer helped, and with the query, "Is the doctor sure he knows what the trouble is, since he was so sure of the cure that failed?" Barbital, grains $2\frac{1}{2}$; sodium bromide[2] grains 10; phenobarbital grain $\frac{1}{2}$ are characteristic sedatives which enable the patient to bear up until the psychotherapy begins to take effect. Sedative medication should *not be given routinely* or at regular

[1] *Vide* p. 92.　　　　　　　　　[2] *Vide* p. 348.

hours for there are many times when the patient has no need for sedation. Instead I tell the patient he can take the sedatives when he feels the need,[1] taking them every half hour but never using more than 4 to 6 tablets a day. "Avoid taking medicine" the patient is told, "unless it is absolutely necessary." In practice, one finds patients will quickly limit their dosage to the equivalent of 1 to 2 grains phenobarbital a day on "bad days" and take no medication on other days. To the patients to whom I give such drugs, I always make some such comment as, "This medicine will help relieve the symptom, but it is not curative: the cure will come only by getting at the cause, and the more you can do to remove the faulty emotions at the bottom of the symptoms, the sooner will you be permanently relieved"; or "The medicine is a crutch which needs to be thrown away as soon as you can stand on your own feet." When one deals honestly and tactfully with the average human being, he generally remains a patient who is willing to return for treatment. Indiscriminate use of medication fails in the long run to produce a cure and turns many patients to "faith" cults or charlatans.[2]

Gradually, such medication is decreased in amount and frequency as the patient becomes able to get along without it. Some patients may discontinue its use after a few weeks, and others may need medication for months. Moreover, the potency and effect of the medication varies with the associated psychotherapy.

Mrs. O. N., aged fifty-eight years, complained of insomnia. Dr. X. had tried all means of treating it. Chloral hydrate, sodium amytal, nembutal, sodium bromide, phenobarbital, and other drugs were used in very large quantities and either failed to produce any sleep or allowed only a few hours sleep. He could discover no organic basis for her sleeplessness. She was referred to the psychiatric dispensary. Two weeks later, Dr. X. accosted me in the hallway: "What is this powerful medicine you are giving her? She takes one capsule and sleeps all night." Dr. X. was surprised to learn that all the patient was getting was $2\frac{1}{2}$ grains of barbital, a dose which the average patient takes three times a day with little effect.

Mrs. O. N. was suffering from a severe emotional strain. Her only support was a twenty-seven year old son who, for the last few years, had been drinking excessively. She cried bitterly and hopelessly as she narrated her sorrows. The son was interviewed and persuaded to drink less, and the mother was overjoyed. The release in tension was sufficient to permit her to sleep

---

[1] The danger of addiction by this method is less than by the routine "dosing" of patients, for before the patient has taken sufficient medication to become addicted the psychotherapeutic idea of "aiding himself" works to reduce the amount needed. Moreover, the sedatives should be alternated from time to time.

[2] *Vide* p. 130.

with very little medication. Some time later, the son began to drink again; but this time he was taken to a hospital, and the social service department made arrangements for the mother's care. Insomnia, which had started to make its appearance again, was immediately checked by proper handling of the stress.

Whenever a person forms a habit of taking a drug excessively it is generally because his neurotic personality is such as to require sedation, and not because of the drug characteristic in itself. To a large extent this statement holds true even of morphine.[1]

Mr. K. L., aged thirty-four years, was a brilliant architect, who unfortunately developed dipsomania. He would drink for two or three months of the year and then be without any taste for alcohol in the intervening time. He came for treatment at the beginning of one of these sprees and seemed to clear up immediately under psychotherapy. One day he complained of insomnia, and was given a half dozen tablets of pentobarbital (nembutal) with directions to take one before retiring. In the next two weeks, he would stagger on entering the office, but he denied alcoholism and had no odor on his breath. His friends remarked also that he staggered on walking in the street, but did not appear "drunk" and had no alcohol odor. Finally, the patient admitted that he had felt calm and relaxed after taking the nembutal and so had ordered them himself and was taking from 6 to 12 capsules (1½ grains each) per day. He in effect had substituted this drug for the alcohol he had given up.

This patient was already an addict and merely shifted the kind of drug he used from alcohol to nembutal. Opiates are to be avoided, as a rule, in the psychoneuroses, but are very helpful in depressions.[2] Insomnia is a problem which will also be discussed in detail in Chapter XIV. Benzedrine sulphate is a valuable stimulant, particularly where there is the element of fatigue or depression. It is best given before noon so as to avoid its stimulating effects producing insomnia. The dosage is usually 10 milligrams at 8 A.M. and at 11 A.M. but this may be twice or one-half the effective dose for a particular patient. As a rule, there is marked effect the first few days, and then the efficacy seemingly wears off and taking the benzedrine produces no results. Moreover, in many patients after stimulation there follows a "let-down" which is so bad as to make these patients forego the drug.

Again it is emphasized that in the giving of sedatives, it should always be stated that the medication is not curative and that it is essential for the patient to solve the emotional conflict which underlies the symptom.[3]

[1] *Vide* p. 397.   [2] *Vide* p. 377.
[3] Other sedative therapy will be discussed in connection with the psychoses. Ch. XV.

CHAPTER XII

ENERGY MOBILIZATION AND EXPRESSION

ONE of the most important aspects of therapy of the neuroses and psychoses concerns itself with the problem of energy mobilization and expression.

Energy is a *force expressible in work* (G. fr. *en*, in, and *ergos*, work). Energy may be stored in the organism very much as electricity may be stored in a battery; and may be utilized under proper conditions. It is inherent in the living cell, and is the basis of the "force of life." Energy is maintained in living matter by such chemicals as food, water, and air; is utilized for such maintenance states as are involved in basal metabolism, circulation, respiration, digestion, etc., and for such functions as the muscle action and cerebration which enable man to obtain these chemicals. The amount of energy possibly available to any given cell or cell groups (*e. g.*, the human being) varies individually, very much as does the electrical capacity of various sizes and types of batteries, the amount present being to a large extent determined by the inherited, genetic, and constitutional factors.

In dealing with this problem, one must keep continuously in mind the difference between energy which is latent and potential, and energy which is expressed in work. Some persons have a large capacity for work, for energy output, which they never express; others may accomplish little for many years and then under proper motivation become very creative. In most persons there is much *potential* energy which does not become transformed into actual observable forms of energy.

From this potential source, all subsequent expressions of energy must derive. But in order for this potential energy to be utilized it must first be mobilized; and this mobilization may be accelerated, retarded, or inadequate. The demands of society and, as we shall discuss later, the inhibitions and frustrations of mankind all serve as stimuli for such mobilization. There are many situations which stimulate the mobilization of energy so that it may be released; but when the energy is not released, tension results. Tension then is to be regarded as a symptom of mobilized but unreleased (bound) energy. Theoretically and practically, *it is possible to stimulate the mobilization of energy in man by motivation, by creating tension states, and by other means, and then to redirect this energy into constructive fields.* This mobilized energy is dependent upon the amount and organization of constitutional energy and differs from spontaneous energy expressions such as are demonstrated in the running and playing of children.

The problem presented to the physician and the patient is a threefold one of: (1) *mobilizing and stimulating energy production* where the supply is insufficient to meet adequately the exigencies of life; (2) *preventing the formation of energy states which may become harmful* to the person; and (3) *providing adequate release for excess energy.*

Before considering techniques for mobilizing and channeling energy, one must focus attention for a moment on the mechanism of energy mobilization.

Reduced to its simplest statement, the fundamental needs of man are to obtain food and sex and to avoid destruction;[1] and the human organism is so constituted as to respond in the presence of these desires by creating the energy necessary for their fulfillment. The amount of effort expended to obtain satisfactions and pleasures and to avoid dangers and pain is proportionate to the intensity of the drive and the amount of environmental resistance. The two—drive and resistance—are rarely if ever perfectly correlated.

Stimulated by desire, the entire organism orients itself in such a manner that it is ready psychologically and biologically to proceed to satisfy the desire. The adrenal-sympathetic-vegetative system is called into play; and by the same token the whole organism is in some degree changed so as to carry out the demand. In the most primitive, non-restraining society, impulse is succeeded by action, for the impulse sets into motion those forces which make the body ready for action; and there is no restraining element to prevent the direct expression, or the attempt at direct expression of the desire. Hunger is satisfied as it is perceived, provided food is available; when food is not easily available, this appetite urges the person on to direct aggression in order to obtain satisfaction. The same is true of other primitive drives and desires; in the absence of restraint there is a direct effort made to satisfy one's needs; in the presence of restraint, efforts to satisfy the desire proceed indirectly, by first dealing with the obstacle. Two complicating factors are at once discernible, though they are in reality but two aspects of one

[1] *Vide* p. 39.

factor: the resistance offered by the environment. The complications may be expressed in the following statements: (1) though the organism orients itself for satisfaction, the satisfaction may not be fulfilled, and (2) the physiologic orientation once set up cannot be turned off as simply as is a water faucet or an electric switch. For example, the sight of food to the hungry animal calls forth a change in the organism preparatory to ingest that food; and there is salivation, increased gastric secretion and motility, etc.; in other words, a psychobiologic orientation is established which urges the hungry animal to eat.[1] Similarly for human beings, *whenever a desire of any intensity is present, the adrenals have begun to pour forth their secretions, the muscles have become more tense, the liver has secreted more sugar; in other words, the organism has made potential energy more readily available* to the system for immediate use. This energy may be said to be *mobilized*. When the organism proceeds to utilize this available energy along the lines of the desire the whole being "feels" well. When, however, this potential energy is not adequately released (when the hungry animal is not permitted to eat the food he has seen), when the desire is inhibited, or when too much energy is produced, then tension arises and symptoms occur.[2] A state of tension results in the organism when the organism prepares to gratify its desires (*i. e.*, becomes psychobiologically oriented toward the desire) but cannot do so. The organism is in a state of preparedness which could best be satisfied by fulfilling the desire; but following the thwarting or frustration, the organism is left seething with mobilized "energy" which is ready for expression but not expressible. Such a state results in a disturbance of the smooth functioning of the total organism, and in the case of human beings, may give rise to psychoneurotic states.

For civilized man the problem is infinitely more involved and more acute.[3] The development of a socially interdependent life, with its greater complexity of existence, the resultant indirect methods of obtaining food and protection from danger, and the necessity for socially approved methods of obtaining sexual gratification, have changed the primitive reactions of man; insomuch as impulse can no longer be succeeded by immediate action, lest some code of the group be violated. Accordingly, delay, restraint, postponement or even discarding of one's impulse rather than seeking its direct expression has become the rule. Not only does he have less direct release of energy, but in addition, civilized man

[1] *Vide* p. 90.   [2] *Vide* p. 78.   [3] *Vide* p. 40.

has pyramided upon his primitive desires a host of secondary ones
with a consequent continued orientation toward these desires with
the result that there is a continued mobilization of energy which
may express itself externally (either constructively or destructively) or internally as a constant state of tension.

There is a paradoxical quality in the role which the social situation plays in the creation and mobilization of energy. As has been
previously stated and implied, the original drives have been endlessly complicated, increased, and extended so that the human
organism is constantly bombarded by countless desires—many of
them self-contradictory, many of them impossible of satisfaction,
and therefore, is in a constant state of mobilizing energy. At the
same time society is so constituted as to offer innumerable prohibitions, inhibitions, and frustrations to energy expressions.
The paradox lies in the fact that the inhibitions themselves usually
result in the further mobilization of additional energy which requires some form of expression (often inhibitions may "paralyze
action").

When an impulse is frustrated and tension results, the resulting
available energy is directed first toward the removal of and attack
upon the frustrating source. When the frustration comes from
society, because of those arbitrary decrees called laws and customs,
the expression of the inhibited tension tends to be directed against
society; and in the child as well as the adult the attack may center
upon the mores, customs, regulations, and institutions. Such
attacks are often ultimately of value to society insomuch as they
may force changes in unhealthful social regulations.[1] When the
frustrations come from inhibitions built up within the person, the
attack tends to be directed at the self, with consequent feelings of
inferiority, irritation, anxiety, and other psychoneurotic symptoms. The lack of release, along with the constant mobilization of
energy makes for disease processes rooted in tension. Not only
does striated muscle tension result, but tension or spasm occurs in
the smooth musculature giving rise to such clinical syndromes as
spastic colitis, paroxysmal tachycardia, hypertension, urinary
retention, etc. Secretory glands are involved, and the whole gamut
of physiologic responses discussed in Chapter IV may be witnessed.
If these attacks upon society or self are open and conscious and the
attitude (orientation) toward the irritant adjusted, the energy behind the attack may be dissipated with a subsequent cessation of

[1] *Vide* pp. 188; 243.

attacks; if the attacks are inhibited, the unreleased energy continues to accumulate and to be a source of unrest. In some countries, the use of "free speech" serves to dissipate the tension or bound energy which otherwise would serve to form violent revolutionary groups.

The presence of inhibitions and frustrations may serve as a valuable stimulus toward making energy available; yet as is the case with most forces in our world, any extreme is detrimental; and excess inhibitions may lead to the *bottling up of energy* so as to make the person at best, unstable and non-productive; at worst, restless, neurotic, or destructive.

One may say, therefore, that there are three types of energy: (1) potential constitutional energy; (2) "mobilized" (pent-up or available) energy; and (3) expressed energy.

Potential constitutional energy is dependent in large part upon the genetic structure, and the resultant type of physique or constitution. In this connection it must be emphasized that by physique is not meant simply the muscle and bone structure, but also the functional anatomy of the cardio-vascular, the respiratory, and other body systems which are intimately correlated with the ability of the organism to adjust and to maintain adjustment. It must again be emphasized that the physique does not *produce* the type of personality response and energy manifestations, but is merely a fairly close correlate to these manifestations, which probably have a common basis in their development. Further, the terms "basic amounts of energy" and "basic personality" are theoretical expressions of energy reaction which the organism might develop if there were no inhibiting or modifying elements. Since, however, all life is constantly molded by forces about it, the resulting personality may have characteristics which are at variance with the underlying tendency.[1] Yet with all these considerations, one is forced to the conclusion that the basic amount of energy available in any given being is primarily dependent upon the type of constitution, and that under ideal but similar circumstances of training, individual differences will occur because of dissimilarity of genes and chromosomes. Such constitutional factors as those involved in manic-depressive swings are illustrative of the underlying physiologic bases. Patients who have manic reactions[2] mobilize and express a great deal of energy; they sing, talk, move about constantly; they have many ideas; and in the hypomanic states at

[1] *Vide* p. 41.   [2] *Vide* p. 358.

least, can accomplish a great deal of constructive work. When the force of the energy becomes so great that it can no longer be controlled, constructive utilization of the energy disappears. In the opposite phase, the depression[1] is characterized by sluggishness, inactivity, few ideas, little speech, seclusiveness, and an inability to accomplish the work which ordinarily would be done. This high or low expression of energy is primarily dependent on the physiologic swings rather than a resultant of environmentally determined forces. The mobilization of this potential energy is a continuous process which once set into motion tends to go on to completion.

In ordinary life the person expresses this state of unreleased mobilized energy in the form of tension and in the subjective feeling of "wanting to tear something to pieces," or "I'll burst if something doesn't happen soon." *This mobilized energy is created by the psychobiologic orientation by which the organism prepares for action* (for example as a response to some irritation which one wishes to remove, or in preparation for some pleasure one desires to obtain). This form of energy is reduced either by changing the psychobiologic orientation (which keeps the organism in a state of continued preparedness to act with the memory of the irritation acting as a stimulus in itself) or by providing some form of energy release. If neither step is taken, the person will remain tense, and his bound energy may result either in a general state of tension or in some substitute type of release such as spastic colitis, essential hypertension, psychogenic vomiting, etc.

Expressed energy may appear in the form of physical or mental work. It may be constructive, destructive or undirected. The child spontaneously expresses his energy in play, in running, jumping, shouting, and various enthusiasms. Depending upon the milieu, some of this undirected energy in the child may be constructive or destructive. Whether existing energy is utilized later in life systematically or sporadically is dependent in large part upon the training received. The early habit patterns[2] are of utmost importance and good work habits should be inculcated early in life. The amount of energy which is expressed varies with many factors, including internal changes of growth and disease, as well as external factors of conflict and opportunity.

The role of motivation is an important one in the mobilization of energy. By means of motivation, the person sets up goals which

---

[1] *Vide* p. 356.   [2] *Vide* p. 253.

16

he wishes to obtain. The organism keeps energy constantly *mobilized*, by repeatedly orienting itself in the direction of this goal. Thus energy may be made available in the negative manner of inhibitions as well as the positive manner of motivations.

In the physician's effort to mobilize energy in those patients who are inert, it becomes necessary to carry out the principles stated above. A vast literature on motivation deals with this problem. *The problem resolves itself into one of stimulating the person to consistent mobilization of energy which can be used in work, while at the same time (a) avoiding the production of such excess energy mobilization as to result in neurotic tension symptoms, and (b) providing adequate release of unutilized mobilized energy.* Such an ideal is difficult to realize in its entirety; though many persons violate all the principles involved, it is, nevertheless, possible adequately to approximate such working states. Many persons, "normal" as well as neurotic, do not mobilize their energy in any consistent manner, produce (via the mechanisms described in the early chapters of this book) energy which gives rise to psychoneurotic states, and have no mechanisms for release of their excess energy.

In the development of the person, the ordinary inhibitions of civilized life will stimulate the mobilization of energy. It is necessary, *very early in life,* to develop *habits of work* so that what energy arises will flow easily through proper constructive channels. These habits of work are difficult to acquire, particularly after adolescence, and the child should have more or less definite periods in which he learns to concentrate and work, as well as time for play. If the child develops these habits adequately, they serve then as means of energy mobilization when the person wishes to do something but "can't bring himself to do it." In other words, the very mobilization of energy becomes automatic and habitual.

The next step in mobilization is the setting up of goals, which are specific pleasures to be obtained in the future after over-coming the intervening difficulties. These goals should be of two types, the long term and the short term goals. The long term goal is a guiding star, toward which an *orientation* can be directed. The high school boy who wishes to become a physician, the laborer who wishes to buy a house, the scientist who aims at finding the cure for cancer are examples of persons who orient their lives and mobilize their energies to attain their goal. The strength of their desire determines the amount of energy they put forth. A practical goal which can be achieved generally offers a greater incentive to most

persons than does some vague ideal and almost impossible goal.
With such an orientation, whatever the person does at the moment
has a bearing on the future; and the early rising, the working late
at night, the self-denial of pleasures are all expressions of energy
mobilized to obtain some future pleasure.

In addition to having these long term goals, the person needs
to have immediate goals which offer some prospect of relatively
quick accomplishment. There are comparatively few men who can
carry on work with satisfaction and continued drive, in the face of
repeated disappointments and with no temporary satisfactions.
In practice one outlines the steps necessary to follow in order to
obtain the long term goal, and keeps in mind that each step gives
pleasure, thereby permitting the constant mobilization of fresh
energy. The high school student's wish to become a physician is
held as the guiding goal, but immediate energy is mobilized to be
able to enter college—and then to complete each of the college
courses, and then to enter medical school, and so on. Each tangible goal completed increases confidence and furnishes further
incentive to carry on, so that the subsequent short time goals are
obtained in turn.

So much for the vocation in everyone's life. The avocations and
the spontaneous expressions of energy and pleasure form an equally
if not more important part of life. From the energy mobilized by
inhibitions and motivations, much energy will be created which
needs release in ways other than "work." In addition there is a
great amount of spontaneous energy which needs satisfaction, not
necessarily along any constructive and directed lines, but in direct
and simple expression. (This spontaneous energy is so-called because it is not "mobilized" but rather is an expression of constitutional drives, comparable to Bergson's Élan Vital.) The carrying out of an impulse as it arises, the indulgence of an idle wish,
bursting into song, dance, frolic and play, are spontaneous expressions of well being (i. e., "natural" potential energy). These are
methods of release which are to be encouraged rather than discouraged. There is danger for society in the insistence that all
activity follow a standard pattern, for *frequently progress is brought
about by the person who does not conform.* Presumably, the major
restriction on spontaneous activity is the prevention of harm to
one's fellow men; otherwise, restraint needs to be avoided.

As will be discussed, the prevention of the formation of excess
energy which may lead to neurotic states, is primarily via relaxed

attitudes[1] and decreasing one's desires to a level which is theoretic-ally, at any rate, possible of attainment.[2] It is difficult to make a definite demarcation as to where one's limitations begin and capaci-ties end; often one is capable of more than is realized, while the reverse is also true. The problem of energy mobilization is of the utmost importance, for all constructive (and destructive) activity is the result of utilized energy. *Intelligence is the guiding principle which utilizes force toward its own ends; but it is the mobilized energy which actually does the work.*

MANAGEMENT OF ENERGY PROBLEMS

The multifarious sources of tension; *e. g.*, unsolved conflicts,[3] guilt feelings, self-intolerance,[4] grudge bearing,[5] etc., may often, in the last analysis, be expressed in terms of inadequate or unsatis-factory energy creation and consumption. In the psychoneurotic and psychotic patient, as well as in many "normal" persons, it is possible to correct the production and utilization of energy so that the person becomes more useful to himself and to others. The set-up of our modern world is such that a vast number of persons generate more energy than they expend; *i. e.*, the demands and desires—often synthetic[6]—foisted on them by the social situation orient the organism but do not implement it; or, in other words, produce the energy necessary for satisfaction but do not channelize it. It is as though vast reservoirs of water which should and could be utilized to irrigate the waste places of life were dammed, with-out outlet, either to stagnate or, where the restraining wall is weakened, to offer flood peril. There *are* ways of channeling excess and pent-up energy, through vocalization, socialization, cultiva-tion of avocations, devotion to work, etc.; but before the indi-vidual patient can work out the necessary plans, he must be incul-cated with and make automatic for himself the attitude of relaxa-tion and learn to reduce the number of his desires to what is possi-ble of fulfillment.

RELAXED ATTITUDES[7]

Every physician is familiar with the type of patient whose fatigue manifests itself in spastic colitis,[8] peptic ulcer,[9] certain types of vomiting,[10] paroxysmal tachycardia,[11] asthma,[12] and a whole host of

[1] *Vide* p. 245 *ff.*   [2] *Vide* p. 205.   [3] *Vide* p. 41.   [4] *Vide* p. 202 *ff.*
[5] *Vide* p. 214.   [6] *Vide* p. 170.   [7] *Vide* p. 171.   [8] *Cf.* p. 306.
[9] *Vide* p. 302.   [10] *Vide* p. 256 (Case H. H.).   [11] *Vide* p. 294.
[12] *Vide* p. 298.

similar psychoneurotic states. (This discussion proceeds on the premise that organic bases have been ruled out.) Often such persons appear "normal" to the casual observer and to their friends. I have heard physicians, judging from the quiet composure of a patient state: "He does not look like a neurotic." Tension, after all, is not simply a matter of the contracted state of individual muscle groups; muscle tension is the result of increased nerve impulses going to the muscles, and these in turn are the result of the psychobiologic orientation and emotional tone. By means of great effort it is possible to relax many muscles and to appear composed;[1] but actually, if the person "feels" tense or is emotionally concerned, some part of his body will express tension; and so far as the therapeutic aim is concerned, such apparent muscle relaxation is of little value.

These patients suffering from unreleased energy (tension) often are the reverse of the complaining, fault-finding variety; they are proud and have a strict pattern of social standards and an entirely praise-worthy code of ethics and manner of conduct toward their fellow men. They work diligently and conscientiously, refusing to be satisfied with a task until it is perfectly done. They become perfectionists[2]—at the opposite pole from those who care little for the tasks they do or for the manner in which they do them. It is the over-doing and the over-expectation that result in their collapse. Many of these persons develop a high standard of living and reach personal or social success by virtue of those very traits which later result in their undoing. The force which produces tension in these persons is not the thoroughness with which they do their work; but rather the thoroughness is indicative of the fact that their total organism is constantly oriented toward expending energy. Their supply of energy exceeds the amount required by their customary tasks; hence the meticulous attention given to detail. The pattern is a vicious circle: the more demands they make on themselves, the more energy they generate, and the more there is a demand to express the energy.

In order to reduce this tension, the patient must learn to relax. However, to relax the muscles it is first necessary to "relax the mind";[3] the success of relaxation lies not in muscle training as some claim, but in training the psychologic (psychobiologic) atti-

---

[1] *Vide* p. 139.   [2] *Vide* p. 264.
[3] There is, of course, no such entity as "the mind," but the term is of value in treating patients.

tude. Therapy consists (through analysis and discussion) in teaching the patient: (1) to understand the mechanism of his tension;[1] (2) to see his problems and himself in a true perspective;[2] (3) to realize that anger and impatience retard rather than facilitate his plans;[3] (4) to cultivate the attitude of self-tolerance (*cf.* indifference[4]), and (5) to substitute reasonable planning for emotional demanding.[5] Here as elsewhere, intellectual comprehension and assent are but the first step; the physician must offer moral support to the patient in his task of making such attitudes habitual and automatic. The motive behind these principles is to train the person to produce adequate but not excess energy with which to deal with his problems.

As an adjunct one may teach the patient (by means of a very light hypnotic state)[6] how to relax his muscular system. The patient reclines on a couch, is told to make himself as comfortable as possible, and then is told to relax his hands, his legs, his jaws, his eyes, etc. Next he is told to "relax his mind," and feel drowsy. The suggestion of drowsiness is repeated over and over. Then the patient is informed that he will feel this way every time he tries to relax, and that he will be able by himself to induce this condition. Such suggestion on many occasions is followed by the ability of the subject to relax deeply at will, and particularly after meals and on going to bed. It is important that the subject does not go into a deep hypnotic stage, for he should be aware of the way his muscles feel on relaxing and thus be able to imitate the state when he tries it alone. Occasionally several such sessions are necessary to train the subject to relax. Once he learns this technique, it is simple to suggest that he be relaxed even when he sits at his desk; *i. e.*, that all muscles be relaxed and all general tension be absent except as is necessary in the pursuance of his work. Some persons find it extremely difficult to carry out these procedures at first.

During this suggestive state, the patient is frequently told that he is no longer tense, that he regards all difficulties that come to him with equanimity, that he has the attitude of doing as much as is possible, but without being emotional. This *relaxed "attitude" does more to release tension in the muscles than does any other single technique.*

---

[1] *Vide* p. 216.   [2] *Vide* p. 205.   [3] *Vide* p. 193.
[4] *Vide* p. 202.   [5] *Vide* p. 193 *ff.*   [6] *Vide* p. 227.

Reducing the number of unfulfillable desires is another method of reducing the number of impulses which lead to tension producing orientations. In many instances, the person has too many ambitions which in the nature of things cannot be attained at once, and yet which may create such tension over not being fulfilled as to give rise to undesirable symptoms. It is of great value to discuss the personal drives and desires (the very fact of stating in concrete and precise terms what one wishes to obtain or to avoid is therapeutic; a definite goal is thus created in place of a vague wish), and counsel the patient to modify them within the limits of capacity and time.[1] In this way less energy will be formed and relaxed attitudes will be more easily achieved. In some instances where the ambition is such as to be impossible of fulfilment, yet where it continues to operate, it is often possible to change the trend of the wish and desire into some related field where it is capable of fulfilment.[2]

It will of course have been observed that the two techniques just discussed—cultivation of relaxed attitudes and reduction of the number of desires—are methods of reducing the amount of excess mobilized energy. There are positive and direct techniques as well of handling excess energy and one of the most readily accessible and effective is *vocalization*.

Vocalization of one's emotions is often more tension releasing than is a substitute or vicarious expression of them. If one is angry with another and refrains from expressing that anger, it may accumulate to form "bound" energy, which in turn may lead to rationalizations,[3] suspiciousness,[4] irritability,[5] and that paranoid state which is an integral part of hate. Moreover the memory of the irritation serves as a continued stimulus—as effective as the real stimulus—continually to generate mobilized energy. It is often better frankly and honestly to express one's disagreement[6] or annoyance and thus be able to forget the irritating stimulus than to "repress" it and allow the memory of the irritation to act as a persistent stimulus, producing constant anger reactions which are then repeatedly, though perhaps indirectly expressed.

If for example, Mr. A. is angry at Mr. B. because of some slight or wrong, and conceals his sense of injury but continues to harbor

---

[1] *Vide* p. 205 (Evaluating liabilities and assets).
[2] *Vide* p. 79.
[3] *Vide* p. 71.   [4] *Vide* p. 331 (Case G. N.).   [5] *Vide* p. 58.
[6] To vocalize one's pleasure tends to create pleasant emotions (self-reflexive) within one's self as well as within one's fellowman.

ill thoughts and ideas of revenge, and then becomes irritated with the institutions or people associated with B., his anger is self-reflexive[1] and operates against himself as well as against his irritator. Anger will be expressed and continued; and irritability will be present, continuing from the one case (among others) so that the irritations are constantly generating pent-up energy. However, when the primary emotion (that is, the irritation with Mr. B.) is expressed directly to Mr. B., most of the irritation is removed and the secondary effects disappear. It is a common, every day experience to find that one is greatly relieved when the emotion is expressed, when "one gets it off his chest" as the common expression goes. This technique of releasing pent-up energy by vocalization is particularly of value in marriages[2] wherein the friction between husband and wife is often based on minor irritations which convert the marital into a martial state. Pride, hypersensitivity, and the desire to have one's own way create difficulties which could quickly disappear in the light of expression and discussion. It is neither excusable nor desirable that one become eloquently articulate about every inconsequential and momentary irritation that one may feel (there are bound to be many in any situation in which persons are constantly and closely associated); but it is highly desirable to recognize the fact that even a microscopic splinter can become the source of a serious or even a fatal infection!

Too often unnecessary "scenes" are created because the persons involved do not as a rule frankly discuss their points of difference or honestly express their mild irritation over some minor situation. Instead, they repress their many small angers, permitting them to fester and spread poison so that when a break does come, the relatively unimportant precipitating factor is lost and forgotten in a welter of recrimination, abuse, parade of past mistakes, and airing of ancient injuries. The violence of expression is out of all proportion to the gravity of the immediate situation and results either in a counterattack of equal virulence or in a feeling of bitterness or rankling injustice which bodes no good for the future. Discussions, if they are to eventuate in the release of pent-up emotions, or if they are to further understanding, must be objectively concerned with the point at issue and not disguises for an attack on the other person's self-respect and pride.

Though granting the therapeutic value of "vocalization," one must realize that it is not always either feasible or possible thus

[1] *Vide* p. 191 (Case K.).   [2] *Vide* p. 162 *ff.*

directly to express and dissipate one's irritation. For example, one cannot freely vocalize one's anger at one's host or at one's employer; and such inhibiting factors call for other forms of release, some of which have been mentioned in the discussion of substitution and sublimation.[1] Though only common sense[2] can dictate procedure in a particular situation, it is as a general rule, better to err on the side of expression than on repression.[3] Politeness, essential and born of the need to facilitate easier adjustment between men, can become a vice when overdone, and may lead to abnormal repression, stagnation, or sadism. Similarly, insufficient politeness leads to excessive irritations between men and to friction which interferes with accomplishment.

When one is thoroughly angry and because of the situation is unable to express himself, it is not always easy to sublimate this anger into "sweet and forgiving" channels. Too often persons who remain outwardly saccharine under marked irritations evidence a steady flow of malicious gossip or sadistic domination in realms which they can control. In the psychoneurotic person, these expressions of anger and hate result in chronic nagging and vicious innuendos; and are part of intense dissatisfaction with the self, and often are accompanied by many hypochondriacal phenomena.[4] The entire symptom complex is an expression in part of this repressed anger, anger which needs to be curbed in its formation and which when formed needs open and direct expression.

One of the best forms of constructive outlets for the pent-up energy is in *socialization*. Visiting with one's friends, going to group affairs, interesting one's self in organizational activities are excellent means of utilizing energy.[5] Too often patients become seclusive and almost asocial when their neurotic symptoms develop; and this seclusiveness creates a vicious cycle, wherein the patient has more time to think of his own ailments which thus become exaggerated, and also, because loss of contact with others means loss of the opportunity to orient one's self toward realities as others see them. The fact that patients state that they have no satisfaction in going out, or that the association with others merely makes them feel worse, should be overcome by the explanation given above; and the patients should be urged to enter social activities, despite their reluctance to do so. It will be found in the average patient that after the first two or three visits to friends,

---

[1] *Vide* p. 79.   [2] *Vide* p. 119 (footnote).   [3] *Vide* p. 63 *ff*.
[4] *Vide* p. 279 (Case B. M.).   [5] *Vide* pp. 165 (Case F. S.); 308 (Case U.).

the original antipathy disappears and the patient begins to improve. Yet, the physician must persist in urging the patient, for without the moral suasion, many patients will relapse and lose all the value they gained from their contacts.

Recreation and hobbies are also extremely important energy release techniques. Moreover, recreation is a direct pleasure obtaining method. Recreation may be in almost any form; and from society's point of view, the form is immaterial as long as others are not harmed thereby. It is difficult to tell any one person how to enjoy himself; rather the person should be canvassed for the pleasures which he knows he cares for, and then the physician may be in a position to advise how these pleasures may be more constructively and enjoyably utilized. Hobbies, similarly, vary so widely and may be so accidentally determined that rather than recommend any one hobby, the physician should urge the patient to choose whatever he likes best. Energy discharge will be greatest in that hobby which is most interesting to the person. Work created for the sole purpose of helping a patient may be of inestimable value; but many of the negative results of "occupational therapy" occur because it is blindly assumed that all will benefit, because some do, from a particular kind of activity. While one person may find release for his mobilized energy through physical activity; *e. g.*, in carpentry, another, having neither manual dexterity nor building interest would through the same medium but increase his tension, add to his store of unreleased energy. To be released adequately, energy needs not only "labor" but also the proper attitude. It is interesting in this connection to note the paradoxical nature of many energy outlets. It might seem that games requiring great physical exertion and intensified by keen competition would be too exciting for an already excitable person; yet they actually are relaxing both to the participant and to the spectator because they release pent-up energy. On the other hand, the apparently passive listening to music[1] may accomplish an identical end. The passivity is only seeming. A person in following the music tends by identification to swing muscularly with the music, nodding his head, tapping his feet; and even when there is no manifest movement, there is often a non-observable but yet definite movement. In many forms of music such rhythmic movements can be performed only by relaxed muscles; and tense persons, who are influenced by harmonious music, are perforce relaxed. Some sani-

[1] *Vide* p. 207.

tariums very effectively utilize dancing to music as a means of relaxing patients. Moreover in this general relaxation and harmonious appeal to the senses, the person "feels" that peace and harmony do exist outside himself and will continue to exist despite his own troubles; and by such general "feeling tone," the person puts aside his conflicts for the while. On the other hand, some types of music will stimulate persons into increased activity (*e. g.*, martial music, dance music) by reason of the tendency to make rapid and staccato rhythmic movements in time with the music. The rhythmic muscle movements can, under the influence of a skillful composer, increase to such a pitch as to make the person excited, exhilarated,[1] etc. The associated words with all their connotations aid in determining the stimulated person's attitudes.

It is important again to emphasize that *energy release occurs not primarily from physical activity, but from the psychobiologic orientation.* If the set of the body is such as to facilitate energy release, such release will occur on proper stimulation. On the other hand, if the person is in continual conflict severe physical labor will not be useful in releasing energy. Thus, persons may release energy in witnessing an exciting ball game, or in watching a boxing spectacle, or a bull fight, or, as occurs today in some modern nations, by concentrating attention upon some public scapegoat. The energy release in these instances is effective because the subject identifies[2] himself as the hero of the event, and projects himself into the real or imagined action, so that his body acts out (by muscle tension, by shouting, and excitement) what he envisions, and he thus secures a release of his energy which may have been mobilized to combat the irritations of daily life. On the other hand, persons obsessed with some concern, or drive, may seek to forget their troubles in physical labor; and whereas there may be some relief, the energy is so continually mobilized by the problem that real relief is not usual. This fact is the reason why, in specific advice to patients, it is important to stress the need for selecting outlets enjoyed by the person (*i. e.*, outlets toward which he is properly oriented rather than those which are merely time consuming).

---

[1] Hence quick staccato music results in quick staccato muscle movement which, in turn, is associated with a feeling of quick movement, of exhilaration. Thus by proper knowledge of music one may "produce" almost any kind of emotion in a "normal" person.

[2] *Vide* p. 73.

Without at all minimizing the value of recreation, hobbies, avocations, social activities, and vocalization, one must in the last analysis admit that for most persons and in most instances there is no other energy outlet so releasing, so rewarding, so universally effective as work: work which requires daily arising and constant attention to duty, irrespective of the way one may feel or of his wishes of the moment; work in which one has certain responsibilities; work which is not only of value but is in itself a value. Accordingly, all males, should work unless there is actual disabling physical disease. And women, despite the special role they occupy in society today, do not differ essentially from men either in their ability of accomplishment in most tasks, or in their need for release from tension. Even married women, whose husbands insist on placing a pedestal beneath them, should find some occupation to take up their time. Having served their primary usefulness in the rearing of children, women, with all the labor saving machinery now available, find time hanging heavily upon their hands.[1] The conventional ideas which force women to stay at home or visit day in and day out over bridge tables are conducive more to boredom and tension neuroses than to a state of well being. There are many activities, useful to society as well as to the individual person, which can supply a zest for life and for creation, which these often highly intelligent and able married women are capable of both doing and enjoying.

It must be borne in mind that the above glorification is of *work and not of drudgery*. Our highly mechanized civilization calls for increasing hordes of human robots; and the monotonous routine performance of a task, while it may be physically exhausting, rarely serves as a safety valve for pent-up energy. Ideally speaking, one would say that whether a work is monotonous depends upon the individual point of view and that rarely should one particular task be forced upon anyone who deems it uninteresting; practically speaking, one would be forced to say that since so much of the "world's work" is dull and unrewarding for the worker, society will eventually have to provide other channels through which energy can be constructively expended.

On the other hand, almost any work which one undertakes because one is interested in it involves many tasks which are not liked but which need to be carried out as part of the total program. So often one meets with persons who by virtue of untrained habits of

[1] *Vide* p. 62 (Case I.).

work, and of desires for an "easy" position, will object to various tasks on the ground of lack of interest. Fond mothers aid and abet their children in many of these idle wishes. While the individual preference should always be given as much consideration as is possible, the tendency to avoid the expenditure of energy should not be permitted to guide the waking activity of the patient. Not only adolescents present this problem; supposedly mature persons shift aimlessly from position to position,[1] with many unformed and vague wishes, and with little organized expenditure of energy.

The factor of habit training as mentioned above is an important one in the carrying out of consistent work efforts. Habits of study for example, if not inculcated in early life are difficult to develop later. The ability to work consistently is often dependent not only upon the amount of energy present but also upon the habit patterns of work, in reality conditioned habit patterns, which facilitate the systematic utilization of energy. This force of habit is important as prophylaxis in the training of children for their adult life. It is difficult to establish the habit in later years.

The influence of an *incentive* in the mobilization of energy and in its persistent direction cannot be over-exaggerated. The very concept of systematized effort, which is so necessary for the advancement of society, implies that the effort is directed toward some goal. When such a goal will in some measure benefit the person, the amount of energy expended in that direction will be greater than if the goal has little relation to the person. In our changing society, however, the possible goals available are becoming more and more limited; so that personal satisfactions in the ultimate goal tend to become more and more identified with social gains. The minimization of the ego-importance in such instances will undoubtedly subtract much effort from many persons, and society will lose thereby. In the therapy of patients, the physician should attempt to direct the person toward a goal, which will furnish some personal satisfactions should it be obtained rather than simply urge the patient to do something because it is generally recognized to be "good." The force of incentive should always be made use of.

Another means of mobilizing energy is through association with persons who are active. If the deficiency is primarily a psychologic one, the problem becomes one of creating desires or demands which the patient will recognize as compelling. Much human

[1] *Vide* p. 62 (Case W. K.).

behavior is imitative; so that often the person apparently lacking sufficient native energy for personally initiated effort, will, if thrown into association with others who are active, make their interests his; and the stimulation having been provided, the organism will orient itself by the creation of energy to meet the new demand.

Psychotic and psychoneurotic patients are notorious for their failure to utilize such *constructive* methods of energy release, and as a consequence develop symptoms which are often expressions of the aberrant and unorganized methods of release. Many such patients would not develop a personality disorder if society avoided inhibition of action which results in the formation of energy; for the less energy created, the less irritating release there would be and the better the adjustment. Feebleminded persons for example who are subject to but unable to meet the demands of adult society mobilize energy which is released in the form of behavior disorders. Psychopathic personalities not infrequently may be unable to adjust in open society for the same reason and yet be almost model citizens in a small controlled hospital group where little is demanded of them.[1] Many such persons and others in related categories are constitutionally unable to utilize constructive techniques for energy release; while many other patients, the psychoneurotic group particularly, just do not know or have not learned how to use the proper methods of energy release, and yet can be taught how to use constructive instead of destructive mechanisms. Therein lies one of the bases for the cure of many psychoneurotic phenomena.

The social implications of the foregoing discussion of energy mobilization and expression are significant and far reaching; for, insomuch as society stimulates the mobilization of energy, it has perforce the responsibility of channeling and directing the energy toward socially valuable goals. As has been previously stated, the social environment superimposes on man countless desires and demands so that he is forever dissatisfied with his status quo, and is accordingly constantly mobilizing energy with which to change his situation. Progress, with its increase in the standards of living and thinking, is essentially based in this dissatisfaction. Left to himself, in the midst of plenty, man would do little and progress would be absent. The "laziness" of man has its origin in the inertia which is a tendency inherent in inanimate as well as animate

[1] *Cf.* p. 394.

objects. Inertia tends to bring all forces to a balanced dynamic state, and where there is any friction (as is the case with inanimate objects) or obstacles (as with animate things), this balance eventually results in cessation of activity. (The Freudian concept of the death instinct,[1] and the desire of man to return to the rest of the mother's womb, is a highly poetic manner of expressing such a tendency toward inertia.)

It is a fundamental law of physics that energy cannot be created; but it is possible to mobilize energy which is latent so that constructive work can be done. Our civilized state has without conscious purpose created situations which tended to result in energy mobilization, and also in an almost equally unconscious fashion rewarded and encouraged energy expression which has been utilized in the first place, to meet the self preservative needs of the individual man and which in the second place has contributed to the welfare of society. Training, schooling, learning of skills, provision of pleasure giving outlets, offering incentives which will enlist man's endeavors toward socially desirable activities, are all methods by which society can channelize constructively the energy mobilized by the necessary (sometimes unnecessary) social and personal frustrations.

Cf. p. 431.

CHAPTER XIII

PROGNOSIS AND THE CURVE OF IMPROVEMENT

THE prognosis of patients suffering from a psychoneurosis varies with many factors. These factors include among others: hereditary predisposition; maladjustment in childhood; an exacting, excessively conscientious personality, or conversely an overly self-indulgent and unself-disciplined personality; the age of onset; environmental stress; sex maladjustments; coexistent physical disease; fatigue; the presence of manic-depressive depressions; the amount of brain damage, as for example in senile patients and in patients with brain injury; the duration of the neurosis prior to treatment, etc. In order to forecast exactly the outcome of such an illness, one would need to know in great detail much that is difficult or impossible to ascertain, for the variations and modifications are as individual as the individual patient. The following statements, then, must be understood to represent only a general picture, the broad outlines within which the particular prognosis will be made.

The prognosis as to life is good. Patients as a rule do not die of a psychoneurosis. However, this statement is not altogether true. Patients may die as the end result of a neurotic symptom, for if the cardiac musculature is poor, for example, they may die of the exertion accompanying emotion. Some patients develop essential hypertension on an emotional basis, and the apoplectic stroke which carries that patient away may truly be said to be the result of emotion. Hysterical asthma may so affect the person's breathing and respiration that pneumonia may set in more easily than is usual. Chronic mucous colitis may succeed in so lowering the patient's resistance that he is carried away by an infection which he could ordinarily resist. A peptic ulcer may be so aggravated by tension as to facilitate the onset of perforation and hemorrhage. The neurosis itself may seem relatively free from the final responsibility; but it nevertheless may indirectly be the determining one. In some instances, indeed, it may bring about actual death.

Mrs. H. H., aged sixty-seven years, was in good health and boasted of never having been ill or in a hospital. She was quite deaf, but could read lips and understand words spoken very loudly. Her husband, with whom she was deeply in love, was killed in an automobile accident. The patient was prostrated with grief, and developed vaginal bleeding. The diagnosis of myomata of the uterus was made, and a vaginal hysterectomy was performed. She made an uneventful recovery, except that she developed persistent vomiting. No cause could be determined for this vomiting, in which not even fluids could be kept down. She was fed intravenously, but her strength gradually grew less and less. She called her children to her side and told them that it was best that she go and not be a burden since her husband had gone. The vomiting was a psychogenic vomiting. Attempt at psychotherapy failed because the patient had lost all desire to continue with her existence and she refused to discuss her attitudes. Her deafness made it impossible to break down the barrier of her indifference and the patient died soon thereafter from exhaustion and malnutrition. Autopsy showed no pathology which might have been of importance in producing the vomiting, except the recent operation, which was significant only as a contributory factor to the psychoneurotic vomiting. Death in this case was the end result of a neurotic symptom.

Prognosis as to recovery may further be classified as: (1) complete recovery, or (2) partial recovery. *Partial recovery* may occur when, though the symptom is temporarily removed, the basis of the neurosis is still uncorrected; and thus the same symptom may recur again under mild stress; or some other psychoneurotic expression of the underlying tension may come to the fore. This type of recovery is common; and may be obtained by many and devious methods. So-called miracle cures are on the basis of suggestion,[1] but their permanency is open to question. Strong suggestion either directly or in the form of medication or operative procedures, may also bring about temporary remissions. The author has seen many psychoneurotic patients with no organic pathology, on whom thyroidectomies, cholecystectomies, appendectomies, coccyxectomies, and other operations were performed, primarily because of the insistence of the patient that "something be done" about his complaint.[2]   Many of these patients will undergo severe operative procedures rather than face the conflicts which while dissociated and split off from the symptom are at the basis of their emotional overtones and their pains.[3] On the other hand, removal from an irritating situation such as occurs when one takes a vacation, often results in temporary alleviation of the symptom, which recurs with the return of the patient to his former surroundings. In children this experience is extremely common: the child who represents a marked behavior problem will often do very well in camp away from his family, but will have a complete recurrence of his symp-

---

[1] *Vide* p. 219.   [2] *Vide* p. 308 (Case B. U.).   [3] *Vide* p. 276.

17

toms once he returns home. Some patients, however, can "manage to stick it out" in a neurosis producing situation provided they can "escape" several times a year by taking vacations. However, where such relief can occur, there is little seriously wrong with the underlying personality. Severe psychoneuroses can never be dealt with in such a simple manner. It must seem obvious that the only treatment that will permanently remove any symptom is that treatment which attacks the cause; and since the "causes" of the neuroses usually have their roots in the diseased personality, the cure must come by changing the diseased parts for more healthy ones. One should always gaze critically upon any miraculous changes wrought overnight; for while they do occur, they rarely are permanent. As mentioned previously, by use of hypnosis, I have frequently removed the presenting symptom in patients on their first visit,[1] but these symptoms almost invariably return and are not permanently removed until the more fundamental bases are reached.

Mrs. H. I., aged forty-three years, was referred to the dispensary for chronic alcoholism. The patient was interviewed for some twenty minutes, and a brief review of her problems made. A general "mental hygiene" formulation was given her; and she was urged to view and deal with her problems in a direct and frank fashion, instead of trying to avoid them by the use of alcohol. She seemed greatly impressed. Two weeks later a letter was received from the social agency caring for this patient, stating, "Mrs. H. I. reports phenomenal results from the treatment." Nothing was heard of the patient till three years later, when the agency asked that this patient again be taken for treatment since she had been drinking for a long period of time.

What had happened during that one interview was: (1) an intellectual appreciation of the method suggested, but no "dynamic conviction"[2] which would enable her to implement her new attitude; (2) strong suggestion as to her ability to do without alcohol should she follow the method of mental hygiene, the effect of the suggestion wearing off in a short period of time; (3) a temporary lessening of the emotional tension surrounding the patient's problems (and hence the cause of the drinking) by giving the patient a general perspective of her liabilities and assets, putting her problems in their rightful place; and (4) the focusing of her efforts not at stopping the alcoholism but at the removal of her emotional difficulties behind it. These influences nevertheless were quickly dissipated in the absence of the sustained therapy necessary to

---

[1] *Vide* p. 32 (Case K. U.).   [2] *Vide* p. 193.

make them part of the patient's personality. Such brilliant initial results are always impressive but can be truly evaluated only by follow-up studies.

Partial recovery may occur in the setting of treatment for a complete recovery, and may be sufficiently adequate so that the patient can adjust on a social level and be able to carry on with routine duties of work or household activity, even though he does not fully complete his therapeutic course. Such temporary removal of symptoms is rather an amelioration, and is of value in that it permits the patient to be concerned about work and social affairs which in themselves are of value. In a number of patients, once one is able even temporarily to remove the symptom so that the patient can return to a normal routine of life, spontaneous improvement will continue, and the patient may make a seemingly complete recovery. Whether the recovery is or is not complete depends on the degree and amount of personality readjustment that has occurred during therapy or during the influence of the demands of the "normal" environment.

Partial recoveries may occur without any formal psychotherapy. In psychotherapy one tries essentially to make the person normal[1] by a critical examination and retraining of the attitudes and reaction patterns. In ordinary society, however, normal attitudes and reaction patterns are constantly voiced and, more important, acted upon; this "living example" of "normal" persons in itself tends to be corrective and may in many instances influence the patient favorably. In fact, *one of the most important factors in the cure of a disturbed personality is a normal, relaxed environment.* This relaxed environment does not necessarily mean one of peace and quiet. Places of rest may be very beneficial, if other persons in the company set examples of relaxation. "Retreats" are used for this purpose and they have the additional value of reëstablishing a more general orientation toward life, and a better perspective which relegates the person's own particular difficulty to the small corner where it really belongs. This change is brought about in part by prayer and faith, which constitute a powerful influence in changing

---

[1] The word "normal" whenever used in this book, means not merely average or usual. Normalcy consists of a type of adjustment which often, though by no means always, makes for a minimum of discord between the person and society. Members of society in the modal range (*i. e.*, between the extremes) have managed to work out a fairly "livable" adjustment. Normal adjustment does not mean the most perfect adjustment possible. What is "normal" for one person or group may be abnormal for another. Time, place, group, and previous state all enter into determining what is "normal."

the person's attitude. Of great, though often unrecognized import is the fact that in such a "retreat" the person is surrounded by like-minded persons who by their very community of ideas offer moral support. When this "like-mindedness" is unhealthy, however, detrimental effects will be intensified. Many of the converts to various oriental philosophies are enthusiastic in their praise, and claim such marvelous results because in these religious experiences they have found peace and quiet, and they have been able to shelve their more or less petty strivings by gaining a perspective which demonstrates how small a role the person or even his group plays in the world as a whole and in the endless passage of time. Unless, however, the philosophic attitude becomes an implemental part of their personality, and unless the specific emotional disturbances at the root of their neurosis is removed, persons who experience a religious conversion often relapse to their former state; and seek solace elsewhere. Often too, such changed attitudes are of value only as long as the person remains in surroundings conducive thereto; and as long as he is encouraged by the presence of others who are striving for the same goal; but on leaving such environment, he soon falls back to his old ways of thinking and feeling. Then too, in those in whom the emotional disturbance is great, relief afforded by the strong religious philosophy is only temporary —for the cause of the difficulty continues to exist.

Mr. K. M., aged thirty-five years, reared in a rigidly orthodox family, was intensely unhappy. He had always been fearful, more of the possibility of showing fear than of dangerous situations themselves. He was a quiet person who preferred his books to people, yet when alone he was tortured by doubts of his ability, and angry with himself for his lack of accomplishments. He was afraid of "sin" to the degree that he would weep bitterly at confession over childish untruths he had told in his games with boys. He was extremely kind and tolerant of others, but of himself he was almost masochistically intolerant. He did excellent work at school, and entered a retreat before preparing for priesthood. When he first came there, he states that a peace settled over him such as he had never known and he was almost supremely happy. He prayed frequently and forgot about his own "petty inadequacies" in consideration of the problems of mankind. After several weeks, however, he found thoughts intruding which had been present before and which he was trying to escape. When he saw worldy persons he began to think of himself; and the problems of sex came strongly to the fore. At the end of the second month, the patient was in a state of greater agitation than when he went into the retreat, for the sense of "thinking unholy thoughts" was added to his former fears. This experience occurred when he was at the age of twenty. He finally became an alcoholic.[1]

<hr>

[1] *Vide* p. 404.

But for many persons, relaxation of spirit and a more effective reorientation of self in relation to others and to time can be brought about in certain situations; e. g., in camps and vacation spots, where strife and stresses are minor and normal healthy expression in play and fun provides outlets which the person can carry back to his daily and routine life. In a similar manner, removal of the subject from an irritating situation, and permitting residence in a non-stress providing place will often produce partial cures of psychoneurotic symptoms.

If a "normal" person is wearied by the work and strain of life, if his efficiency is lowered by fatigue, then a "retreat" whether it be found in cloister or camp, in philosophical or physical gymnastics may be of inestimable value. It offers rest and refreshment; it enables him to return with new zest to whatever may be his task and problem. If, however, it is used as a permanent escape or as a substitute for facing his actual situation, then inevitably it fails.

Partial recoveries may continue for long periods of time if the person is intense enough in his attitudes and is able to bury himself sufficiently in what ever philosophy he has accepted. Yet even during this period of remission from his emotional ailment, the patient still is not completely recovered, for his recovery tends to fail quickly when he takes up his routine and daily tasks in the community at large. Some groups try to overcome this handicap by making their constituents spend from one to several hours daily reviewing tenets of their special philosophies; but this is not an adequate substitute and the original relief dwindles considerably in time. Permanent relief from psychoneurotic symptoms can come only when the etiologic factors have been unearthed and the existent attitude of the patient toward them has been remedied.[1]

One of the most important elements in partial and even in complete recoveries and the prognosis for their continuance, is the ability of the subject to shift the responsibility[2] of his actions to someone else. In the relationship of the patient to the therapist the patient is often relieved in proportion to the degree to which the therapist will assume the responsibility for directing a course of action, and basically *the patient feels relieved because someone else makes his decision for him.*[3] Many persons are immensely relieved

---

[1] *Vide* p. 125.

[2] This tendency to perform unpleasant tasks rather than take the responsibility of making a decision on some forbidden topic is found too often in some totalitarian countries.

[3] *Vide* p. 195.

even when told to do things which are obnoxious to them, if by so doing they can be relieved of thinking about their conflicts or deciding which pole of their desires should be carried out. It is this putting in abeyance the conflictual drives, that quiets the emotional tension about the drives, and thus secures relief for the patient. The more effectively the therapist can succeed in doing this at first, the greater will be the relief. In psychotherapy, however, it must be remembered that such release from tension is only the initial stage during which adequate mental hygiene may be incorporated into the patient's personality; and is to be succeeded by the stage of *training the patient to accept responsibilities and to be self-reliant.* In many cults on the other hand, this first stage is never passed, and the person remains bound to and dependent on the central figure of the cult; and although temporarily aided, remains only partially recovered and forever unable to make his own decisions and supply his own faith.

Even when the proper technique is followed, and an effort is made to resynthesize the personality to a more healthful state, one may fall far short of complete recovery. There are many elements which militate against perfect results, some of which are inherent in the personality, some of which are inherent in the environment, and some of which are inherent in the therapeutic situation.

One of the most difficult factors is the *hereditary*[1] one. Little is as yet known of the subject but it may be easily understood that when the substance is poor, the results of molding that substance cannot always be satisfactory. Feebleminded patients springing from a long line of feebleminded ancestors can rarely be made into "intellectual giants." The manic-depressive patient, subject to intense moods of elation alternating with intense moods of depression, is often the end result of his forefathers, and often is relatively unmodifiable by therapeutic efforts.[2] In the psychoneuroses this clear-cut picture of hereditary influence is less obvious, while the very nature of the illness emphasizes the importance of training elements as well as heredity; yet clinically, the role of heredity seems indisputable in its significance. The alcoholic, K. M.,[3] whose drinking seemed to be the result of emotional maladjustment, and who was later helped by psychotherapy, sprang from a line of alcoholics: his father and his uncle died as the direct result of alcoholism, his cousin and his brother both were drunkards. The strain which drove this man to drink may have been environ-

[1] *Vide* p. 340.   [2] *Vide* p. 357.   [3] *Vide* p. 260 (Case K. M..

mental in large part; but while it is difficult to prove, it is likewise illogical to dismiss as entirely non-contributory, the familial drunkness.   Similarly Miss S. G.,[1] who had a severe obsessive compulsive neurosis gave the history of a sister who had a "breakdown" at a similar age, of a mother who had "breakdowns," and an aunt who was extremely neurotic.   It is impossible to give in specific proportions the relative importance of heredity and environment, for both undoubtedly play important roles; but when one meets with such a family history, one can understand why the emotional illness is of such intensity and of such long duration. The prognosis in these situations is often the prognosis of what has happened to the forebears.

Emotionalism inculcated in early childhood[2] may remain for the duration of one's existence, although its intensity may be ameliorated by psychotherapy.   The child's personality is very much like soft putty, plastic and easily malleable.   Yet it quickly becomes set and hardened, retaining all the impressions inflicted on it during its plastic phase, and exhibiting in adult life many reaction patterns which are but the expression of the formative ruts.   These *childhood influences are not so much specific memories, but general reaction patterns.*[3]   Thus the child may grow up with a tendency to fearfulness, to self-sympathy, to over-compensation, etc. which attitudes will manifest themselves in all spheres.   Later in childhood, specific emotional discharges will occur on the basis of their general pattern but in relation to specific stimuli; so that there will be finickiness about certain foods, hates directed toward specific objects, over solicitude toward oneself or toward certain persons, etc.   The earlier in life the emotional force has its effect the more general will the reaction of the patient be later in life; and the more difficult to alleviate.   Earliest memories of most persons begin after the age of four, five, and six years[4]; and as a consequence, it is difficult to determine from the patient just what role was played by various experiences.   For research purposes, direct observation of children and of the effect on them by their parents is far more reliable for gaining information than are many so-called "memories" in adult life.   Then, too, one must be careful of "retrospective falsification" wherein what is remembered as having occurred is incorrect.

---

[1] *Vide* p. 80 *ff* (Case S. G.).   [2] *Vide* p. 46 *ff*.   [3] *Vide* p. 171 *ff*.
[4] Psychoanalysts maintain that patients can remember what their emotional states were at two and three years of age.

Thus one schizophrenic patient stated that when he was in school some boys pushed him with deliberate intent to harm; yet when this patient was asked whether he knew at the time the incident was supposed to have occurred that they wished to hurt him, he replied that he did not, but that it "just came to him." In other words he was reading meanings into events which may not even have happened. It is difficult to tell whether this same unconscious falsification is not characteristic of many of the patients' accounts of what they did before the age of five.

One of the forces which are inculcated early in life and which tend to make for a guarded prognosis is the drive to exaggerated preciseness, definiteness, certainty, and thoroughness.[1] These qualities are extremely valuable to the person as well as to the society in which he lives; but when they become intensified to the point where the patient is emotionally disturbed at not obtaining perfection, they are conducive to rigidity of personality and to difficulty in molding. In many such persons, the necessity for precision has become a fetish, and operates habitually and automatically. Generally this trait is the result of early environmental inculcation; and these patients may "crack" under the pressure of their own drives. Perfection in action is a matter of degree and it can never be obtained in absolute form by any man; yet many persons demand of themselves, the impossible.[2] They tend to lose their plasticity; and when psychotherapy is begun, one encounters great difficulty in "softening" this rigidity into "normal" human plasticity. It is this group of patients who often are subject to "smiling depressions," wherein they are deeply depressed internally but have learned to present a composed and pleasant exterior. It is this group that is particularly liable to suicide and, therefore, to a guarded prognosis in therapy.

Will power is a term which has fallen into disfavor, yet the principles involved in it are of great value in psychotherapy. The exercise of will power consists in the forcing of one's self to do that which should or must be done, irrespective of whether one wishes to do it. Will power is subject to many modifications which in themselves may be extreme, and harmful: variations from the over-indulgent, perpetually self-gratifying hysterical woman,[3] to the unyielding, uncompromising, dogmatic "iron-willed" tyrant.[4] Yet between these two extremes, there is room for the exercise of *will power*, and it forms *the basis for the self-discipline*[5] *essential to life at a high social level.* In using "will power," the person volun-

---

[1] *Vide* p. 212.   [2] *Vide* p. 202.   [3] *Vide* p. 62 (Case I.).
[4] *Vide* p. 213 (Case D. I.)   [5] *Vide* p. 217.

tarily sets up standards which he desires to obtain, usually the
desire being an idealized wish (goals forced on one are in another
category); and often the steps necessary for accomplishment of
that wish are difficult, unpleasant, or even distasteful. The ability
of a person to hold to such a line of endeavor is roughly a measure
of his will power, and it is of great aid in the overcoming of many
unhygienic emotional habits. When one encounters a patient who
can force himself to follow the basic principles of mental hygiene,
cures will come far more quickly than if he habitually follows the
desires of the moment and shys away from difficulties. The
amount of effort or the will which a patient can exert is of prognostic significance.

However, a word of warning is important. It is not easy nor at
times possible, simply by an effort of will to "forget" certain obsessions. In many patients suffering from anxiety states, with symptoms involving the heart and gastrointestinal tract, one reason for
their symptoms is the attempt to control emotional drives purely
by an effort of will. Such efforts create tension, and many patients
suffering from a depression[1] may, by the condemnation of others
or even of themselves, be driven to suicide. In manic-depressive
depressions, patients frequently complain of having "lost their
will power." In general it may be stated that where the symptom
is the vicarious manifestation of some underlying conflict, the
"will" to forget the symptom is exceedingly difficult to carry out,
unless at the same time there is an effort to understand the causative psychologic mechanisms.

The *age of onset* of symptoms in the neurotic is of significance.
In the psychoses the earlier the onset of the illness, the greater, as a
rule, is the potency of the hereditary element.[2] In the psychoneuroses on the other hand, the symptoms are often the reaction
to a situational stress,[3] and once this stress is terminated, or the
person trained to deal with the stress without being disturbed, the
personality reorientation may go on in a normal fashion. Behavior
disturbances may be particularly frequent at puberty, and depressed symptoms may appear in the forties, as the result of diminished personality resistance to the stress of physiologic changes at
these periods; but even here, the determining forces of attitude and
stress actually are the important elements in producing the neuroses. These periods in life are associated with physiological

[1] *Vide* p. 363.   [2] *Cf.* p. 262.   [3] *Vide* Ch. VIII.

changes, and the personality which may previously have been able to get along by effort, fails to adjust under such stress.[1] Symptoms at these periods indicate either that the physiologic changes are unduly strong or that the personality is poorly balanced. Prognostically, it may be said that if one does nothing to ameliorate the pre-neurotic personality, and granting that it does not become worse, the neurosis will disappear and the former adjustment will be reached with the cessation of the physical changes. Such a person, however, remains potentially neurotic, and will be precipitated into an illness should sufficient stress arise. Indeed in patients suffering from a manic-depressive depression, neurotic traits may come to the fore during the depression and continue long after the depression has disappeared.[2]

The sudden onset of a neurosis following a strong precipitating stress carries a good prognosis; for the implication is, in these instances, that the personality itself is relatively little at fault, and that when the stress is removed, the symptoms will clear up. The residual emotional trauma occasioned by this stress, may or may not remain; generally if it is treated soon after it occurs, it will disappear. On the other hand, the less obvious the precipitating factor, the more severe the neurosis will tend to be.[3] This severity is the result of two forces: first, that of the greater susceptibility, in general, of the personality even to minor stresses; and second, that although the stress may be severe, and its very lack of obviousness may indicate that it is more of a pride or personality wounding factor (*e. g.*, lack of attention from one's husband) less of a direct attack upon the person (as for example occurs in financial difficulty), and therefore it will be less easy to approach and remedy. In reality this second reason is a corollary of the first, for the severity of the stress depends upon the sensitivity of the patient.[4] When a patient who apparently has financial security, what appears to be good domestic situation, and no physical defects, yet suffers from neurotic symptoms, then the cause of those symptoms must lie in deepseated emotional conflicts, which have finally culminated, or which have been unduly intensified by some trivial incident. When a patient complains of suddenly developing a neurosis over some trivial incident, the physician may suspect strongly that the personality was predisposed to it, and that if not this incident, then some other would have precipitated the condition.

[1] *Vide* p. 357 (Case K. H.).   [2] *Vide* p. 371.
[3] *Cf.* p. 360 (Case C. C.).   [4] *Vide* p. 153.

Mr. D. G.[1] developed intense vertigo, the result of worrying about the possible loss of his position. He had good grounds for concern. However, when he was shown how to handle the situation, the symptoms cleared up quickly.

On the other hand:

Mrs. K. T.[2] was seemingly well, until she went to a motion picture where suddenly she became very frightened at some scene, and had to leave. Since that time she had been very emotional, fearful of leaving her home and suffering from the syndrome of anxiety attacks. In point of fact, her difficulty had very little actual relation to what she saw at the theater. That incident was so trifling as to be practically unrelated to her illness. On the other hand, the emotional disturbance existing in this patient was so strong that any incident would have brought the illness to the fore. Deeper personality studies had to be undertaken to determine the bases of her condition, and many months were spent in retraining the constitution so that it could be more adjustable.

Recovery rate may be greatly impaired by *continuation of the stress in the environment*.[3] If a child continues to live in a home full of strife and anxieties, his behavior problems will rarely clear up easily. If a woman develops neurotic symptoms on the basis of her husband's drunkenness and infidelity, her neurosis will tend to remain if she has to continue living with him. It is possible at times to modify the person in the environment; but here again, everything depends on the intensity of the irritating forces.

Disturbance over such stresses as accompany *sexual maladjustments*[4] is often difficult to treat. When a woman is married and her husband for some reason or other fails to satisfy her sexually, she may develop a neurosis on this basis and find it difficult to readjust. Occasionally, the development of outside interests will suffice to permit the escape of tension accumulated by the unreleased sex tension;[5] and occasionally, only the advent of increased age, particularly after the menopause,[6] is sufficient to still the emotional tone aroused by unfulfilled sex desires. Too often, however, the patient goes along on a level of superficial adjustment without any real cure. In many instances, the desire for actual sex contact can be satisfied by receiving much loving attention and devotion;[7] for women who are unsatisfied sexually often feel that the reason is their husband's lack of interest in them.

---

[1] *Vide* p. 196 (Case D. G.).   [2] *Vide* p. 27.   [3] *Vide* Ch. VIII.   [4] *Vide* p. 162 *ff.*
[5] *Vide* p. 165 (Case F. S.).   [6] *Vide* p. 164 (Case H. I.).   [7] *Vide* p. 109.

The sex problem is different in unmarried and married persons, because in the former there is not the constant contact with stimulation and the constant expectation of that which "should occur." Under comparable circumstances the unmarried person can divert more of his or her energies into other spheres in a more satisfactory fashion. It must not be understood from this statement, however, that marriage or lack of it is the determining factor; for very severe maladjustments can and do occur in either situation. Society has as yet not found an adequate solution of this basic and fundamental drive; more needs to be known about how and when to curb it, and how and in what manner it may be developed so that its expression is not inconsistent with the highest development of man.

Mrs. I. L., aged forty-five years, criticized her husband and his friends constantly. Her biting criticism developed to the point that no persons ever came to the house, and they were rarely invited elsewhere. Her husband was a sociable person who was the manager of a large farm, was well liked and very efficient. He had worked at this place ever since his marriage, and had developed it to be the admiration of the countryside. He could not tolerate his wife's behavior, had threatened her with divorce, sent her away to her sister in a neighboring city, given her a long vacation in Florida, and done everything else he could think of from extreme kindness to the greatest strictness. He was an eminently sensible man, kindly and tolerant in his way but a perfectionist and intolerant of his own, and often of others lack of thoroughness.

When first married they were happy, but shortly afterward her nagging and criticizing tendency developed. She found fault with everything and everybody. Even in a situation which apparently demanded nothing but praise she managed to put in a damaging word. In the last four years this this attitude had become intolerable.

The difficulty, in essence, lay in the patient's disturbance over sex. She was apparently normal in her desires, but her husband, although physically strong, had little sex desire. Sex relations once a week were sufficient for him even during the first year of marriage; and since then his desire had become progressively less. He denied having extramarital affairs and since she "checked on" his every move, she could confirm this statement. He simply was without great sex desire and preferred to spend his time in work or in large parties. The patient on the other hand desired actual sex contact more often. Not receiving it, she became irritable and the expression of her irritability took the form of criticism. A vicious cycle was thereby produced. The more she criticized, the less affection her husband had for her, and thereby the less sex desire he had for her; the more infrequently they had sex relations the more she criticized. In the last four years (he was fifty-three) he stated that he was so incensed at her irritability that he could not bring himself to have sex relations with her. It is an interesting proof of his lack of sex drive, that he could also go that entire time with no sex contact.

His wife, constantly suspicious was with him constantly (they worked and lived on the farm) and became more and more enraged at him, and by irradiation at all others.

In therapy, not only was it pointed out to the patient that her emotional unrest lay at the bottom of her criticism, but she was also urged to seek outlets in social activities and her husband was asked to cease his "abstinence." In spite of his assurances, he made no attempt to "be with his wife" and although her symptoms were somewhat ameliorated by psychotherapy, she tended to revert to her former self. The patient stated that she felt that he didn't care for her, and that she was just tolerated in the house, but was not loved as a wife should be. She further stated that at this age she had less sex desire than formerly, and that she wished more tenderness and affection than actual physical contact. An effort was made to ameliorate her anger against her husband by explaining to her, that he had not avoided her, at least early in their marriage, because he disliked her, and that though he was strong physically, constitutionally he had little sex desire, She had to learn that this lack of desire was not a personal affront, until later in their life. She was to try to understand him, and not be angry at him. This advice was given in an effort to minimize her resentment, and to have her make an effort to avoid being irritable. The husband, on the other hand, was urged to give his wife as much attention as possible, and to be particularly considerate of her even in the face of irritating statements.

The patient was followed for several months, and the husband reported an improvement but not complete rehabilitation.

Sex difficulties have many ramifications, as illustrated in the following case, and are always difficult to treat.

Mrs. T. K., aged fifty-three years, had a severe skin ailment over her wrists. Nothing that the dermatologists could do changed its appearance or intensity of itching. The diagnosis was "neurodermatosis." She had consulted many physicians in all fields and finally came to the psychiatrist.

She enjoyed being a housewife. She liked to cook, to prepare for parties, and reveled in the fact that she held an excellent position in her local society. Her husband was well thought of, and was a prominent architect. He was short tempered at home, in sharp contrast to his even disposition away from home. Ten years ago, an anonymous telephone call had warned Mrs. K. and on investigation she found that her husband was "having an affair" with his stenographer. She would have left him and sought a divorce, had it not been for pride and the knowledge of the gossip which would be caused thereby. She became nagging; and he, his conscience troubling him, developed a defense mechanism which made him sensitive to the slightest insinuation. Moreover, he ceased to have sex contact with his wife, again on the basis of being so sensitized by the scandal of his affair, that he had become practically impotent in the presence of his wife. It is an interesting note, on the actual workings of the sex impulse, that during his affair, his sex activity with his wife had been greater than usual. The patient, had thus an added emotional difficulty: not only the remembrance of his straying from the path of virtue, with its implication that he cared more for someone else than for her and that she was insufficient to satisfy him, but also the actual deprivation of sex contact which she had always enjoyed in a normal fashion, and which she doubly desired now because its lack implied an insult to her. In spite of her injured pride, she still loved her husband. In this setting, the skin lesion developed and under tension, she scratched at it unmercifully. Any healing that might have occurred was given no chance. Again, an interesting sidelight on the expression of tension was her smoking of innumerable cigarettes, lighting one off the tip of the other. The psychiatric problem was then twofold: one to remove from the patient her constant condemnation of her husband for an act which, however greatly it had made her suffer, should not on the other hand be permitted to ruin her life; second, to deal with the husband and similarly remove from him the intense feeling of guilt and his abnormal sensitivity which was at the basis of his relative impotence. In practice, the difficulty was great for the patient was willing to change, but the husband was adamant. The patient finding her husband's unwillingness to change, quickly reverted to her former attitude. For a while she obtained slight relief from tension by an enforced changed philosophy, but this relief was partially dissipated. Superficially, the two lived together harmoniously; in private there was constant bickering.

Improvement through psychotherapy is less likely to occur in these cases than in other types of neuroses, for there is a definite sexual drive which calls for satisfaction. Various channels may be devised to release the sex tension but they are after all sublimatory, and therefore offer only an attenuated satisfaction. When in addition to suffering from this unfulfilled need, the person has come to surround sex with a halo[1] and to overevaluate its psychic aspects, the problem of therapy becomes exceedingly difficult. Treatment should be directed toward managing the marital situation where possible, toward redirecting the person's energy into other channels,[2] toward removing by psychotherapy all the unnatural and artificially created ideas about sex,[3] and finally by a lessening of the person's general tension,[4] which in itself tends to aggravate any situation. In those instances where the mate refuses to cooperate, therapy is made doubly difficult because, as stated above, the constant sex stimulus is present and implicit in the marriage relationship, and is difficult to forget. Moreover where the sex drive is innately strong, many of these suggestions will fail. In the cases cited, the factor of wounded pride over not being loved as "one should be" also played its detrimental role, and the tension resulting therefrom was one of the bases of the psychoneurotic complaints.

[1] *Vide* p. 107.   [2] *Vide* p. 244.   [3] *Vide* p. 121.   [4] *Vide* p. 126.

Solutions of sex difficulties are easier in "extrovert" (social, jovial, active) types of personalities than in "introvert" (shy, retiring, dreaming) types for two primary reasons: first, that in the former, the person finds it easier to become interested in activities outside himself; and second, that the introvert personality tends to day dream more and surrounds the sexual act with emotions and attitudes which have no counterpart in actuality. Although this statement is generally true there are many exceptions and variations.

Mrs. J. K., aged thirty-four years, complained of typical anxiety attacks. She woke in the middle of the night, was fearful of impending death, found her heart pounding and had a heavy oppression on the chest. During the day she was tense, anxious, and "nervous." The patient had been married for six years, had two children, and a husband who was out of work more often than he was at work. In the past three years, her husband had been particularly desirous of avoiding having more children and so practiced coitus interruptus, as a birth control measure. This technique of withdrawal of the penis just before orgasm resulted in an interrupted orgasm for the patient and she found herself crying and irritable after sex relations. It was then that the symptoms of anxiety appeared. Her husband tried to use contraceptives but disliked them intensely; and when the patient used a pessary, she found herself just as irritated. She began nagging her husband and developed a temper which she had not had before. In the discussion, the patient in one breath denied that she was interested in sex, and in the next, said that it was the basis for her nervous symptoms. This contradictory statement is common in psychoneurotic patients in general and particularly in situations where sex is involved, often because of the conflict within the person between "that which one ought to feel" and "that which one actually feels." In this instance, the patient's difficulties were explained (with her permission) to her husband, and he was asked to try to substitute in some measure for the sex difficulty, by increased personal attention to his wife, personal attention which consisted not necessarily in giving gifts, but in thoughtful remembrances, and commending and appreciative remarks. Secondly, the patient who used to be a salesgirl, was urged to seek a similar position even if the wages she earned went in large part toward the upkeep of a maid to take care of the children, since having a position would get her out of the house, and provide an occupation which would take her mind off herself as well as provide some extra funds. This suggestion was made only because the patient did not particularly care for housework, and on the other hand, did not mind outside work. In the third place, she was urged on returning home, after the children were in bed, to go out with friends, or to have friends come to her house, for this social life would give her husband and her a greater community of interest. This patient's social tendency permitted her to carry out this prescription with pleasure. In the fourth place, she discussed in detail her concepts of sex, the influence of her friends who dilated greatly on the subject; and in the discussion she learned of the normalcy of the desire, and the fact was stressed that sex is not the only source of happiness. She learned that the energy which is usually released in sex activity may be well expended and somewhat released into other non-sexual channels. She was taught that in the interest of an active life, she could minimize and to some extent forget the sex desire, if she had such a goal in mind. Since her husband demanded sex contact, and insisted on with-drawal, there was little that the patient could do other than attempt to avoid becoming aroused. She was to try definitely to avoid the degree of arousal which demanded an orgasm which could not, in the nature of the situation, be satisfied. Lastly, her general tension in regard to the financial difficulties was treated.[1] The patient responded extremely well to these prescriptions and in a short period of time lost her anxiety symptoms.

In the above case, the particular technique of dealing with sex frustrations was applied because the husband as well as the socio-economic system almost precluded any real satisfaction in sex relationships. The physician could not change mates nor the financial background and had to do the next best thing to relieve symptoms. The patient learned to adjust on a different level. As society progresses and the ills of our civilized life are removed, many of these forced solutions will become unnecessary; but in dealing with society as it is, the physician must realize that for the patient who is sick and needs treatment, the substitute method of reaction is better than a continuously frustrating direct reaction. This patient, moreover, was fortunate in having sufficient "extro-vert" tendencies so that such substitution could be carried out. Where such an adjustability is not possible, the patient tends to remain "a chronic neurotic."

The *type of personality* presented by the patient before the neu-rosis is often an indication of the relative ease of recovery from a neurosis. It is difficult to make any personality classification that is generally accepted, and only a few of the traits which make for difficulty will be discussed. It must be borne in mind, however, that these traits may be offset by compensating characteristics; and what follows must be qualified by realization of this fact. Persons who have from adolescence been sensitive, shy, intelli-gent, and energetic, but more inclined than their siblings or com-panions to be moralistic, and who in later life evidence a drive which brings them some measure of success, who have much pride and are looked upon as solid substantial persons, who tend to be kindhearted and generous without being taken advantage of—in short, persons who seem to be almost the ideal which society has

[1] *Vide* Ch. IX.

set up—when such persons develop a neurosis, the symptoms are deep, severe, and resistant to therapy. The difficulty in these persons lies in their chronic and constant state of tension. Although this tension may not affect their poise, yet it does affect their attitudes. These persons are inclined to be somewhat impatient,[1] to be restless, and seem to be constantly striving. It is this striving which brings about both the success in worldly matters, and the inner tension which, when exploded, produces a neurosis or a tension depression. This neurosis tends to be characterized by tension symptoms[2] and frequently manifests itself in spasticity of smooth musculature, in excess activity of the autonomic system, with the result that there often develops paroxysmal tachycardia, essential hypertension, mucous colitis, severe asthmatic attacks, unrelievable headaches,[3] etc. These persons present so little in their personality that to the outsider appears wrong, that it is commonly said of them "They do not appear neurotic."[4] The fact remains, however, that they have a tense, restless, never content attitude which pervades all their activities. So deeply ingrained is this tendency, and so early does it present itself in life, that it is difficult to insist that its etiology is entirely psychogenic and not constitutional. From a social point of view, these persons accomplish much, and many go through life without a breakdown, presumably because they have enough balance through the operation of relaxing tendencies to release their otherwise constant tension.

The form of "breakdown" in these persons varies with many factors. With the tension type of personality just described, the patient may develop a neurosis, the presenting symptom of which is one of the physiologic disturbances listed above. If the illness does not occur until the "involutional" decades (from thirty-five to fifty-five) it may take the form of a depression with all the elements found in the manic-depressive psychosis,[5] except that agitation replaces the silent brooding, and the tendency to suicide is greater. Often too, paranoid ideas may insidiously assert themselves; and although the patient is primarily depressed, the picture may appear to be that of schizophrenia. Recovery is delayed because the patient makes constant effort to perform normal tasks,[6] their attempts, failing because of the depressive state and at the same time creating further tension which aggravates their agitation. In "normal" life, these persons have the energy and "will power"

---

[1] *Vide* p. 212.   [2] *Vide* p. 24.   [3] *Vide* p. 337.
[4] *Vide* p. 139.   [5] *Vide* p. 355.   [6] *Vide* p. 265.

18

to carry out what they think they ought to do; and they cannot understand their failure to do the same thing in their depressed state, and thus their tension increases. Obsessions[1] are common, and dermatoses[2] spring without apparent cause. Therapy in these cases consists in addition to usual psychotherapy, of long drawn out training in how to relax.[3] They need to learn to avoid keeping their emotions "locked up inside" and to express them without going to the extreme of temper outbursts. They need to learn the philosophy and the practice of tolerance and contentment, without becoming smug. One might say, even more significantly, that *not they, but their autonomic nervous systems, must learn these things.* And by consistent and persistent effort, these tenets may be learned and put into practice.

At the other extreme, there is a group of patients subject to the use of symbolic symptoms,[4] who are also resistant to therapy. This group of persons also are often very intelligent, yet they are inclined to permit the slightest caprice or wish to determine their course of action. They have insufficient "will power" to carry out the ordinary, unpleasant duties inherent in the daily routine; yet at the same time they may have a martyr-like ability to withstand pain in crucial heroic moments.[5] Actual sensuousness may be absent, in the sense of sex pleasures, but whatever pleases their vanity, or is flattering to their ego, is not only desired but demanded, in the most petty of fashions. Accordingly, the opinion of others[6] is far more important to them, than what they themselves think is right. Superficially these persons are pleasant and may be very winning. They are often capable of great dramatic appeal; and often tend to be basically insincere. Many of these persons will deny experiencing sex orgasms while at the same time conducting numerous amorous affairs, primarily because in the amorous situation they obtain more flattery and attention than in any other situation, and not because of actual erotic satisfaction. Lying is far more common than facing the facts and telling the truth. The psychoneurotic disturbances to which they are subject may be in any of the groups, but most frequently are symbolic in nature and have a minimum of tension symptoms. Their deep-seated tendency to give in weakly to whatever pressure or desire is present at the moment and their basic insincerity make therapy exceedingly difficult.

---

[1] *Vide* p. 35.   [2] *Vide* p. 312 *ff.*   [3] *Vide* p. 244.
[4] *Vide* p. 28 *ff.*   [5] *Vide* p. 276.   [6] *Vide* p. 215.

The characteristics summed up in these two extreme types of personality patterns represent a conglomeration not often found in one person. Nevertheless, they represent the extremes, between which there is an infinite number of variations and combinations. The more persons tend to group themselves around either pole, the less easily will they yield to therapy. These traits are found in varying proportions in most normal persons; and it is only when they become intensified or combined with other inadequate reaction patterns that the traits assume a pathologic character. In order to evaluate the personality reactions accurately, the physician must always consider the patient as a total organism, and according to the total situation existing at the time.[1] It is impossible to make any hard and fast rule that will apply to all. Psychotherapy must take these variations into consideration, and accordingly *two patients with apparently the same type of complaint may receive opposite forms of therapy.* For example, Mr. X. Y., who had "spastic colitis" was urged to work less and be unconcerned about whether he finished his work as it should be done; whereas Mrs. X. Z. with spastic colitis, was told to find work to do, and to keep at her work until it was done, regardless of how her abdomen pained her. In the first case, the man was a tense, over-conscientious person, who worked too hard and who needed to learn how to relax; in the second case the woman sat about the house all day, her work done by a maid, and with no interests to occupy her.

The *coexistence of physical disease* often retards improvement of the neurosis. For this reason, as well as others, it is important that thorough investigation, by physical and laboratory examination, be made of the patient's complaint. It is important to be able not only to tell the patient about how much actual physical justification there is for the pain, but also to be able to judge how far the patient may be pushed psychically in overcoming it.[2]

In many instances, a person may ordinarily be able to adjust fairly well in spite of many personality problems; yet at the advent of an illness, may become a whining, complaining, childish invalid, who demands constant attention and is petulant when he does not receive it. This regression[3] of the subject to childish levels is a rather common form of neuroticism, but it tends to disappear with the disappearance of the illness. If the illness lasts too long or is serious and exhausting, these neurotic complaints may persist

[1] *Vide* p. 39.   [2] *Vide* p. 118.   [3] *Vide* p. 77.

long after the disappearance of the physical basis for the complaint. In chorea, for example, aimless movements may continue for years in emotional children. On the other hand, if the personality is undergoing severe emotional upheavals, even a slight illness may be sufficient to precipitate a chronic and disturbing neurosis, which far outlasts the organic disturbance. Moreover, physical illness often comes as a welcome relief to many of these patients for they then have some focal point which is "respectable" and acceptable for expressing their tension. These patients tend to cling to a supposed physical ailment with great tenacity, rather than release it and face the personality problems which are always surrounded by fear and unrest.[1] The numerous operations these patients will submit themselves to is a testimony to the intensity of the fears and emotionality surrounding their problems, and to the fact that physical pain is less painful than "personality pain."[2]

Mr. B. B., aged twenty-seven years, worked in the post office in the evenings and went to school during the day time. He wished to become a lawyer but he had much opposition at home from his father who spoke derisively about "snobs" and "college boys," and from his mother who felt that he should contribute to the family's income instead of "wasting his money going to school." His only encouragement came from his younger sister. The instability of his parents communicated itself to him and his feeling of loneliness made for a strong feeling of inadequacy; and he was determined to finish his law course to prove himself capable and adequate. He worked very hard and frequently went with but a few hours sleep.

He developed a cough which he treated himself. One day he coughed up some blood, and on examination was found to have an apical tuberculosis. He was in his last year of law school and the necessity of sanitarium treatment meant that he had to give up all that he had dreamed of. The argument that he could go back to school after his cure did not cheer him, and he was certain that he was doomed. His family were suddenly shocked into the fact that his career was seriously threatened; his father began to talk about his son's becoming a great lawyer and making enough money to "support him in style" but that now "all his sacrifices for his son's education were in vain"; his mother had an awakening of mother love and would pour out all the tales she heard of how dreadful the sickness was, and how many persons died of it, and that even if they seemed to recover, were never really well again. The patient had never before received so much attention from his family as he did at the sanitarium. His lesion gradually cleared up, and after a year he had a clinical and x-ray recovery. He gained 20 pounds and looked very well.

However, on returning to his studies, he complained of great fatigue on the slightest effort. He ate large quantities of food and insisted that his family have special egg and cream dishes; he retired at nine every evening and

[1] *Vide* p. 216.   [2] *Vide* p. 274.

would become almost panic stricken at the slightest suggestion of a cold. He complained of many aches and pains, and walked very gingerly to avoid "a strain on his lungs." He was three years in finishing the last year of law study and another two in preparing for the bar examination. When he was seen by the psychiatrist he was discouraged over his inability to secure a position in a law office, and he was as full of aches and pains, and as careful about his health as the proverbial "old maid."

Behind these neurotic complaints lay the satisfaction that he obtained from the attention his family gave him because he was "sickly" and a sadistic pleasure from his parents' disappointment that he had not become a great lawyer.

Fatigue.—In a similar manner, fatigue, the result of excessive work, or malnutrition, or some persistent physical difficulty such as a neuritis may undermine the person's resistance to the point where a neurosis may occur, and which may prevent the neurosis, once present, from being resolved. In general it may be stated that physical ailments should be removed first or tackled at least simultaneously with psychotherapy. It makes the task much easier.

Brain Damage.—The amount of brain damage present is an important contributing factor in the persistence of behavior disturbances.[1] In this situation, however, that which ordinarily would be classified as a psychoneurosis, is termed a psychosis, because the person's reactions are associated with signs of intellectual impairment. The alleviation of these behavior disturbances in senile or arteriosclerotic brain changes, is generally brought about by changes in the environmental pressure, rather than by psychotherapy. Many patients cannot get along at home because of family difficulties, which usually have their origin in the patient's vague realization that he has become inadequate, and inferior in a situation wherein he once may have been dominant. Since there is actual brain damage, full realization and understanding by the patient is almost impossible, and the irritability which is acute enough at times to give rise to paranoid and violent trends at home, may clear up when the patient is transferred to a quiet and undemanding environment, such as a rest home.[2]

Psychotherapy in patients who have sustained brain injury after trauma, is, as a rule, difficult. Many of these patients were well adjusted and normal prior to injury; following it, they develop dizziness, particularly on stooping; they have headaches that may be one-sided; there is a general irritability and a moodiness, with crying spells; the memory is often impaired; and there

[1] *Vide* p. 343.   [2] *Vide* p. 161.

is physical weakness which prevents their going back to work. X-ray findings in many of these patients do not reveal skull fracture, and neurologic examination is often negative; nevertheless, it is my impression that in most of these instances the "neurosis" that follows is frequently based on definite injury to brain tissue which involves the silent area in the brain and thus does not give rise to focal neurologic signs, but does give rise to personality changes. Autopsy findings for such cases are difficult to get; but those findings which have been obtained are confirmative of this conclusion. There is a general tendency to speak of these patients as having a "compensation neurosis," implying thereby that the patient's illness is the direct result of his desire to obtain compensation. While there are undoubtedly numerous instances of this sort, there are many others in which there is definite brain damage. Such patients may be referred for treatment of their neurosis, yet, it is often impossible to obtain any improvement in their condition by psychotherapy. (Intracerebral air injection as advocated by Penfield, often is of value.) Modification of stress in the environment, and the development of an occupation which the patient can perform without difficulty are of great help. Some of these patients may develop epileptic attacks and others become so difficult to manage that they need to be hospitalized.

Mr. S. M. was a window washer in a large firm. He fell three stories one day and fractured his skull, wrists, and nose, and was unconscious for about an hour. He remained several weeks in the hospital; but when he recovered from his physical bruises and injuries he found that he could not concentrate; forgot easily; was dizzy most of the time, had frontal and right-sided headaches, slept poorly, saw double at times, and at other times "couldn't see for a moment or two"; always felt tired; was unable to read even the daily newspaper; and worst of all, flew easily into rages at the slightest irritation, and on occasion had struck his wife. He was home for six months, and then was given a position as a janitor. He had a cash settlement for his injury and was content therewith. Since that time, however, the symptoms enumerated above had continued despite the fact that all physical examinations were negative. He was diagnosed as a neurotic because there was no physical indication of his disabilities, and because of his emotional outbursts.

Study of his background revealed the ordinary difficulties and the usual mother-in-law problems, but these same problems had existed before the accident, and he not only was unaffected by them but was a happy and hard working person. Psychotherapy was useful only in that it made the patient less intolerant of his inability to work, but it essentially did not change his symptoms. The so-called neurotic symptoms were in all probability based on actual damage to his brain tissue, the damage probably being multiple petechial hemorrhages in the silent areas. In this case there was definite evidence of skull fracture, but in many instances there may not be any skull fracture, and the damage to the brain and personality may be as great or greater.[1]

Manic-depressive Depression.—One of the most difficult obstacles to overcome in a psychoneurotic patient is the coexistence of a manic-depressive depression.[2] Far more persons are subject to mood swings[3] than is generally recognized, and many of the psychoneurotic situations have their basis in the brooding and self-accusations which accompany the downward phase of such a swing. In its purest form the depression is characterized by "blueness," inactivity, and retardation of thought processes. In the setting of psychoneurotic phenomena, the patient may express the depression by agitation instead of simple melancholia; he may become restless, though unable to work, instead of purely inactive; and his thoughts may center upon one or two self-condemnatory ideas instead of his being simply unable to concentrate and remember. In other words, the depression is influenced by the patient's personality traits and by the patient's attitude toward his problems.

If then, one is able to remove most of the psychologic difficulties in the sense that they are psychoneurotic in character, there still is left the basic depressive tendency. This tendency is, as we shall see later, physiologic in nature, although its effects express themselves primarily by means of the personality response; *i. e.,* in a general sluggishness of the entire person. Removal of the neurosis is possible, but what usually happens in the psychotherapy of these patients is that the continued existence of the depressive tendency, serves to retain the psychoneurotic reaction patterns. In such situations, either time or metrazol is necessary to clear up the depression in addition to the psychotherapy of the personality problem. Likewise many patients who are suffering from a true manic-depressive reaction, may continue to be problems long after their depression is cleared up, primarily because of the continued existence of the psychoneurosis. In these instances, the completion of the cure is brought about by psychotherapy.

Mrs. C. N., aged thirty-four years, was weak, irritable, nauseated, and constipated. She was more or less a chronic invalid, and complained bitterly about her physical and emotional instability. She was very difficult to get

---

[1] *Vide* p. 160 (Case L. M.).   [2] *Vide* p. 371.   [3] *Vide* p. 283 *ff.*

along with, and her children reflected her own insecurity in their behavior problems. When first seen, she had the usual hypochondriacal outlook. She gave a history of being dominated by her parents, who would not let her go about alone until she was nineteen, and even then so arranged the situation, that she married the first man with whom she had a "date." She entered marriage in a period of financial stress, and the marriage was not a happy one. Later she listened enviously when her girl friends would speak of the men they went with and the good times they had. She felt inadequate and inferior and longed to have had the experience of others. She had never been free; for even after her marriage, her parents still dominated her, coming to her home, criticizing her husband, and in general, interfering in the domestic life. In this setting her hypochondriacal symptoms developed. She felt too weak to get out of bed, she was nauseated so that she could not eat, she had constant headaches, her children irritated her easily, she was depressed, she slept poorly, etc.

Psychotherapy was instituted, and the patient soon lost her nausea, became stronger, was able to do some house work, learned not to be upset by her parents, developed emotional independence of them and persuaded them to see her only once a week, and lost most of her headaches. As these symptoms disappeared, there was uncovered a definite picture of a manic-depressive depression. The patient felt blue, could not concentrate, was more depressed in the morning than in the afternoon (a depressive phenomenon in contrast to the neurotic tiredness and melancholia which is greater as the day wears on), was constipated, slept poorly, and felt no interest in activities which she had formerly enjoyed. These later symptoms were not those of the neurosis but of a depression and had been present during the entire illness but had been modified by her psychogenic difficulties. These symptoms were the result of an underlying physiologic depression, which came clearly to light on the removal of the defective reaction patterns. For this depression, metrazol shock therapy was instituted, and after eight treatments, the patient recovered completely. If the metrazol therapy had been given before the psychotherapy, the reverse situation would have occurred: the depression which was physiological in nature would have cleared up, but it would have been difficult to determine when to cease the metrazol therapy because the neurotic symptoms would have continued and confused the picture.

In all these patients, one must remember that in addition to physical ailments there may be personality difficulties, and both need to be treated. The occurrence of manic-depressive depressions in their minor form often goes unrecognized. When they do occur, they may aggravate any existing difficulty and retard or prevent what would otherwise be a cure. It is interesting to observe how clearly a manic-depressive symptom complex may come to the fore after the psychoneurotic symptoms are removed. Moreover in such a combination of conditions, the physiologic depression is undoubtedly of etiologic importance in precipitating the neurotic symptoms, and in the prognosis of their disappearance.

Duration of Neurosis.—The duration of the neurosis prior to treatment is also of prognostic significance. Usually (again with many exceptions) the shorter the duration of the neurosis, the easier it is to cure it; and the reverse is true with neurotic illnesses of long duration. One reason for this fact is the tendency toward habit formation, for the symptom once being established tends to perpetuate itself.[1] This tendency is an important element in such conditions as hysterical paralysis, in spastic colitis, in stammering, in paroxysmal tachycardia, and particularly in any ailment involving the use of smooth or striated muscle. Muscle tissue is very susceptible to conditioning, and to repetition of similar actions. However, even *emotional responses may take on the characteristic of being habitual*, and so require the breaking down of a habit in addition to the removal of the basic emotional strain.

Even this statement has many exceptions. For example, some patients may develop a neurosis on the basis of intense environmental stress (this in itself has a better prognosis than do the cases with little environmental stress[2]) and as time passes, the stress may disappear, so that by the time the patient comes for treatment, it may be easier to remove the neurosis than it would have been if the patient had come while the stress was still quite strong. Again, some neuroses may be based on internal drives resulting, for example, in sex dissatisfaction, or ambitional unrest; and these too, may tend to diminish during the later decades of life.[3] There are variations even to these variations, for in some persons the sex drive may even increase after menopause.[4] Again, the passage of time may be helpful, where there has been a great hurt, or where the pride has been wounded severely, and the healing element of time is important.

Occasionally neurotic symptoms are of value to a patient. In certain situations a person may, by having symptoms, be able to work on the sympathies of others and obtain concessions and attentions which he would otherwise never achieve. The case of the man with the paralyzed legs[5] is in point. Often such symptoms are symbolic in nature. As a rule, the symptoms are not the result of conscious malingering, but occur either in the setting of great stress, or against the background of an immature personality. Not infrequently do they occur in aged persons after the death of a mate,[6] or with the beginning of senile brain changes. Mothers may

---

[1] *Vide* p. 42. [2] *Vide* p. 266. [3] *Vide* p. 99.
[4] *Vide* p. 164 (Case H. I.) [5] *Vide* p. 30 (Case D. W.). [6] *Vide* p. 256 (Case H. H.).

use this technique to blame their children for the "awful way in which they treat their parents who 'sacrificed their all' to give them a happy life"; and on occasion adolescents, or unmarried women past thirty-five will make the most of their symptoms in order to dominate their household.[1] Such symptoms and such situations are so related that psychotherapy must usually be preceded by changing the environmental stress in order to obtain satisfactory results. Strictness in these instances fails more often than it is successful for these patients if treated with severity tend to adopt a martyr-like attitude, and will suffer much pain and torment rather than admit they are wrong. Adequate therapy should remove the cause for the patient's actions as well as very gently persuade the patient to deal frankly and directly with his difficulties.

THE HOMEOSTATIC CURVE OF IMPROVEMENT

When a patient begins to recover from his psychoneurotic illness, the improvement rarely follows a steady path in which every day his condition is better than it was the day before. Improvement, diagrammatically speaking, is not a perpendicular rising from the nadir of illness, but an irregularly curved line moving steadily though not smoothly away from the depths of illness and up toward the base line of normal health. Progress is made from the "lows" of the illness very much as the terrain proceeds from the plains through rising foothills with intervening valleys, and comes finally to the high point of the mountains.

It is important alike for physician and patient to recognize that this type of recovery is to be expected, for then the inevitable "set backs"[2] can be objectively evaluated and their attendant discouragement discounted. Frequently, a patient responding well, benefiting greatly from the first psychotherapeutic session is sure that he is on the high road to immediate recovery, only to return two or three visits later, depressed and discouraged because he has not maintained his improvement, and anxious to try some new remedy. If by positive clinical and laboratory findings the physician has ascertained the absence of physical disease, and if he has uncovered precipitating emotional factors, then recognizing the patient's temporary remission as being an implicit part of the "curve of improvement" he will not be tempted to change his

---

[1] *Vide* p. 33 (Case L.).   [2] *Vide* p. 132.

psychotherapeutic procedure; and his confidence will, in turn, communicate itself to the patient. Here as elsewhere, "to be fore-warned is to be forearmed"; and the patient having been told what to expect, will be less discouraged by the temporary return or aggravation of his symptoms than he otherwise would be. These remissions in the curve of improvement are part of a natural tendency toward swings in all psychobiologic activity.

NORMAL SWINGS

When one uses the word *normal*,[1] he must bear in mind the fact that it is a relative and not an absolute term, a descriptive and not a scientifically accurate expression. The range of normalcy is great, and within its confines is to be found an infinite variety of types and combinations of types. If one were to draw a straight horizontal line to represent "normal" psychobiologic activity, and then attempt to measure by it the activity of any given "normal" person, two interesting facts would at once become apparent: (1) the two lines would be only roughly parallel; (2) the line for the individual case would not be straight but wavy. In other words, no person exactly corresponds with an arbitrarily established norm; nor does his own base line of activity and mood proceed in a straight line, at a constant level.

In all persons there are definite fluctuations in at least three spheres: (1) mood, (2) activity, and (3) flow of speech. These three personality characteristics appear in various proportions and combinations in each person but commonly increase or de-crease as a unit. Thus when a person is "happy," he also as a rule, is more active and speaks more freely; and conversely, when a per-son becomes comparatively inactive (compared with his usual self) he also tends to be less gay and more silent. Though it may be generally stated that these three elements (mood, activity, speech) move in the same direction at the same time, the physician in evaluating any set of personality changes must be careful to re-member the individual differences which always exist. For exam-ple, in some persons the speech output is habitually great as com-pared to their activity, so that when the activity decreases and there is corresponding decrease in the flow of speech, they may still be loquacious as compared with others, though taciturn as com-pared with their former state.

[1] *Vide* p. 259 *ff.*

For most persons there is a definite and more or less consistently characteristic baseline of mood, speech, and activity. This baseline may be set higher; *i. e.*, higher than the arbitrarily established norm, in some than in others; and among normal persons there are some who are generally energetic, and some who are usually passive. The difference in energy output is markedly influenced by many factors: the state of physical well being, the requirements of work and social activity, meteorologic changes, psychologic factors, internal diurnal fluctuations, etc. Nevertheless, each person tends to have a definite and characteristic minimum expenditure of "energy,"[1] and the daily averages are the same over a period of years.

F<small>IG</small>. 1.—Every person has varying levels of at least three functions: first, mood; second, frequency of ideas and, third, activity, all roughly parallel and all fluctuating within a given range peculiar to the person.

Fluctuations occur in this baseline as the result of internal homeostatic physiologic mechanisms as well as of external forces (see Fig. 1). These fluctuations vary with the person, apparently with some correlation between these fluctuations and the type of constitution. The person with the pyknic habitus is inclined to have long waves of elevations or of depressions in activity, each "wave" lasting for many weeks or months; the asthenic person tends to have a relatively consistent baseline with sudden outbursts of energy and activity during which he may accomplish much but which are of short duration. The pyknic[2] person tends to be consistent and persistent; the asthenic, sporadic, with brilliant but brief flashes. Between these two extremes are countless variations, and the "normal" person does not lend himself easily to classification because of the inseparable and complex admixtures of these types.

"Ups and downs" in mood are every-day experiences; and their causes are legion. There are diurnal fluctuations in moods just as there are similar variations in body temperatures, many persons consistently feeling better in the morning than in the evening, or vice versa. Acutely disturbing or exceedingly pleasing events may sharply elevate or depress the baseline of mood; and obviously

[1] *Vide* p. 240.   [2] *Vide* pp. 355; 379.

psychologic factors are pervasive in their influence. Yet even where there is a constant psychologic stress or when there is external stress of a compelling nature, fluctuations which are primarily physiologic in nature occur in such a way as to provide periods of relatively less depression. To speak more succinctly, one may say that no person whether he be "normal," "manic," or "depressive" pursues the even tenor of his way, variations (swings, curves) apparently being an inherent physiologic basis in personality development. Once more attention is called to the fact that the differences between the psychobiologic attitudes of normal (average) persons and psychotic or psychoneurotic patients are not differences in kind but of degree.

PATHOLOGIC SWINGS

The fluctuations mentioned above occur within a relatively small range in the average person. Rarely do normal persons swing so "high" that they become euphoric and ecstatic; nor on the other hand, seldom do they swing so "low" as to develop persistent suicidal thoughts. These extreme swings often do occur, however, in psychopathic personalities[1] and in manic-depressive psychoses.[2] Between the pole of average variations in mood and the pole of pathologic swings fall the many persons who in common parlance are said to be "subject to moods." Primarily, such swings, varying in height and duration, are *physiologically* determined even though psychologically precipitated and so are resistant to modification, though the average person by properly directed efforts may succeed in controlling their manifestations.

It is important to emphasize the relative independence of psychologic factors and "swings." When a person is "high" as the result of a spontaneous swing in his baseline, stresses and irritating news have comparatively little power to depress him; he is "able to take everything in his stride"; and is relatively unimpressed and unaffected by any other than the most acutely disturbing events. Conversely, when a person is "low," he will become melancholic over some minor difficulty which ordinarily he would disregard; and even unusually good fortune will be so discounted that only momentarily does it raise the level of depression.

The significant implication of the foregoing discussion is that the total response of a person depends not only on the strength of the

---

[1] *Vide* p. 393 *ff.*   [2] *Vide* p. 355 *ff.*

depressing (or stimulating) factor but also upon the position with reference to his baseline. In figure 2, for example, a depressing factor at A will be much more keenly felt than the same factor at B. In manic-depressive states such relationships are obvious; in the normal and psychoneurotic states these reactions, though less obvious, are just as true.

FIG. 2.—In unstable persons, these levels fluctuate widely, from exaltation to depression, from scintillating wit to mental dulness, from great activity to sluggishness. These fluctuations vary in intensity, as a rule, with *physiologic* instability though psychologic factors play important roles. Psychologic irritations may be minimized or intensified depending on the time they occur. Thus if irritating circumstances were to occur at *A*, they might be regarded lightly; whereas if they occurred at *B* when the person was already depressed they might drive the person to suicide.

Disease processes, emotional or physical, can so disturb the organism that these swings in mood are more apparent and more marked than at a time when the person is in an excellent state of health, and his homeostatic mechanism[1] is so efficient that fluctuations are checked quickly enough to keep the subject on a relatively even course. Disease adds an extra load to the organism;[2] and should there exist a basic instability,[3] the extra stress of the illness may be sufficient to uncover swings which ordinarily would be well compensated and therefore obscured.

THE CURVE OF IMPROVEMENT

A graph representing the improvement which takes place after psychotherapy has been instituted is like the graphs of "normal" persons in that the progress is not straight but made up of a series of curves. The early stages of treatment are often characterized by periods of amelioration of symptoms followed by periods of exacerbation. A graph of improvement, however, will be different from a graph of pathologic swings in two important respects: (1) the line will not be horizontal, but inclined away from the level of illness and toward that of normal health, and (2) as it approaches the upper level the line will tend to straighten out; *i. e.*, the "ups

---

[1] *Vide* p. 215.   [2] *Vide* p. 275.   [3] *Vide* p. 339.

and downs" will more closely approximate in appearance those of normal health. Diagrammatically, this progress—this curve of improvement—may be represented as in figure 3.

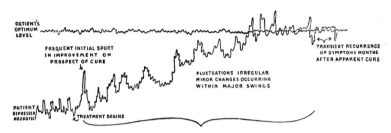

FIG. 3.—Recovery time varies from a few weeks to years according to the patient and his illness.

The specific neurotic symptoms will tend to fluctuate in their intensity just as the mood fluctuates. One can more easily understand this variation if he remembers that the specific neurotic complaint is only a focal expression of a general emotional difficulty.[1] Moreover, during psychotherapy itself, there will be a shifting of the patient's emphasis to the etiologic factor; and the general improvement will therefore be accompanied by a lessening of the focal complaint.

As the therapy continues and the patient continues to improve, exacerbations and remissions of symptoms continue also. When a patient has a remission in his upward curve of improvement, he almost invariably will contrast his present mood with that which has immediately preceded and as a consequence may "feel" just as depressed as he did early in the treatment. However, in actuality, at his new level, he has far fewer neurotic symptoms and is far better able to carry out his desires than he was formerly. In other words, the emotional evaluation of his status is essentially dependent upon the immediately preceding "feeling"; but an intellectual understanding[2] of his changes as presented and interpreted by the physician may ameliorate his mood, and enable him to appreciate his continued progress. Although a down swing is almost always accompanied by general hopelessness, tiredness, and irritability, symptoms which seem to have no end, and a future which appears black, if the patient forces himself to observe these symptoms objectively and for proof gazes at the exacerbations

[1] *Vide* p. 300 (Case N. T.).   [2] *Vide* p. 216.

and remissions which he has already passed through, he can then not only "know" but also in part "feel" that he is improving. The duration of these swings varies greatly from patient to patient, but in the improving psychoneurotic patient the swing frequently lasts from several days to several weeks. There is a tendency, however, for the depressive swings to be of longer duration early in the illness, with the remission of symptoms at first lasting only a few hours, then increasing to a day, and finally lasting longer than does the depressive phase. Even when the patient seems to have recovered, he may months later have mild recurrent attacks. Some manic-depressive patients have had attacks lasting several days each, occurring first a month after the patient was apparently well; then two months later; then six months; and so on until the time when they ceased altogether.

The steepness of the recovery curve varies with each patient. Commonly, if the illness began suddenly, the time required for recovery is relatively short;[1] whereas if the illness had a prodromal period of many months, the recovery curve is also long delayed.[2] The recovery rate also is dependent upon many factors: environmental hindrances,[3] the degree of rapport[4] between patient and physician, the amount of cooperation from the patient,[5] and the type of neurosis, and all the other factors mentioned under prognosis.

Within these fluctuations from day to day and week to week, there exist almost hourly fluctuations. Thus when patients are asked to record their emotional status for each day, using as a measure a numerical scale (where 1 is marked depression, 3 is "fair," and 5, a feeling of well being, they will record several values, indicating marked fluctuations within the day. One patient, for example, remarked that she "felt differently every fifteen minutes."

If the therapy is discontinued before a cure is established, and if the patient is not able to continue the improvement himself, the fluctuations tend to continue at a slightly lower level than they were at the end of the treatment. In some instances, the curve having reached an almost "normal" level, reverses itself, and pursues a downward course until the patient is again at his "illness" level. If he maintains the highest point that he reaches during therapy and does not advance, he learns to adjust on an inferior level so far as his neurosis is concerned.

---

[1] *Vide* p. 135 (Case F. B.).   [2] *Vide* p. 135 (Case B. M.).   [3] *Vide* p. 321 (Case C. D.).
[4] *Vide* p. 129.   [5] *Vide* p. 224.

CHAPTER XIV

ILLUSTRATIVE PSYCHONEUROTIC SYMPTOMS AND THEIR TREATMENT

THE symptoms listed below are for the most part presumed to be without "organic pathology." This presumption implies that no symptom is diagnosed as psychoneurotic until a thorough clinical and laboratory examination is made. This point cannot be stressed too strongly, for many persons who are "emotional" and who have much psychopathology, may still have organic disease. The physician will be more certain of his therapy, and the patient will be more amenable to psychotherapy if both have the knowledge that all possible examinations were made to rule out physical defect.[1]

Symptoms do not, as a rule, have a *simple* cause and any one of those discussed in this chapter may result from organogenic as well as psychogenic forces. In spastic constipation, for example, it is not sufficient to presuppose merely an emotional etiology; although in many cases emotional stress is the primary factor in development. A symptom is only the outward recognizable sign of the existence of something else (symptom; fr. G. chance, to happen). Only by thorough analysis can the proper basis of the symptom be established.

It is not always clear, why, in the psychoneuroses, two persons with apparently identical emotional stresses; *e. g.*, financial difficulty, should have symptoms in different parts of the body. Of several patients with apparently identical stress, one may have headaches;[2] another, cardiac pains;[3] a third, spastic colitis;[4] a fourth, neurodermatoses,[5] etc. Several possible explanations arise: (1) there may be *constitutional differences,* such as the family in whom peptic ulcer developed through several generations although the ulcer symptoms often were precipitated by emotional stress;[6] (2) the organ involved may have been subject to *some initial physical disturbance* upon which the emotional distress becomes centered and fixed, as for example the "psychogenic vomiting" which may come to be the habitual response to the eating of any food several years following the eating of a particular nauseating food; (3) *the*

---

[1] *Vide* p. 118.
[2] *Vide* p. 165 (Case F. S.).
[3] *Vide* p. 293 (Case H. F.).
[4] *Vide* p. 307 (Case S. B.)
[5] *Vide* p. 316 (Case S. L.).
[6] *Vide p.* 302 (Case S. T.).

physical dysfunction may be symbolic of the patient's emotional prob-lem, as was the blushing of the woman whose husband was unfaith-ful;[1] or the throat spasm in the interne who feared insanity (rabies in this case) over his "unsolvable" problems;[2] (4) the stresses may be, and usually are, only "apparently" but not actually identical.

It is commonly found that the patient misleads the physician by focusing on one complaint;[3] whereas a careful history reveals that although the one complaint may be the dominant one, there are many other complaints. Patients referred for pseudo angina pectoris, for aphonia, for mucous colitis, are found to have symp-toms in other parts of the body. The diagnosis of neurosis is aided by the ubiquity of the patient's emotional response.

Psychoneurotic symptoms are not "imagined." The pain which such a patient experiences is as real to the patient and as difficult to bear as "organic" pain. In addition, the pain has the added qualities of fear and anxiety which make it still worse.

Such fear and anxiety, stemming as they do from the same source as the symptom itself; *i. e.,* basic emotional maladjustment, are even more intense than are the fear and anxiety concerning an organic difficulty.

Moreover, it is a mistake to presume that there is no change in the tissue complained of. Generally there are alterations in the tone of the autonomic nervous system[4] which produce "real" dis-turbances; and these are perceived by the patient as being very intense. There may be tachycardia, extrasystoles, definite and painful spasms of the intestine, increased secretion of hydrochloric acid, etc. These physiologic reactions may be psychogenic in origin, but they are none the less real; and may be the basis of further anxiety. In summary one may say: The *determining mechanism* of so-called functional disorders lies in the constitutional predisposition, in the shaping influences of the environment, and in the precipitating factors of stress. The *mediating mechanism* is tension, with the resulting increased activity of the vegetative nervous and endocrine systems, its associated tenseness of smooth and striated muscle, and the psychologic accompaniment of appre-hension and unrest. Such tension is practically always general, although its most annoying manifestation and the chief complaint may be focal. The *determination of the site* of the main manifesta-tion of this general tension may be by psychologic stimuli, physical

---

[1] *Vide* p. 64 (Case X. F.). [2] *Vide* p. 52 (Case N. D.).
[3] *Vide* p. 320 (Case W. H.). [4] *Vide* p. 81 (footnote).

predisposition, or by more fundamental inheritable or constitutional predispositions. It is difficult to separate the etiologic factors. In the case of the interne[1] the spasm of the throat was "caused" by a fear of rabies. Mr. G. H.[2] developed tics of grunting after an irritated sore throat. Mrs. X. F.[3] blushed constantly after initially being concerned over an obscenity and so on. In these instances all the forces necessary to produce tension were present, and the patients seized upon any unrelated physical reaction or physical disturbance of the moment and used it as the focal point of release from then on. This general truth is the primary reason for paying relatively little attention in most cases to the symptom although it appears to be the most disturbing element; this is the reason why dealing with emotional tension and relieving pent-up energies is automatically followed by disappearance of the symptom. Accordingly, the physician though he may at times deem it advisable to have recourse to palliative therapy,[4] will know that permanent cure will come about only if the cause of the symptom is removed. He will realize that the patient is unconsciously telling a falsehood when he insists that if only his symptom were removed, his worry would disappear. The principle of treatment must therefore be a thorough analysis of the socio-psychobiologic factors which have brought about the symptoms,[5] followed by a socio-psychobiologic resynthesis[6] of the personality so that unhygienic traits are removed and mental hygiene attitudes substituted.

The number of psychoneurotic symptoms is legion.[7] Those discussed below are only a few which illustrate some of the mechanisms.

---

[1] *Vide* p. 52 (Case N. A.).   [2] *Vide* p. 297.   [3] *Vide* p. 64 Case X. F.).
[4] *Vide* p. 233.   [5] *Vide* p. 118.   [6] *Vide* p. 121.

[7] In an effort to emphasize the interrelationship between the psychiatric approach and the medical approach, one may divide all medical ailments into three groups: (1) those illnesses which result primarily from external physical sources such as the toxic-infectious traumatic diseases, and which are appropriately treated primarily by physico-chemical agents; (2) those diseases which result primarily from internal sources such as the degenerative diseases of arteriosclerosis, senile dementia, some forms of nephritis, and from neoplastic changes; and (3) psychosomatic diseases which result primarily from the pressure of emotional factors upon constitutional predisposition, and which are best treated by the combination of physical and psycho-therapy. The psychosomatic diseases include such conditions as essential hypertension, paroxysmal tachycardia, hyperthyroidism, certain forms of arthritis, peptic ulcer, spastic colitis, many forms of headaches, diabetes, and so forth. In many of these conditions, the most important factor may be the constitutional predisposition (*vide* the formula S x E x Inh. C., Chap. IX, page 182), and in many others the precipitating forces may be in the nature of diet, of climate, of associated infection, etc.

CARDIOVASCULAR SYSTEM[1]

Pain Over the Heart.—This is a frequent complaint. It is usually associated with palpitation, dermographia, moist palms, and a fear of heart failure or impending death. The pain tends to be constant and aching in nature. It is present in rest as well as in activity; but may disappear when the person's attention is distracted. Auscultation, and even electrocardiographic studies reveal no pathology. The cardiac rate varies, but is usually rapid. Extrasystoles may occur.

Mr. A. S., aged forty-two years, was referred because of an intractable pain over the heart from which he had suffered for two years. Studies in the clinic gave negative results. There was some local tenderness, but no signs of disease could be found. The patient was worried about his complaint, and feared it was heart trouble which would cause his death. The skin over the tender area had even been infiltrated with novocain, but no relief was obtained. The patient was a house painter of average intelligence. He worked during the day and at home in the evening, helped his wife with household tasks, and after reading the paper went to bed. He had no "bad habits," was very conscientious, serious minded, and devoted to his family, made up of his wife and two children. Some five years ago, his two year old daughter had a broken leg which was followed by osteomyelitis. Treatment for this bone disease had drained his resources. Two years ago, his five year old son had had scarlet fever which "left bad kidneys," and the patient worried greatly because he had heard some neighbor remark that bad kidneys cause high blood pressure and strokes. Shortly after his son's illness, his wife became emotional and disturbed and the patient felt the burden of the entire family on his shoulders. He felt helpless and hopeless. One morning his wife complained of pain in her chest, and the patient immediately felt pain (identification)[2] over his chest. The fear then entered that he might have heart trouble. The pain persisted. He became so weighed down by his troubles that he had thought of suicide and death; his thoughts were centered on physical ailments; and he literally "took things too much to heart."

In essence then, this man's cardiac pain was the result of tension and concern over his problems. To cure the pain, he had to learn to be less tense and to avoid thinking of his difficulties except in those aspects wherein he could actually and practically help. He was told that his heart was normal (he had been told that repeatedly before without avail), but it was further explained[3] that his pain could come from some muscle tension in his chest. This tension was the result of his general emotional tension. He was overly concerned with his problems and needed to subordinate them. To accomplish this purpose he was first to make the conscious attempt

---

[1] *Vide* p. 84 *ff.*   [2] *Vide* p. 73.   [3] *Vide* pp. 178; 304.

to put his worries out of his thoughts as soon as they entered, and secondly he was to find outlets of a social and recreational nature. Detailed methods for doing these two things were discussed with him. He was then taught, by the methods previously described, how to relax.[1] In addition, barbital 2½ grains three times a day was given and its tension releasing action explained to him. After two discussions the pain disappeared and remained away for four weeks, after which time it recurred only to disappear with further discussions about his emotional problems pointing out wherein he was tense and how he could relieve the tension.

Palpitation.—Palpitation is one of the most common of cardiac symptoms. It is usually accompanied by tachycardia, though often the heart rate is normal, the pathology lying in an abnormal *awareness* of the heart action. Physical functions do not as a rule enter consciousness, and we are not aware of our teeth, or our intestines, or any other parts of our body unless they are diseased or painful, or unless our awareness of them increases. *Extrasystoles* or "heart jumps" are a frequent complaint; although pathology is rarely found. These symptoms are usually the result of tension.

Mr. H. F., aged forty-nine years, complained of palpitation and marked skipping of beats. He was very worried about his condition and thought of all sorts of dire possibilities. Examination disclosed definite extrasystoles. However, auscultation revealed no other pathology; response to exercise was normal; and the electrocardiograph showed no pathology. Mr. H. F. was a successful business man occupying a position of importance in a national concern. He had had only high school training but was ambitious and read widely. He was very conscientious and took his business problems home with him. His superior in the office had grudgingly advanced him but disliked the patient and frequently spoke in his presence about the need for better trained college men. The patient felt that insinuations were directed against him and brooded constantly over the possibility of losing his position. Further in the background and revealed only accidentally through conversation with his wife, was the fear that he might become insane as his mother had. His mother had died in an institution.

Essentially then this man's symptoms were based on: (1) his insecurity in his position; (2) his general tendency to worry and concern even over business details; and (3) a lifelong fear of insanity. Treatment was directed towards having him adopt a philosophic attitude towards his position, teaching him how to avoid worry[2] and reassuring him on the influence of heredity and

[1] *Vide* p. 244.　　　　　　　　[2] *Vide* p. 193 *ff.*

the influence of environment and disease in the production of insanity. In addition he was given instruction on how to learn to relax by means of recreation and socialization.[1] He responded quickly to therapy.

Paroxysmal Tachycardia.—Paroxysmal tachycardia[2] is poorly understood as to pathology. When it does occur it usually is in a setting of tension. It is generally found in "vagotonic" persons who are sensitive, proud, and capable of working hard. These persons tend to "worry inwardly"; *i. e.*, though they appear to shake off any trouble and worry, in reality they "tremble inside" and react to the worry by increased response of the vegetative system. These persons are difficult to treat for they are overtrained and have overdeveloped their conscious control over the expression of emotions without removing the tension associated with those emotions in contradistinction to the more emotional hypochondriac in whom the emotional tension overflows into conscious feeling, thinking, and acting. The attacks frequently occur hours or even days after an emotional incident.

Miss N. L. was hanging curtains when her heart began to pound rapidly and she felt faint. The physician when called could not count the pulse because of its rapidity. She continued to have attacks which lasted from one-half hour to one-half day. They seemed to come on without any provocation, while she was sitting quietly or while she was working. Examination showed no pathology.

On closer questioning, this patient revealed that the night before the first attack she had gone to a dance, and her escort had neglected her all evening in favor of another young woman. She pretended to pay no attention and seemingly was unconcerned about the matter. However, she lay awake a long time thinking of it and was depressed on arising. The attack came on shortly after lunch. (Many of these *cardiac symptoms seem to occur after a large meal*, possibly because of the extra load a dilated stomach makes on the heart, and because of reflex action.) This simple disappointment occurred in the setting of a rather intense person. She was twenty-five and wished to be married; such a disappointment was therefore all the greater. She was closely bound to her mother and did not have many friends. She was an active person who liked to work and could not bear idleness, and she had been two years without employment. She had had a bleeding peptic ulcer, and a mild form of Raynaud's disease. Though she was somewhat benefited by reassurance and suggestions aimed at socialization, recreation and diminishing of general tension, her tachycardia continued to occur spasmodically until she procured a position and was married. She had no further attacks in the five years during which her case was followed, an important therapeutic factor probably being her marriage.

[1] *Vide* p. 249.   [2] *Vide* p. 85.

Essential Hypertension.[1]—The response of blood pressure to emotional states is well known. When a patient enters the office for the first time, the blood pressure is often found to be from 10 to 50 points higher than it is after a half hour of reassuring conversation. These patients are apprehensive, and fearful of the examination and what it may reveal. Such rises in pressure are usually temporary. In some patients, however, there is a chronic state of anxiety and fearfulness, associated with a chronic state of elevated blood pressure. The condition called essential hypertension tends to occur in tense persons, in whom there is less of a definite precipitating emotional difficulty, and more of a subtle, pride wounding, or insecurity producing situation. In these patients the overly tense attitude which for years they have had toward their personal problems is the basic factor. This fact is important to remember, for the casual history often fails to reveal any emotional difficulty. The treatment for these patients, in addition to pertinent medical procedures, is prolonged psychotherapy in the form of retraining their attitudes toward their personal problems.

Mr. K. N., aged fifty-three years, complained of dizziness, of headache and of "high blood pressure." Examination revealed no pertinent pathology in the cardiovascular system or elsewhere except for a blood pressure reading of 176/104. He stated that he was without any special irritations, "except of course those occurring in business," which was running smoothly. Wife and children were congenial and he could list no emotional difficulties. His son, however, gave some significant information. The patient was in the laundry business with several partners. Financially he was successful; but there was intense rivalry among the various partners as to efficiency, and there was constant fault finding. It had been to their financial advantage to remain together; but "there was constant grief and aggravation." The patient was a conscientious person who "carried his business troubles to bed," and in the last few years he had become exceedingly irritable and had violent temper outbursts. Moreover, he had no outlets and no recreation other than his work. On Sundays and holidays he was restless, not knowing how to relax or what to do. His symptoms were thus the result of his way of living, and of his continuous irritation.

The therapy in this case was relatively simple. Since his financial status was secure, he was persuaded to sell his share of the business and seek methods of relaxation. He was not allowed to be idle, however; for *sudden idleness in a person who has been active all his life is often followed by such consequences as depression, malaise, restlessness, and unhappiness.* He was persuaded to enter his son's

[1] *Vide* p. 86.

organization on a part time basis, spending his leisure time in gardening, bowling, and golf. Three months later, his blood pressure was down to 140/90, and his entire outlook on life had so changed that he stated, "For the first time in my life, I'm really enjoying myself."

Most patients with such emotional hypertension do not yield so readily to therapy. In patients who have had high blood pressures for long periods of time, some permanent change seems to have occurred which prevents much lowering. Moreover, the arteriole spasm which presumably is at the basis of the emotional hypertension, has taken much time to develop, and is in itself a difficult process to reverse. Psychotherapy in such patients accomplishes most by removing further emotional trauma, and by making it possible for the patient to adjust himself to his physical condition with a minimum of difficulty.

The author has treated with metrazol shock therapy several patients who were suffering from a depression of the manic-depressive variety,[1] and who were observed to have hypertension before the treatment began. Six or 7 treatments resulted in the blood pressure's dropping to within normal limits and a subjective feeling of relaxation. The cardiovascular system was normal at the end of the treatment. It is possible that as these patients lose their tension by means of this chemotherapy, the vascular tension also disappears.

Respiratory Tract—Chest.[2]—Sighing and inability to take a deep breath are very common complaints among psychoneurotic persons. Many such patients are observed to breathe relatively quickly and shallowly, with interspersions of deep sighs. It is possible that the frequent short respirations are insufficient to remove all the carbon dioxide from the blood, and that when this accumulates, a deep respiration occurs to aid in its removal. The cause of the frequent short respirations is excitement, anger, fear, or other emotional tension. The irritability of the respiratory centers may be so increased in the psychoneurotic patient that reflex irritability may bring about premature discharges and thus prevent deep breaths being readily taken and so give rise to the feeling of heaviness on the chest and difficulty in taking a deep breath. Whatever the precise explanation, however, the treatment of this state is directed not toward the respiratory tract but toward the emotional tone behind it.

[1] *Vide* p. 355 *ff*.   [2] *Vide* p. 87 *ff*.

Tics.[1]—Tics of grunting, snorting, and coughing have the same general genesis as do all tics, and are classified as symbolic symptoms. Tics are often of long standing, appearing early in life, and disappearing for various periods only to reappear again. Since tics require the movement of voluntary muscle, and since voluntary muscle (as well as smooth muscle) actions can easily become habitual, the treatment of tics has two components: (1) the usual one of determining and removing the underlying emotional difficulty, and (2) the breaking of the habit tendency. This latter is greatly aided by hypnosis,[2] in conjunction with psychotherapy.

Mr. G. H., aged twenty-seven years, made grunting noises and shrugged his shoulders. This condition had been present for fifteen years, appearing and disappearing at irregular intervals. He was married and had a small son. His domestic life was excellent and he was able to live on his income without undue stress. He had had this tic for the last five years, but it had increased in intensity so that his wife and friends could not tolerate him for any length of time in their presence. At work, he hardly ever manifested his peculiarity, but when he returned home all the restraint he was capable of exercising while at work disappeared and his grunting and neck twisting became pronounced. His background was a very disturbed one: his father was a drunkard who had made the boy feel miserable. There was a constant feeling of inadequacy, irritation, and unhappiness, so that the patient had run away from home at the age of thirteen. A year before he left home, he had had a sore throat, during which time there were a great number of family arguments. The clearing of his throat had persisted thereafter, and eventually became habitual. The memory of his unhappy childhood was always with him, and the grunting noises became a conditioned reflex response to his memories. He was able to control himself to large extent at work, but this control failed him toward evening when he was at home. Therapy was directed toward desensitizing him to his childhood memories by airing them completely and removing his attitudes of hostility, and by hypnosis directed toward relaxation of all his muscles as well as those involved in his tic. There was marked improvement after the first few visits, but the complete cessation of his symptoms did not occur until after many months of therapy.

Pain Beneath the Sternum.[3]—Pain beneath the sternum, heaviness on the chest, a lump in the throat are not infrequent physical manifestations of emotional difficulties. The mechanism for the production of these symptoms may be spasm of the smooth or striated musculature in the larynx and esophagus, but the relief of these symptoms is produced by relief of generalized spasm and tension.

[1] *Vide* p. 25.   [2] *Vide* p. 227.   [3] *Vide* p. 87.

Mrs. K. I., aged fifty-four years, complained of constant pains in her chest, going from side to side and associated with a feeling of oppression. The pains were not particularly intense but they were constant, and the patient "imagined" every conceivable complication from cancer to heart trouble. Not obtaining any satisfaction from local physicians, she traveled to a famous clinic where the absence of physical disease was confirmed and the patient returned to Chicago unrelieved.

She was married to a fairly successful business man who, however, drank frequently, and attended parties alone. His wife would wait up for him and there would be frequent clashes and stormy scenes. During the day she brooded constantly, and she could not fall asleep waiting for him to come home. "It was like a knife going through me to have him call and say 'he had to go to a business meeting that night.' " The pains in her chest developed after one such telephone call. The children had grown up, married and left home so that the patient had no one to confide in, and no immediate interest in which to lose herself. The husband labeled the wife a "nag," and refused to change his ways of living, unless his wife "acted differently." Divorce was not possible. The only solution was for the patient to attempt so to change her attitudes and manner of living that she would be less concerned about her husband's indiscretions, and at the same time more occupied and interested herself so as to have little time for reflection on her problem. Moreover, she had to realize that "nagging" serves only to defeat one's purpose, and she had to learn to control herself on this score. By following this procedure and with the occasional aid of $\frac{1}{2}$ grain phenobarbital (she had been taking as much as $1\frac{1}{2}$ grains t.i.d.) she lost her physical symptoms. She was far from happy, but she managed to readjust her life sufficiently so that she secured the return of some measure of self respect and some degree of peace.

Asthma.—Asthma[1] is a controversial topic. There are some who say it is entirely the result of the influence of some sensitizing protein, and there are those at the other extreme who insist that it is purely a "psychic" disease. The question, however, would appear to be rather how much of a particular asthmatic reaction is organogenic and how much is psychogenic. There are probably many cases which fit fairly well into one or other causation; but as a rule, asthma tends to occur in tense, determined persons, or in those who have some manifestation of neurosis. One physician quotes the case of a patient who is sensitive to ragweed pollen and who has typical asthmatic attacks in the ragweed season, but who, interestingly enough, does *not* have these attacks when his mother-in-law is *out* of town! Emotional tone always plays a role in these patients; in some it plays the major role. Effective treatment depends on a true analysis of the factors involved with adequate treatment toward all the causes.

[1] *Vide* p. 88.

Mrs. O. G., aged fifty-three years, had severe asthmatic attacks which were unrelieved by medication. She was sensitive to ragweed pollen, but her attacks began early in the summer and lasted far into the fall. Occasionally, she had attacks in midwinter. Adrenalin would bring some relief but this would be temporary. Sedatives, desensitization procedures, rest in bed, a sojourn in northern Wisconsin during the ragweed season, all proved futile. The patient had to stay in bed and "suffer" for long periods of time.

This woman was a very intelligent, unselfish person. She belonged to many social groups, worked diligently and conscientiously with little thought to her own welfare. Her finances were limited, but she would contribute out of her food money for some worthy cause. She had many friends and was married a second time, seemingly content and companionable with her husband. Her only son was a professional person and had been married for several years. Superficially there seemed to be no discernible emotional causes of tension.

A close friend, however, suggested that the patient was concerned over her son; and with this clue it was possible to direct discussions with the patient so as to reveal the following. The patient who had come from Europe in her teens had lived her childhood against a deplorable background. She had become an intense person, matured too early for her years, and cherished deeply whatever was close to her. Her only child gave her an outlet for her sympathy, and she gave to him the love which she had always desired and had never experienced. She struggled against many odds, and even after her first husband's death labored to send her boy through school and into professional life. She had dreamed of his future and gloried in the idea of being by his side throughout life. When after graduation, her son spent little time with her, she consoled herself with the belief that he was busy and had little time for persons outside his work. When, however, he married, and her daughter-in-law, jealous of the mother's attention and suffering from emotional difficulties of her own, managed so that her son saw her hardly at all, she broke down completely. Her breakdown, however, came with the onset of an acute attack of asthma. Skin tests revealed ragweed sensitization, but the attacks were continuous and unrelieved. For several years these attacks continued, becoming more and more severe.

The therapy in this situation was directed toward bringing to light all these conflicts, and getting the patient to view them objectively. Her own overly intense attachment[1] to her son and the dreams she had of being by his side throughout life were shown to her to be both impracticable and undesirable. Children when mature must lead their own lives, and no parent should expect to remain the center of their attention. The children have their own problems which often unwittingly make them forget about home. Children often are needlessly selfish and thoughtless, but the parent must think back on his own life, and understand the nature of things. Moreover, no parent should put all or most of his life into

[1] *Vide* p. 200 *ff.*

rearing children.[1] Parents need other interests to balance them
and keep them from being so involved in the lives of their offspring
as to render both themselves and their children unhappy. These
facts she had to learn. She needed to understand life in a manner
different from that which she had accustomed herself to. She
discussed her "emotional" ideas and wishes, and viewing them in
the mirror of the psychiatrist's interpretation saw reflected undistorted and objective wishes. The changed attitude brought about
in several weeks of discussion resulted in complete relief of her
asthma. The only medication used was $2\frac{1}{2}$ grains barbital p.r.n.
The life-long tendencies and sympathies and desires were not
removed; but by virtue of a sympathetic presentation of a more
self-disciplined and less emotional way of living she obtained sufficient objectivity to start in the direction desired, and to remove the
tension which in large part had produced the asthma.

GASTROINTESTINAL SYSTEM AND ABDOMEN[2]

The gastrointestinal tract is particularly subject to disturbances
of emotional tone. A possible reason for this sensitivity is the rich
sympathetic and parasympathetic nerve supply existent in almost
every part of the abdominal viscera, plus the existence of a motile
structure, the muscles, which may respond quickly to stimuli, the
response being by spasms. Moreover, the brain has a close relationship to the stomach and intestines, via the hypothalamus.
It has been found that perforations of the stomach and intussuscep-
tion may occur after operations on the diencephalon. Whether
these connections are primarily by means of nerve impulses, or
via hormonal activity is as yet not definitely established. At any
rate, many gastrointestinal symptoms are commonly spoken of as
being the result of emotional upsets.

Difficulty in Swallowing.—Difficulty in swallowing is a common complaint. It is usually referred to as a "lump in the throat,"
and is probably associated with spasm of the throat and upper
esophageal muscles. It has frequently been termed a cardinal
symptom of hysteria, but it is one of the symptoms of tension
which may be present in any of the neuroses.

Mr. N. T., aged twenty-two years, complained of a burning sensation in
his throat and a difficulty in swallowing. This symptom had existed for
two years. Since no physician had been able to find any definite pathology,
it was hypothesized that he had hyperthyroidism (even though the B.M.R.

---

[1] *Vide* p. 202.   [2] *Vide* p. 89 *ff.*

was only plus 5) and he was treated with Lugol's solution. The symptoms were temporarily relieved but soon returned in full force. On further investigation I found many other psychoneurotic complaints but they were subordinated in the patient's mind to the above. The history in part is significant. The young man suffered from an overly devoted mother who wished to protect her darling from all harm and desired him to be perfect. She had taken him to Florida for "a rest." "The first time I got this trouble in swallowing was one day when we were walking along the boardwalk. Mother kept talking to me about how terrible it was that I had taken a drink the night before. She kept bawling me out, over and over, and I begged her to stop it even for a minute; but she kept right on, and I suddenly became faint and couldn't swallow my saliva. Since then I can't swallow food, even though I'm hungry." Behind this apparently simple precipitating factor was an entire background of an unemancipated, overdominated child. When this basic factor was treated, by counselling with the mother, and by training the boy, the symptoms disappeared and did not recur.

Fullness, Tightness.

Fullness, tightness, "a knot in the pit of my stomach" are symptoms which may be the forerunner of active organic gastric pathology. They also however are common symptions of emotional difficulties. The heart and gastrointestinal tract are exceedingly sensitive to the influence of emotions. "Normal" persons develop a "lump in the stomach" on hearing some distressing news, or on being frightened in some way. In chronic emotional disturbances these sensations tend to persist. Their most probable physical basis is pylorospasm.

Miss K. D., aged thirty-eight years, was referred after x-ray and laboratory examination because of a constant feeling of heaviness in the epigastrium over which the patient appeared unduly distressed. The examinations had not revealed any organic pathology. Psychiatric history revealed an emotional upheaval following disinterestedness by her "boy friend." In her lonely unmarried existence, such a loss was a tremendous calamity second not even to loss of financial support. She was wounded deeply, and the conflict resulted in the tension which in turn resulted in her symptoms. Once a patient has a focal point of complaint, it serves to draw one's attention from the main difficulties and provides an outlet for the pent-up energies. Such dissociation then goes to the point where the patient insists that all would be well if only his symptom cleared up. But the symptom cannot be cleared up until the basic causes are remedied. Therapy in this instance was rather simple for the causation of the illness was primarily the loss of her escort and she was able to reorient herself quickly, particularly when she plunged enthusiastically into social and recreational life.

Hyperchlorhydria.

Hyperchlorhydria or "acid indigestion" may be either indicative of an early stage of peptic ulcer or an expression of anxiety, or both. Many patients feel pain, burning, and heaviness "in the stomach" after eating; but on more detailed questioning they reveal that these sensations occurred before eating and also at other times of the day. Not infrequently an Ewald test meal reveals a great amount of free acid in the stomach, but there is no direct laboratory evidence of ulcer. These symptoms tend to disappear very quickly under psychotherapy and without any change in diet.

Mr. O. P., aged twenty-eight years, had persistent "acid stomach" for which the medical department could find no organic cause. In addition he spoke of being nervous and easily irritated. He had been out of work for several years and was worried about his future. However, he admitted that he had been worrying for many years before his loss of position. At the age of seventeen, he had contracted gonorrhea and this was followed by constant fears of impotence and sterility. The memory produced a constant aggravation, and so the patient deprived himself of all female company. His tension manifested itself in part by this hyperchlorhydria. Therapy was directed toward giving him exact knowledge as to just what happens after gonorrhea (an examination had revealed no pathology), toward removing his tense attitudes, and toward better social readjustment. Incidentally, in one month, the patient reported a gain of 6 pounds in weight, although he had not consciously increased his food intake. This gain in weight is frequently seen after psychotherapy; possibly it is produced because of increased appetite, through less energy consumption in agitation, and by improved processes of digestion.

Peptic Ulcer.—Peptic ulcer[1] may or may not be secondary to psychologic difficulties, but regardless of the original causation, ulcer symptoms are markedly influenced by emotional states. Patients who may have their ulcer "under control" will have a recurrence of their symptoms when subject to intense concern. The ulcer syndrome may prove recalcitrant to treatment in the presence of apprehension, anguish, or fear. A "silent" ulcer may manifest itself in periods of tension. Pains may be more intense and the subject suffer more distress in these situations. As a consequence, in the therapy of peptic ulcer it is important to use, besides diet and medication, psychotherapy. Correction of unhygienic patterns of reaction by removing emotional instability may be the determining force in obtaining cures.

Mrs. S. L., aged fifty-two years, complained of pains in the "pit of the stomach" and below the left scapula, occurring from one-half to one hour after meals. The pain was burning in character associated with sour eructations, and was worse after eating meat. Relief was obtained by using baking soda. Gastric analysis revealed a high free acid content, and x-ray films showed a persistent filling defect in the duodenal cap. The diagnosis

1 *Vide* p. 91.

of duodenal ulcer was made and the patient was placed on a milk diet and alkalies. The patient responded well and was symptom free for about three months, when the symptoms recurred. An indiscretion in diet was said to be the cause. Removal to a hospital was necessary in order to bring about complete relief of symptoms again; but thereafter the ulcer symptoms would recur at irregular intervals and at times when the patient insisted that she was following her usual routine in eating.

A psychiatric consultation revealed a self-contained, well poised person who, however, appeared somewhat tense. She had three children all of whom were adults. She had separated from her husband several years before and was living on the earnings of her oldest son. This son had obligations of his own, and though he gave willingly, the mother grieved, feeling that she was depriving him of some of his needs. She insisted on taking only enough to provide for her minimum needs. One daughter was married, had one child, and a husband who was an alcoholic and who finally ceased to earn a living so that it was necessary for his wife to go to work. The patient stayed home with the child, and witnessed the violent altercations between her daughter and son-in-law. She dared not interfere, and "had to keep everything I felt inside." The other daughter was unmarried, and being without work was irritable and restless. This background made for an almost unbearable situation, and every attack of ulcer symptoms could be traced to some violent outburst or disturbance in the environment. The very nature of the environmental stress made therapy difficult. Psychotherapy was directed toward showing the patient the relationships between her symptoms and emotional problems;[1] toward trying to develop as much as possible an attitude of passivity and objective calmness; toward creating outside interests and diversions.[2] This régime definitely alleviated but did not entirely remove the symptoms. Within the following year her youngest daughter married, her son's financial condition improved, and the alcoholic son-in-law disappeared, permitting his wife to adjust on a difficult but certainly less irritating level. As time brought about these changes, the ulcer symptoms gradually subsided and finally on a relatively meat-free diet the patient remained completely well during the follow-up period of three years.

"Nervous Stomach," "Quivering Inside," "Hungry But Can't Eat."—These are common complaints. Very rarely however are these the sole complaints; as with other neurotic complaints, they are generally but a few of the symptoms in a con-

---

[1] *Vide* p. 126 *ff*.   [2] *Vide* p. 249.

stellation of psychoneurotic features. In therapy the patient is given some such explanation:[1] "Your stomach is just as irritable as you are. When you hear the slightest noise you jump; when you are irritated, every muscle in your body is irritated and jumps, including the muscles of your stomach. The quivering inside you is but a reflection of your quivering outside. When you put food into your stomach, the stomach is too irritable to be relaxed and hold very much, and so you feel full with very little, although you seemed quite hungry at the outset. The treatment of your irritable stomach is to remove the cause, which is your general irritability."

Mrs. C. O., aged thirty-eight years, complained of nervousness, feeling quivery in the stomach, and general trembling. This condition had been present for several years. She spoke of being hungry but said, "as soon as I have one or two bites I feel full and can't eat any more." There was a constant "trembling inside" and this would come on whenever there were periods of tension. Sedatives of all sorts had been given her with relatively little effect.

This patient on questioning spoke of herself as "always having been nervous." She told of her early years, of her strong affection for her father who was very kind to her; of her shyness, timidity, and overwhelming sense of duty and prudishness. There was little in the way of external stress but modesty, shyness, and propriety were always overemphasized. The patient never learned these in proper balance, but overevaluated them to the point where she remained continually unhappy at her inability to live up to what she termed "adequate standards." She came to the point where she thought of "earthly pleasures" as sinful. When she married, therefore, it was from a sense of duty, to relieve her parents of herself as a burden and to bear children. The sexual act was not only distasteful but left the patient in a state of tension and hysterics after it was over. She had four children. Her husband never shouldered any responsibilities; he turned over his check to the patient who then managed the household affairs. When any question arose, the husband evaded the issue by telling her that she had the money and could do what she wished. To the neighbors she appeared fortunate in having that sort of husband, but she felt keenly the absence of someone whom she could look up to, someone as strong and powerful as her father. (Psychoanalysts would speak of this attachment as an Oedipus situation: see Chapter XVII.) The strain of these various factors had made for her "constant nervousness." Several years earlier her son had been apprehended as a member of a gang engaged in stealing automobiles; and to a person of her moral scruples, this experience was a most difficult blow. She became nervous and upset, easily irritated, and could not do anything without her hands trembling. She lost her appetite and felt "quiverings" in the abdomen. After a few weeks her appetite returned, but as soon as she would eat she would vomit. This symptom disappeared, but thereafter although she would be hungry, she would "feel full" after a few bites.

[1] *Vide* pp. 178; 216.

Therapy for this patient was a long term one, directed at so reorienting her personality as to obtain satisfaction and pleasure out of "normal" pastimes. This end was accomplished first, by discussions to remove all her intellectual objections, and then by directing her into one social activity after another until she reacted favorably. For example she never in her life had appeared on a beach in a bathing suit, because it was "immodest" and she was persuaded to go swimming with her neighbors. Again, after dinner, her family would visit friends or go to a motion picture, while she felt that it was her duty to stay home, clean up the house, and sit up until they returned. She was persuaded to change, to be firm and insist that her two daughters and daughter-in-law help with the housework, and then to go out with them. This patient came once a week to the dispensary for over a year. After the first month there was a marked improvement, and her eating became normal. However, to pronounce her cured at that point would have been fallacious, for the background of excessive inhibitions remained; and it was necessary to continue with the therapy until her personality was fairly completely reoriented. She has been seen twice a year since then and is a different person, according both to herself and her friends.

Constipation and Diarrhea.—Constipation and diarrhea[1] may be spoken of together, for particularly when without "organic" etiology such as dysentery, obstruction, etc., constipation often alternates with diarrhea. Homeostatic[2] phenomena are an essential part of physiologic processes, and when one extreme is present in the body, these processes tend to swing to the other extreme continuing until the normal balance is reached. However, constipation is by far the more common and is of greater duration than the diarrhea. The whole subject is too complex to present in detail in this book, and only a few of the facts relating to it can be reviewed. In health there is a formed fecal movement about once a day. In some it may occur several times a day, and in others once in several days. The person feels the urge to defecation and responding is able to empty the lower rectum easily. Usually the entire process is an uncomplicated one performed automatically. In modern life, however, there are many disturbances which interfere with this automatic process. One of the most important interferences is the rush and hurry demanded by our existence. Many persons rush to stool, and strain, doing what they can to force the process. If

[1] *Vide* p. 91.   [2] *Vide* p. 215.

20

no immediate results occur, they leave the toilet. Constipation results. The peristaltic waves of the intestine are usually not in a hurry, and this bustle and rush of the person are not conducive to intestinal activity. By the same token as above, those who are in such a rush are generally tense, and there fails to be adequate relaxation of the anal sphincter, which again retards evacuation. Moreover, tension is accompanied by an alteration of the intestinal peristalsis which also interferes with evacuation. In addition, there are many sensitivities and fears connected with the elimination processes. Women particularly are subject to an exaggerated false modesty which prevents them from going to the toilet or staying there any length of time when they are among people. As a result constipation occurs, with irritation of the bowel and the advent of other symptoms. But even men have such a false modesty. One person, a man, aged forty-two years, would hesitate to go to the toilet when visiting the home of his friends. If he did go, he would turn on the faucets and even the shower, in an apparent and obvious effort to drown out any sounds of urination. At times even this was not sufficient and he would leave the house on some excuse, so that he could go to a toilet in a hotel or other public place. It is an interesting symbolism that he would return on these occasions to the home of his hostess with a purchase which invariably consisted of bananas! All these and other "psychic" factors play a large role in the development of fecal retention.

Even more important, however, is the effect of emotion on the intestinal tract. Peristalsis may be increased, decreased, or normal. Fear and anger tend to produce spastic-like conditions lasting for the duration of the emotion. When fear and anger become mixed and chilled and constant, when irritation, resentment, or despair are prevalent and persistent, the spastic states also become constant and persistent. In those persons in whom the gastrointestinal tract is for some reason predisposed, there may develop ulcers, spastic colitis, or mucous colitis. In these persons the primary "cause" of the focal illness is the general emotional disturbance.

Spastic Colitis.—Spastic colitis[1] has for some years been a "fashionable" diagnosis. The diagnosis is based on an account of abdominal pains or cramps, diarrhea alternating with constipation, and x-ray findings of excessive contractibility of the colon. The patients suffering from this condition are said to be nervous and irritable as a result of their spastic colitis. However, the reverse

[1] *Vide* p. 91.

is generally the case; namely, that the nervousness and irritability come first. Accordingly, treatment of the condition of the bowels should be the treatment of the causes of the "nervousness."

Mucous Colitis.—Mucous colitis has a similar background, except that it is one stage further than spastic colitis. The appearance of mucus in the stool points to a more intense aggravation of tension. Should the tension become less the mucous may disappear and permit the more simple "spastic colitis" to appear. The difference is a matter of degree.

Mr. S. B., aged forty-two years, complained among other things, of marked constipation. He spoke at great length about his difficulties, about the amount of medication necessary to produce a bowel movement, about the constant abdominal discomfort and the scybalus or tape-like form of the feces. When he was "very nervous and upset" much mucous would be present but that condition occurred only in very disturbing situations.

He was at one time a manager of stock show companies, but he lost this position soon after 1929. Since then he had worked in various capacities, usually as a salesman and would "have a lot of grief with the jobs." He and his wife lived precariously, and he finally took to drink because the "going was tough." He developed delirium tremens in 1937 and was sufficiently frightened to discontinue drinking. However, he began to notice increasing difficulty with his constipation; and the symptoms continued to become worse until he was seen in 1939. His wife reported that he was a dominating, overbearing person, who was petulant and who sulked if things did not go his own way. He worried constantly and kept criticizing all those about him. He was impatient, tense, and was troubled by insomnia. It was difficult to persuade him to come for therapy "which was talk and not medicine" and after the first visit he did not return. Six months later he returned for treatment and decided to attempt changing his personality. The appearance of a steady position enabled him to feel more secure. Psychotherapy was directed toward changing his personality traits, and increasing his tolerance of himself and others. Gradually his cramps and mucous cleared up, but two months after treatment there still remained some constipation. The medication used consisted of barbital $2\frac{1}{2}$ grains p.r.n. Warm water enemas were used occasionally. The employment of drastic cathartics was avoided because the bowel spasm, ushered in as it may have been by emotional difficulties, could be aggravated by any irritant cathartic and recovery thus be delayed.

Pseudo-appendicitis.—Pseudo-appendicitis has also come into vogue among apprehensive persons who have read a good deal about appendicitis. In these cases, there tends to be constipation and what has been termed "spastic colitis" but the specific complaint lies in vague or sharp pains occurring intermittently in the right lower quadrant, without fever, general cramps, or other signs of acute inflammation. The abdomen is soft, and mild tenderness is often present in all quadrants. The fears of the patient often keep such pains alive, and many an unnecessary appendectomy is carried out because of the patient's insistence.[1]

"Gall Bladder Pains."—Gall bladder pains without any demonstrable pathology are not infrequent. These pains are, however, typical of actual pathology. The pains are constant or intermittent and often without definite relation to food. They radiate across the chest and to all parts of the abdomen. They are associated with many other aches and pains, such as the headaches and weakness found in psychoneurotic illness. Finally, they produce weakness and prostration out of all proportion to the clinical findings. Nevertheless, it is extremely difficult to make a differential diagnosis at times. In many instances there may be some basis of actual pathology, but the emotional tone enhances the subjective findings to the point where operative procedures are carried out. Frequently these pains are the result of spasms of the bile ducts which operate in such a way as to cause a "real" blocking of the gall bladder. Whenever the surgeon finds after operation, that the symptoms were out of proportion to the degree of pathology, he should arrange for further personality study of the patient, if he wishes that the symptoms do not return. As long as the emotional problem remains unsolved, relief from symptoms by other methods will be only temporary.

Mrs. B. U., aged thirty-six years, complained of severe "gall bladder" pain. These symptoms were particularly over the right hypochondrium and were so severe that she was invalided. She had just been hospitalized for several weeks in the County Hospital, and x-rays and stomach tests had revealed nothing. Neurologic examination was negative. Mrs. U. told how her symptoms had originated seven years ago with similar pains. She was treated by several doctors, and finally the pain became so severe that she had to be operated upon. On operation the surgeon found that the gall bladder was "normal" and so he removed the appendix. After operation the patient was well for several months and then the symptoms recurred and continued in full force.

On more detailed questioning the patient admitted to suffering from headaches which were very severe; of occasional blurring of vision which did not seem to be helped by the glasses prescribed for her, of a frequent choking sensation in her throat, which made her inquire anxiously about a "goiter", of pains which spread from the "gall bladder" area to the heart which palpitated often; of vague and peculiar sensations "which flitted through her legs and made her knees weak" and prevented her from much walking. The patient was an excellent demonstration to the students of a frequent

[1] *Vide* p. 276.

type of psychoneurotic patient whose presenting complaint focused attention away from the more general complaints, and the more general complaints included practically every portion of her body.

Mrs. U. came from Italy at the age of nine. She was the only daughter and at fifteen, when her mother was ailing, was given in marriage in order that the mother not have the responsibilities of an unmarried daughter. The patient accepted her lot with stoicism: the man she had married was, according to her standards a "good man"; he did not drink and was good to her. They had three children and the struggle for existence was hard. In 1932, their life savings were lost in a bank crash, and the patient became quite depressed. Shortly thereafter a miscarriage occurred and the patient was so disturbed that in spite of repeated menstrual periods, she kept feeling the movement of a child in her abdomen. Everything "seemed to happen at once" and her husband lost his position and the family had to go on relief. Soon thereafter she developed pains in the upper abdomen. There may have been a predisposition to the site of the pain, in that she was a stout "gall bladder type."

On discussion she admitted that she was always worried, and that the symptoms were all over her body. She admitted that she thoroughly enjoyed the sympathy and commiseration of her friends, and the consolation thus obtained because of her troubles and sickness that baffled all specialists.

In therapy, it was necessary to be very insistent that she change her social situation: that she go out into company regardless of how badly she felt;[1] that she make a firm promise not to discuss her ailments with any one except the physician; that she give up bemoaning the difficulties she had had in the past. The aid of her friends who came with her was enlisted,[2] and they were instructed in her presence to "help her forget" by changing the subject should she talk of herself or her difficulties. Strong reassurance[3] was given the patient that she would get well, and that "the pains which were present in all parts of her body were the result of 'irritable nerves,' which in turn were the result of an irritated 'mind,' which could be cured by giving it an outlet in activities." The immediate relief of symptoms seemed almost miraculous. After several weeks, however, they returned again; and further explanation and insistence on mental hygiene principles had to be carried out for many months before she accepted and made automatic the new way of living.

Itching and Pain About the Perineum.—This is not infrequent, particularly following vaginal or rectal operations. The surgical procedures focus the interest on the area, and the emotional tone, particularly because of the added erotic nature of the area involved, serves to produce these symptoms.

---

[1] *Vide* p. 249.   [2] *Vide* p. 126.   [3] *Vide* p. 219 *ff.*

Mrs. I. Q.[1] had a fibroid uterus removed by vaginal operation. After the operation she convalesced well, and then four days later developed an intense burning and itching about the rectum and vagina. Ointments, heat, and deep diathermy were without avail. The patient spoke at great length of the trials and tribulations to which she was subject, and the lack of attention from her family, friends, and even physician. Discussion with the patient about these emotional difficulties, reassurance, not so much about the physical as the personality problems, resulted in removal of her symptoms in the two succeeding days.

GENITO-URINARY SYSTEM[2]

The kidney and ureters are relatively automatic and independent of emotional tension. More commonly affected by tension, is the act of urination, and the tension may show itself by frequency, by precipitancy, by retention, etc.

Frequency of Urination.—Frequency of urination is much more common among children than adults. When children develop a neurosis it is called a behavior problem, but the mechanisms involved differ little in most respects from those of the adult. Increased frequency is found among many so-called "normal" persons, and in these instances is not constant but fluctuates with the emotional state. On closer observation one finds that many of these same persons can retain their urine for an abnormally long period of time. In the first instance, the bladder is irritable; while in the second, it is relatively insensitive. However, it is not accurate to speak of the bladder as being irritable, indicating thereby a relationship as it may to the bladder irritability associated with inflammatory and irritative illnesses of the bladder. Rather, in the cases of tension frequency and tension retention, there is a change in the excitability of the bladder walls, and vesical sphincter: an excitability integral with the general state, and probably mediated by changed tone in the autonomic nervous system. In these disturbances of urination, minor physical changes often act as the precipitating element; and while in themselves they would be innocuous under other circumstances, they serve to focus the tension on the bladder. For example, concentrated urine, excess phosphates and oxalates, mild endocervicitis, chafing clothing may by themselves have no effect on the bladder irritability but when associated with general tension, will serve to bring about frequency of urination.

Precipitancy.—Precipitancy is but a degree of frequency, just as *delayed starting* of urination is but a degree of *retention*. In the latter instance, the vesical sphincter is spastic, and by reciprocal enervation, the bladder is relatively atonic. As far as therapy is concerned the patient's personality reactions require most attention, and changes thereof will bring about results, even if the apparently irritating local cause is not removed. However, limiting or increasing the fluid intake may be of value for cases in which there is frequency of urination or concentration of urine, respectively. Removal of the focal cause always has some measure of success; but rarely is it in itself sufficient, though the suggestion accompanying it may be important.

Miss G. J.,[1] a stenographer, had precipitancy of urination particularly when she went to take dictation. The generalized tension was associated with her fear of going out into open spaces and brought about not only this extreme urgency in moments of tension, but also brought about a diarrhea. When going to the urinal under these circumstances, she passed very little fluid and there was no subsequent feeling of relief. Repeated examinations showed no evidence of infection, kidney disturbance, or other pathology. The question of some inflammation or swelling in the bladder was also ruled out by the fact that for long periods of time she had no frequency and under certain conditions, such as being embarrassed from false modesty, in a social gathering, she could retain the urine for long periods of time.

The therapy was directed primarily at the cause which was in essence a life-long fear of what others might think of her;[2] toward a deeply ingrained inferiority complex;[3] toward the desire and need for the affection from her parents which was denied her because of the emotional disability of the parents; and toward an unfortunate love affair.

Mrs. I. L., aged thirty-four years, had a tension depression. She had, for little apparent reason, lost interest in people, in events about her, in her husband, and in her home. She was depressed, and felt inadequate to carry on the day's activities. She developed insomnia, constipation, loss of appetite, loss of weight, and loss of libido, in the fashion of the usual manic-depressive depression.[4] In addition, she kept insisting that there was nothing the matter with her, that it was her own fault that she was blue, that she was worthless, and it would be better for her and her husband if she were to die.

She was given a course of metrazol shock therapy, and practically all of the depression left her after 6 convulsive doses. The treatment was discontinued then because of the marked muscle pains; and being unable to

---

[1] *Vide* p. 209 *ff.*   [2] *Vide* p. 215.   [3] *Vide* p. 58.   [4] *Vide* p. 361.

have the completed course, she still retained some of her tension. She began to have frequency of urination, going every hour to the toilet, but passing only an ounce or so of urine at a time. Examination showed no abnormality in the urine, and there were no other indications of disease. The patient was tense, fearful at times, and very anxious to get back to doing what she used to do; but she was prevented by some of the residual depression; and in an effort to overcome this depression and force herself to do what was very difficult to do, she developed tension which reflected itself in the urinary frequency.

This patient had to be told not to try so hard to get well, and to wait until she returned to normalcy before expecting so much of herself. It was difficult to get the patient to follow this advice for part of her depression was the result of her personality trait to get things done regardless of the cost to her in energy and restless-ness. She was taught to relax,[1] however, and her frequency of urination disappeared.

Retention of urine after operations is not an uncommon finding.

Miss T. E., aged thirty-two years, had a cholecystectomy. Following the operation, she made an uneventful recovery. However, from the beginning she had to be catheterized; and two weeks later, still could not pass her urine. On occasion she would go twenty hours and distension would become great and catheterization necessary. Hot packs, belladonna, and straining by the patient were to no avail. Miss E. was dependent solely on her earnings, and the acute attack of cholecystitis, and the hospitalization created expenses which she did not know how to meet. She was very anxious to get well quickly and did all she could to follow directions: the over-intensity in fol-lowing directions, in the setting of financial distress was sufficient to cause spasm of the sphincter and urinary retention. When she was taught to relax (by the use of hypnosis in the beginning),[2] the retention disappeared.

DERMATOLOGY[3]

The skin often reflects the emotional tension of the patient. The mechanism by which this influence takes place is not clearly under-stood. It is possible that the *impairment of circulation*, seen grossly in pallor and blushing under the influence of emotion may, if chronic and long prolonged, produce local physical changes; or disturbances in the balance between the sympathetic and para-sympathetic systems which are so common in emotion, may play some *trophic role*. Regardless of the mechanism, however, the effect is definite. It may involve the sweat glands with excessive perspiration; it may involve the peripheral circulation and produce cold hands, or warm hands, or a feeling of warmth or chilliness,

[1] *Vide* p. 244.   [2] *Vide* p. 227.   [3] *Vide* p. 94 *ff.*

pallor or blushing; it may involve the skin sensibility with the "sensation" of anesthesia, paresthesia, or hyperesthesia; it may involve the skin elements with abnormal changes as seen in eczema, warts, non-specific urticaria, and other "neurodermatosis." In those persons in whom there are definite skin changes,[1] the emotional influence has generally been present over a long period of time and most of these persons are sensitive, intense, and "driving" in character. At first questioning, these patients will often deny the existence of any emotional trauma, and will insist that they have no more difficulties than the ordinary person. This statement is in itself usually true; *i. e.*, that they have no more difficulties than the average person, but their *attitude*[2] toward these "ordinary" difficulties and their response to them are different from the average. Their general response is one of intensity, restlessness, driving ambition, discontent with their situation, or secret remorse and anger over some past or present difficulty,[3] all of which prey upon them. There is relatively little in the way of a precipitating factor; but there is much in the way of a chronic factor. For these reasons and others, therapy is slow, and must be thorough-going. Often therapy of the skin lesion amounts to a complete changing of the personality. Many of these patients are rigid, and tend to be unyielding to advice and suggestion, even in ordinary activities. Clearing up of these neurodermatoses is more difficult than removal of many other emotionally conditioned physical symptoms.

Perspiration of the palms of the hands and of the feet is one of the most common symptoms among the neuroses. Presumably it is the result of excess activity of the cholinergic fibers (even though they travel with fibers from the sympathetic nervous system) and it indicates an overactivity of the autonomic system. Usually the palms and the soles of the feet are involved, but in some persons, perspiration may actually drip from the axilla, beads of sweat may stand out on the forehead and chin. The cheeks, arms, trunk, thighs, and legs rarely perspire as the result of tension; and it is interesting to observe in connection with the mechanisms of tension and of heat dissipation that many persons will at one time perspire profusely on their hands and not on their body; while at another, under violent physical exercise, they will have dry palms and a perspiring body. The treatment of this excess perspiration of the palms of the hands is the same as the general treatment of the neuroses.

[1] *Vide* p. 316 (Case S. L.).   [2] *Vide* p. 153.   [3] *Vide* p. 208.

Cold and bluish hands have a similar genesis. Adolescent persons are particularly liable thereto. Similarly a sensation of chilliness or warmth at variance with others in the room is not uncommon. The basal metabolic rate in such instances tends to be somewhat below normal. Many persons, for example, are said to be hyperthyroid, partly on the basis of this warmth; but a more precise history will reveal that the feeling of warmth will vary with that of chilliness, and that the basal rate is often 10 to 15 points below 0. In some adolescents the hands may have almost a cyanotic character without any physical defect discernible on clinical or laboratory examination. In these patients the main complaint is not directed toward the hands, but toward the "stomach" or "heart" or "nervousness," and the treatment should be directed similarly to the causes of the more general complaints. When the specific difficulty clears up, the perspiration, the cyanosis or the coldness of the hands will also disappear. In many instances the actual status of the vasomotor control may be dependent on the constitution of the nervous system.

Blushing and pallor (vasodilation and vasomotor spasm) may even be spoken of as "normal," under appropriate emotional stress; they become abnormal when they appear frequently and from very little stress. In many persons, the neck and face becomes a mottled pink as they struggle to control the emotion aroused by some stimulus. Here, again, the line between normalcy and abnormalcy is vague and dependent on the frequency and facility of the symptom's appearance. In some instances this symptom may be a presenting complaint; in others it may be part of the personality expression and its cure or removal is best brought about only by a fundamental alteration in the personality attitudes.[1]

Disturbances in skin sensibility without actual nerve injury are really part of the symbolic process.[2] The skin is probably not involved, the fault lying instead with the receptors in the brain. Absence of sensation, numbness, burning, "crawling feelings" all need close investigation. When a patient presents such complaints, great care must be taken to investigate all possible sources of damage to the nervous system; for some of the earliest signs of pernicious anemia, of syringomyelia, alcoholism, peripheral neuritis, diabetic neuritis, etc., may manifest themselves in this way. One patient, a young man, aged twenty-seven years, complained of many obvious psychoneurotic ailments, among which

[1] *Vide* p. 64 (Case X. F.).   [2] *Vide* p. 28 *ff*.

was a peculiar sensation on the outer aspect of both thighs. A general examination revealed no pathology, and the patient improved remarkably under psychotherapy. He gained weight, "felt better than he had in ten years," and most of his symptoms disappeared. Five years later, when this patient was again seen, he had developed a full-fledged syringomyelia, and the anesthesia of his thighs was on an organic basis. The fact that in addition the patient had many psychoneurotic features which yielded to therapy did not exclude the fact that like any other human being he might also have an organic lesion. The two symptom complexes were unrelated for the most part, one being the result of his concern over a gonorrheal infection in youth and a consequent avoidance of women even in ordinary social contacts, and the other being the result of cavitation in the center of his spinal cord.

The variety of complaints along the lines of sensation disturbances is astonishing. One young man, aged twenty-five years, for example, complained of a tingling in his arms, the sensation at times spreading to his legs. This peculiar sensation occurred only when he was expected to address an important meeting, or have an important business conference. The basis for his complaint was a general apprehensiveness, the result in large part of a mild manic-depressive depression. The treatment of these ailments here, as elsewhere, is the discovery and removal of the cause.

Eczema is closely related to tension. *Psoriasis, non-specific urticaria*, and many other neurodermatoses are found in persons subject to tension. The specialist is liable to center his attention on only the one sphere, and overlook the fact that the patient at the same time may be suffering from other ailments than that involving the skin. One patient with psoriasis had a peptic ulcer; one with psoriasis had an intense agoraphobia; one with eczema of the hands and neck had spastic colitis; one with a general "neuro-dermatosis" had intense anxiety feelings, etc. A more intensive study of the background will aid in determining the etiology of the disease of the skin, for tension symptoms tend to show themselves in several parts of the body at the same time.[1]

The treatment of these skin conditions by psychotherapy is made difficult by the rigid personality[2] so common in these patients. Therapy for the skin illness itself dwells not on the skin at all, but on the emotional cause responsible for it. Other factors (allergy,[3] etc.) should be treated simultaneously. Soothing ointments and

---

[1] *Vide* p. 320 (Case W. H.).   [2] *Vide* p. 212 *ff.*   [3] *Vide* p. 88.

heat are often of great help: sensitization tests should always be made: no one method should be relied on, but all should be used. The physician as well as the patient will need much patience; but perseverance will bring about the desired result.

Mr. S. L., aged twenty-nine years, had on the back of his hands and his neck eczema which had been present for several years. *X*-ray therapy as well as soothing and irritative ointments were of no avail.

This man was a lawyer. He had been one of the leading men in his class and had promise of great success. On leaving school, however, he encountered the business depression of 1932, and was unable to establish himself. He finally married the girl he loved, but had to depend in part on her earnings. He was a proud person and could not tolerate the idea of having to depend for his livelihood on the daily work of his wife, whom he wished to see as a home maker. They could not afford to have children because of his financial state, and he developed tension toward all his difficulties. When confronted by a law problem, he was so in earnest and desirous of carrying it through successfully that he would scratch at his hands and neck till the skin would bleed. If he covered the areas with adhesive tape, he would scratch it off in his sleep. Even when he was able to stop the scratching the intensity of the eczematous process would vary with the emotional intensity of the day.

In therapy, an effort was made to have the patient accept the situation more philosophically for the duration of its existence. He was also urged to study the opportunities open to him, and come to some common sense evaluation of his prospects in the field of law, and his prospects elsewhere. He finally decided to go into teaching; and after some preliminary preparation, was able to procure an excellent appointment in a small university where he taught business law, where his income was assured, where his wife could cease her daily work at the office and bear him children. Six months after he had procured this position, he was a cheerful, relaxed, happy person from whom all traces of eczema had vanished.

EYE, EAR, NOSE AND THROAT[1]

Visual disturbances without any observable pathology in the eye should not be labeled neurotic without a competent and thorough neurologic examination. Inability to see to one side of the body (and the various forms of hemianopia) may be the result of pressure on or destruction of the optic tract, the temporal lobe, or the calcarine cortex. Moreover, the accidental discovery of

[1] *Vide* pp. 34 *ff*; 93.

hemianopia in a patient who is not aware of its existence is not an indication of neurosis. Many patients have an unawareness of their visual defect even though it may involve the inability to see anything to the right or the left of the midline. This unawareness results from the fact that brain tissue is insensitive to pain, so that the growth of a tumor, or as in one case the occurrence of a hemorrhage, is unnoticed as such; and the person does not notice the absence of vision until the visual function is called into play (compare, for example, the unawareness of the syringomyelia patient who is not cognizant that he cannot feel pain, until he sees that his hand or finger is burned by a cigarette).[1] Moreover, in many of these patients, central (macular) vision is intact so that reading and all visual acuity may be present (one patient who was unaware of his complete inability to see to the left of center told of having several examinations by non-medical oculists who pronounced him perfect as far as his vision was concerned, and who did not even detect this hemianopia) in spite of the defect in peripheral vision. Visual defects must be carefully studied before they can be pronounced as neurotic.

Changes in visual acuity, are common in patients suffering from neuroses. These changes are more apparent than real. It is not uncommon for a patient to have his glasses changed a dozen times while under an intense but chronic emotional strain.[2] Nevertheless, even in these situations one needs be cautious in making a diagnosis, for some patients with nearsightedness for many years may have an actual improvement in their visual acuity as the result of increased intercranial pressure which may push the elongated myopic eyeball foreward enough so that, as in one case with a cerebellar tumor, glasses could be discarded. Thorough examinations are essential before making a diagnosis of neuroses. In children the determination of visual acuity may be a problem because it is difficult to get complete cooperation; and it may be a similar factor which is responsible for the changing refraction error found in neurotics. Patients who are agitated often will return to the oculist daily for adjustment of their glasses, an adjustment necessary because of the patient's general tendency to complain, and not because of any difficulty with the glasses. Many patients

---

[1] These symptoms would indicate that man is unaware of the presence or absence of any of his functions, until his attention is drawn to them by stimuli (external or internal). Similarly, persons may have various characteristics which they despise and of which they are totally unaware.

[2] *Cf.* p. 361.

complain of tiredness of the eyes or blurring of vision after reading or even on making an attempt to read, and on occasion without reading. Examination of the visual acuity, of the eye muscle strength, etc., reveals no pathology; but a few minutes' discussion with the patient will bring out a vast number of somatic complaints not infrequently associated with a feeling of depression. The reason for the production of these ocular symptoms in neurotic states is unclear. Similarly the reason for the supraorbital headaches which are attributed to eyestrain, but which are part of the psychoneurotic phenomena is unclear. It may possibly be the result of fatigue of the ciliary muscle which is innervated by the autonomic nervous system and is in a constant state of irritability. (Hippus is frequently found in these patients.) In these instances, likewise, treatment is directed not primarily toward the eye, although any error in refraction should be corrected, but toward the basic emotional instability.

The above complaints tend to occur in many psychoneurotic persons, but there may be additional disturbances. These include tubular vision, monocular vision, inconstant diplopia,[1] or various forms of amblyopia, which on examination by the use of prisms or different colored glasses are demonstrated as symbolic disturbances. In many of these patients charting the peripheral field of vision reveals a spiral narrowing of the visual field as the test is repeated. Here again, however, it is necessary to differentiate between paracentral scotomata and hysterical inability to see.

Frequently *the ear* also may be involved, but here, as in the case of the eyes, the disturbance is more in connection with the function of hearing than with the disturbances involving the anatomy of the hearing apparatus. However, *pains and irritations* may occur in connection with the ear just as in any other part of the body. The etiology of these pains has the same background as the etiology of any of the neuroses.

Mr. Y. R., aged twenty-two years, was referred because of extreme intractable pain in the ear from which he could obtain no relief, and for which there did not appear to be any physical basis. The pain was so severe that the patient pounded his fists against the brick wall when he was seized with a paroxysm, and he insisted that his physician perform a mastoidectomy, or cut the "ear nerves." The patient was a well built man, weighing 190 pounds and standing 6 feet tall. He was all muscle; and though he was powerful physically, his intellectual level was below average and his mental age was between eleven and twelve. He stated that several

[1] *Vide* p. 93.

months prior to the onset of his pain he had been working in the basement (he was a janitor) and an explosion had occurred, deafening him. Not until several weeks later, however, did the pain in his ear begin, and then it was so intense that he could not perform his work.

On closer questioning, the patient at first denied that he had anything to worry about, and then blurted out his general hatred of his existence. In effect he said, "I hate my job. When I go down the stairs, the neighbors they holler at me and they want me to do dis and dat and they make me crazy. I sometime don't collect the garbage till early in the morning before they get up and then I go away where they can't find me. I didn't want this job; but when I married my girl her father said this is a good job and he made me take it. I always wanted to be a prize fighter. I used to hang around the clubs and even used to fight as a sparring partner sometimes. I wanted to become a good fighter, but I never get the chance, and my wife don't let me go there anymore. I don't get any fun out of life."

This man was a "child" with the body of an adult. His ambitions were limited, but easily satisfied; yet his mind could not accept the responsibility[1] even of a janitor's position. His wife was of normal intelligence and was constantly angry at his "dumbness." The patient was under pressure to be that which he could not be,[2] and at the same time was denied access to his simple ideal of "fun." The patient was not in any way vicious or sadistic; he was mentally a child with childish concepts. It was the emotional disturbances surrounding this entire situation that gave rise to the psycho-neurotic symptom; and the focusing of the symptom was determined by the accidental centering of his attention on the ear by the boiler explosion. In therapy, the problem was to scale down the stress[3] placed on the patient by his work and his wife and to provide some outlet for his stored up emotion.[4] The patient was urged in the simplest of language not to let himself get excited by the demands of the tenants; and his wife having been told of his mental level was urged to treat him as a child rather than as a responsible husband. She was also urged to make arrangements with her father, who worked in the neighboring buildings as a janitor, to teach the patient some of the more efficient ways of dealing with his work. The patient was then told that he could go to the gymnasium several times a week to watch and engage in his desired sport, and his wife was instructed to encourage him along these lines. Simultaneously, he was hypnotized and the suggestion given that the pain would disappear. The pain did disappear, and when he was seen three months later by the referring physician there had been no recurrence. The emotional basis for

[1] *Vide* p. 217.   [2] *Vide* p. 416.   [3] *Vide* p. 417.   [4] *Vide* Ch. XII.

the pain was relieved.   It is interesting to note that the site[1] of the symptom in this man was determined by accident, and it is probable that if the boiler explosion had not occurred there would have been no ear difficulty but some other symptom.   If he had burned his leg he might have developed a persistent neurotic pain in the leg; if a cinder had gotten in his eye, that organ would have been the center of his complaints, and so on.

Ringing, tickling, throbbing and roaring sounds may occur without organic basis.   Not infrequently persons complain of hearing their pulse when the head is on the pillow, but this sensation carries over into waking hours in some patients.   Many middle ear conditions may be at the basis for these abnormalities of sensation and hearing, yet they may occur without any basis other than emotional tension.   It is an important question to determine whether or not emotional tension may produce tension between the small bones of the middle ear, and on the tympanic membrane sufficient to facilitate the production of these sounds.   The therapy as always must be directed toward the cause.

Mrs. W. H., aged twenty-two years, was referred because of her complaint of ringing in the ears and a vague sensation of itching in the ear.   Auricular and auditory examinations were negative.   It is interesting to note how the patient focused her complaints on one system, sufficiently so that she was sent to a specialist on ear disease, and how these same complaints dwindled to an inferior position when the entire history was taken.

Four years earlier the patient had awakened out of a sound sleep to find her sister having a violent epileptic convulsion, and since then had been nervous and had developed the ear sensations.   In spite of the fact that the ear sensations were the presenting complaint the physician made an inventory by systems, beginning with the head, and the patient brought out the following complaints.   "My *head* feels awfully funny.   I used to have pains in it.   My *mind* isn't right.   I feel as if I'm going crazy.   My imagination gets the best of me; I'm afraid to open windows, and to be where there are knives, lest I hurt myself.   I think I have every disease imaginable.   My *sinuses* used to bother me a lot, but they haven't lately.   My *teeth* aren't good; I think I've got pyorrhea (there was no observable evidence of this on superficial examination).   My *throat* has an awful choking feeling; it's suffocating-like.   My *eyes* have a drawing feeling; at times I can hardly see.   My *heart* pounds so hard at times that you can see it through my dress.   I get sharp pains coming and going around the heart often.   I can't get my *breath* at times and once I was sure I had tuberculosis.   My *stomach* isn't right, I can't eat or drink and feel nauseated.   Everything lays like a lump in the pit of the stomach and hurts.   My *periods* (menses) used to be seven or eight days and I had headaches, was in a daze and felt light-headed.   The "shots" (theelin) cut them down to five days now.   My *legs* always feel

[1] *Vide* p. 289.

shaky-like, as if they'll give way. I tremble all over and feel as if I could drop things. When I move my arms and legs the *bones* crack and make funny sounds. Weak feelings come over the *whole body* and it feels just like I'm passing out, but I never actually faint. It feels just like dying. I've lived a thousand deaths; am afraid and don't know of what; am afraid of dying or something."

The above statements are abstracts from the patient's history taken on the first visit when she was seen. It is indicative of the general nature of emotional expression, even though the presenting symptoms were apparently centered in the ear.

Deafness, complete or partial, is not an uncommon symptom. In general, the etiology of it may be the same as that involving disturbances of vision, a symbolic desire to avoid hearing of difficulties (in visual amblyopia it is often a desire to avoid seeing difficulties). The deafness is bilateral, inconstant, and without any demonstrable organic pathology. It generally is associated with many other neurotic symptoms,[1] and is relieved by psychotherapy.

Mrs. C. D., aged forty-three years, was referred from the department of otolaryngology for partial deafness which had no determinable organic basis. When the patient entered the consulting room, she spoke in a normal toned voice, and yet could not hear unless the examiner raised his voice almost to the shouting stage. The patient told of her husband's death some three years ago, and of her struggle for existence. She had two children aged three and four and a half, and worked in a factory earning a very meager wage. She lived with her sister who was married and had a small crowded apartment. Not only was the physical standard of living very low, but there was intense dissatisfaction between the two sisters. When the patient returned home from work, the sister would begin to nag and complain. The constant whining, the fault finding, the seeming hopelessness of her position discouraged the patient to the point of brooding and frequent tears. One day while preoccupied, the patient did not hear what her sister said, and the sister caustically remarked, "You must be getting deaf." From then on the patient heard less and less in the house, though she managed to make her way about at work and away from home with no difficulty. When the examiner spoke to her, it was necessary almost to shout to be understood, but as the patient began to unfold her story more and more, it was possible to reduce the loudness of the voice to a conversational tone. However, when her story was finished, and she was being given various suggestions, it became necessary to raise the tone again.

The therapeutic situation was prognostically poor. It was suggested that the patient try to become more social and divert her attention and interests into something that she could enjoy; but she was fatigued from the day's labors, and the care of the children

[1] *Vide* p. 93.

and their belongings took up most of her spare time. The persistent nagging made it almost impossible for the patient to get any peace and sympathy; and few results were achieved in the patient's six visits to the dispensary.

Auditory hallucinations are the most common form of hallucinations, but are not properly the result of ear difficulties or even of the neuroses. Hallucinations in general are the result of projection of one's dissociated thoughts,[1] and occur primarily in the psychoses. Illusions, or misinterpretations of actual stimuli, as occur when one hears one's name called only to discover that someone else has been called, or some unexpected sound has occurred are similarly based on the projection into the outside of one's self-consciousness (crudely expressed, it is "hearing what one thinks"). Hallucinations of sight, or sound, or smell are all based on this same mechanism, and occur primarily in the schizophrenias[2] and organic psychoses.

Rhinorrhea is not infrequently found in tension states; it is exceedingly difficult to prove, however, that there is no basic irritant, even if it lies only in the weather. A number of subjects complain among other psychoneurotic symptoms of a profuse secretion from the nose particularly during the spring or fall of the year. It may very well be that these patients are particularly sensitive to some pollen or get colds which under ordinary circumstances would have no effect, but which in these emotionally overreacting persons, will produce an excessive secretion.

Complaint of a fish bone in the throat is not infrequently heard in the E.N.T. office, and yet the most thorough investigation may reveal no fish bone, or any semblance thereof. It is possible for a small bone to lodge in the throat, and be difficult to locate in spite of the most careful examination, and x-ray studies; yet the reverse also occurs: patients complain of such an occurrence with no physical basis therefor. In these instances, as is the case with many other neurotic symptoms, the complaint serves as the focusing point through which their emotional tone created by other problems can be discharged. Patients find it very difficult to give up such a complaint, particularly if their problems continue unabated in intensity.[3]

Mrs. F. Y., aged forty-nine years, was eating a fish dinner, when she suddenly complained of pain in her throat, as if a bone had stuck there. She tried to "brush" it down by eating several leaves of lettuce, and then followed one suggestion of her family after another in an effort to dislodge the

---

[1] *Vide* p. 72.   [2] *Vide* p. 380.   [3] *Vide* p. 216.

bone which she was sure was stuck in her throat. The family physician was called, but since he could not see anything in the throat, advised a specialist's examination. The specialist found no indication in the throat of any bone, or scratch, or irritation. The patient wandered from doctor to doctor, and from dispensary to dispensary making the same complaint and undergoing innumerable investigations. She was referred to the department of psychiatry two years after the onset of her symptoms, which had remained unchanged.

The patient had been married thirty-two years, had three married children, and lived with her husband in a small apartment. Her husband worked at odd hours in a tailor shop and in the evening played cards with his cronies. Toward his wife, he was cross, irritable, and unsympathetic. She awoke in the morning to make him breakfast, but did not see him during the rest of the day. She wandered from one friend to another but she had neither the money nor the educational background to seek out more interesting amusements. She was not intellectual enough to be bored; so she was just plain unhappy. For a number of years she had given voice to her emotional discord by visiting clinics for various hypochondriacal aches and pains. Her children were kind to her, but had their own affairs which concerned them, and she went to their homes only occasionally for meals. It was on just such an occasion that she had received some painful stimulus which she interpreted as a fish bone. She was kept quite busy and occupied going to various clinics and discussing the various tests she was undergoing and whom she was seeing.

This patient's complaint was not set in any serious and deeply repressed unconscious wishes. She had always been more or less unstable; and as her children grew older, and her required work dwindled, she found time hanging heavily on her hands. If her husband had been interesting and conversational, and sympathetic, all might have gone well; but since he was as he was, the patient brooded over the inadequacies of the present life, the deprivations of the past life, and the probable suffering of the future. The "bone in the throat" was a welcome relief from all this monotony, and at the same time a vicarious release mechanism for her emotional brooding. It was a relatively easy matter to interest this patient in a welfare society, where she spent much of her time caring for children who were in actual misery. Not only did her distress over the imaginary fish bone disappear, but the other neurotic symptoms which were present, but in the background, also disappeared.

Aphonia.—Aphonia[1] is another distressing symptom which is often called to the attention of the laryngologist. The onset of these symptoms is usually sudden, following a "sore throat," or as in the case of one young woman following the "scare" of an automobile accident. The aphonic patient can usually whisper and so is able to make his wants known, but otherwise he cannot sing, shout, or call in a loud voice. On laryngoscopic examination the vocal cords are found to be normal.

[1] *Vide* p. 29.

Mr. K. L., aged twenty-six years, was referred to the psychiatric dispensary because of hysterical aphonia. He spoke in a whisper and complained bitterly of his lot.

The patient lived with his father behind a small store where his father sold groceries. The father was a penurious person and complained constantly about the difficult way life had treated him. His wife had died many years before, and he had two children, the older of whom, a daughter, had married. This daughter had seemingly forgotten completely about her father, and he constantly bemoaned the fact that his children did not care for him. He was resolved that his son should aid him and imposed the most menial tasks without compensation. The son was forced to work early and late, and after he had completed the second year high school, was kept home for this purpose. He had always had ambitions of becoming an educated and professional man; and not only were his opportunities thwarted, but he was stunted in every other way by his constant association with his nagging, complaining, irritating father. Several times he had run away, but lack of funds and failure to procure a position had forced him to return; and after each return, his life was made more unbearable by his father. One day, after a great deal of abuse the patient called his father obscene names and fled the home, only to return late at night. He was received in cold silence, and life continued as it had, until late the following night, when the father of the patient developed an apoplectic stroke with left sided hemiparesis. The father had been ill for some time and had visited clinics for his "high blood pressure," but he accused his son of producing this ailment and the son believed he had brought on the stroke. He had nothing to say, and developed his aphonia immediately thereafter. The inability to speak was the result not only of the emotional shock at finding his father thus paralyzed, but of his guilty feelings and on the basis of his life-long emotional instability. The father died shortly thereafter and the boy lived on relief, handicapped all the more in his seeking work by his speech ailment. He had tried several voice trainers, and speech experts who focused all their efforts on trying to have the patient make certain sounds. The fallacy of treating just the symptom was not understood and the patient's aphonia remained.

The principle of therapy was to remove as much as possible this man's guilt feeling,[1] to have him cultivate his ambition in a practical fashion, and develop outlets for his energies. In the ensuing discussions the patient was made to view his relationship with his father in an objective fashion, and to understand how abusive language might come from anyone under stress; to realize that his father's hypertension was the responsible cause of his stroke; to believe that if he devoted himself he could finish his high school education and take college work sufficient to become a laboratory technician; and he was persuaded that he had to seek some day work by which he could support himself as an independent

[1] *Vide* p. 179.

adult. Hypnosis[1] was a valuable aid in obtaining relief from the aphonic state, and the fulfilment of the above conditions maintained his improvement. When he was seen three years later he was working as an orderly in a large hospital, had married an attendant on the ward, and though he had given up all idea of taking college work, he was interested in his work, content, and without any sign of neurosis.

OBSTETRICS AND GYNECOLOGY[2]

The reproductive tract of the female is very susceptible to the influence of emotional changes. Menstruation and pregnancy are frequently involved. The menstrual cycle may be delayed or precipitated, it may become irregular, it may be associated with severe cramps, or with an excessive feeling of irritability. The uterus is plentifully supplied by sympathetic and parasympathetic nerves, but the nervous influence on the uterus may also come from the emotional excitation which directly or indirectly undoubtedly influences the hypothalamus.

Menstrual delay may occur in many instances and under widely varying circumstances. It is not infrequently found in unmarried women who fear conception, or in married women who also do not wish (or for that matter strongly wish) pregnancy.[3] Emotional tension does not particularly accommodate these patients; it exerts its usual inhibiting effect on the menstrual cycle. On the other hand, if there has been prolonged inhibition and emotional tension, the menses may become first irregularly delayed and after a while, quite profuse and frequent. Deficiencies of the glands of internal secretion play a vital role, and often produce therapeutic effects when supplied; but the intercorrelation between emotional tension and endocrine secretion is such as to make the separation of the two extremely difficult. It is important to check every possible factor when treating these conditions. Delayed onset of menses in the adolescent girl may be more closely associated with ovarian dysfunction than with a psychobiologic unrest resulting from puberty; but an unhealthful atmosphere in the home, may, from the psychologic point of view, play an important role. Similarly in middle age, the early signs of menopause may be the essential element in menstrual dysfunction, but the emotional element should not be overlooked. In other words, disturbances in

---

[1] *Vide* p. 227.   [2] *Vide* p. 91 *ff.*   [3] *Vide* p. 108.

menstruation should be thoroughly studied from all possible aspects; but not the least of these should be the sociopsychologic aspects.

Fear of pregnancy is commonly associated with menstrual delay. Usually, the patient sees the physician within two days after the expected period has passed without the onset of menses; but delays may occur for several weeks or months. Not infrequently the patient gives a history of irregular menstruation, but it is not uncommon for the interruption to occur in a setting of regularity. The treatment is two-fold: one to determine whether the patient is pregnant or not, a difficult task insomuch as the Aschheim-Zondek pregnancy tests are usually not positive for several weeks in pregnant cases; and secondly to reassure the patient emotionally. The practical situation may be such as to make the advent of a child a difficult strain; the financial status of the family may be inadequate to support the existing children let alone a new addition; the physical condition may be such as to make it inadvisable to bear another child. As physicians, we must face the actual situation with its attendant complications. The physician must determine for himself what advice he will give; yet he must do what he can to give the patient courage and reassurance to face the outcome with as few fears or tears as possible. The release of emotional tension will permit the uterus to operate in its normal fashion and in the absence of pregnancy the flow will soon return. It is reassurance plus the increased morale on the part of the patient which releases this tension; and time itself is cooperative. Many abortions done behind locked doors are simply the scraping of normal uteri, wherein the menstrual flow was emotionally inhibited.

Miss A. B., aged twenty-three years, was in an intense state of apprehension. She had not slept for several nights, could not eat, and at the office could not concentrate on her work. She burst into tears at the slightest provocation. She was engaged to be married, but the ceremony was not to be performed for six months by which time the combined earnings would be sufficient to purchase furniture and outfit their home. They had been engaged for three years, and the necessity of supporting their respective families had limited their ability to save for their home, and even to support themselves adequately. Three weeks earlier, sex relations had occurred; and ever since, the patient had been certain that she had become pregnant. Her guilt feelings were so great that she had not dared to mention her fears even at confession. Her period had been expected two weeks ago, and when it did not come she was certain of pregnancy and began to dwell on all the "horrible" complications; all the symptoms of an intense anxiety state came to the fore.

It was necessary to reassure the patient, to show her that she had overemphasized the difficulties of the situation and was foreseeing possibilities which were unlikely, and, moreover, that she was overly sensitive to what others might think of her. If she were pregnant, it was pointed out, she could have a quiet wedding and continue to live as she had until she and her husband were ready to live together. The situation was not the happiest one, it was true; but on the other hand, it was not the calamitous one she had imagined. The first thing to do was to have a pregnancy test. She was to bring a sample of urine to the laboratory the next morning. In the meantime she was to take phenobarbital every three hours and whenever she felt "nervous,"[1] the purpose of the medicine being to quiet her and reduce her tension. She was urged consciously to do what she could to avoid thinking of the subject,[2] and to enter into as many diverting activities as she could.[3] She was reassured that since her intended husband had used a contraceptive, she probably had no real pregnancy. Two days later the patient phoned to say that the menses had begun.

This experience is an extremely common one; and whereas one can do little as far as changing the actual situation if pregnancy occurs, one can do much so to change the patient's attitude that the situation can be handled with less perturbation and with more intelligent planning.

The reverse situation is also frequently found; *i. e.*, the patient desires a child and may be so affected by her desire that menstrual delay will occur. These persons do not need psychotherapy as much as a capable obstetrician, and time and effort often do what medication cannot do.

In many instances the menstrual period will come on earlier than usual, and may be prolonged. In some patients the period will last from ten to fourteen days, and occur with only a week's intermission. Rarely can any definite pathology be proved, though usually the diagnosis is made of an endocrine dysfunction. Clinically, many of these patients are in an intense emotional state, and have so been for some time.

It is difficult to state, post hoc, proper hoc, but it appears that the menstrual difficulty manifests itself in a setting of chronic anxiety attacks. In many patients the physician can discover the existence of a fibroid uterus, or ovarian pathology, or actual glandular deficiencies; yet in a large number no such organic basis can

[1] *Vide* p. 233 *ff*.   [2] *Vide* p. 194 *ff*.   [3] *Vide* p. 249 *ff*.

be found. Moreover, in the course of psychotherapy, there is a spontaneous readjustment of many of these chronic uterine difficulties. Patients who come in with psychoneurotic complaints mention in the course of their discussion their chronic difficulty with menses, and while the menstrual complaint is not the primary one, there is frequently a spontaneous readjustment of it as the patient recovers. In these instances little is done in the way of direct treatment of the uterus or ovaries, nor is there any suggestion given or discussion of this problem other than the preliminary one. The improvement occurs simultaneously with the improvement of the neurosis.[1] In these situations, as in most others, the point of attack does not lie in the uterus but in the emotional tension.

Miss K. L., aged nineteen years, complained of excessive irritability, crying spells, a sleep troubled constantly by dreams, and marked palpitation. Her general physical history revealed a tendency to chronic constipation, and menstrual irregularity. For several months she had periods lasting twelve to fourteen days, and it seemed to her that hardly had she ceased to flow than she began again. There was a constant feeling of tiredness, and her blood count was just under four million.

She lived in a very unhealthy environment. Her mother was emotionally unstable and suffered frequently from all sorts of aches and pains. The mother used the patient as an outlet for her own unhappy existence. She nagged and scolded and criticized everything the patient did. The economic situation was in itself depressing, and the patient compared herself and her "unhappy plight" with that of other girls of her acquaintance. Her father was a sullen person, driven into verbal retirement before the constant onslaught of his wife's fault-finding; he gave no comfort to his children. The patient had wished to have a career, possibly in law; but the demands of the mother and family were such that she could not go beyond a two year high school course. She was taking courses in night school, and had avoided the company of her own or the opposite sex. She was extremely unhappy, her ambitional thwartings adding to the nagging and irritations which occurred at the home.

It was these factors which were at the basis for her psychoneurotic complaints and her menstrual difficulty. The excessive loss of blood resulted in her anemia; and her poor habits of health, of eating and sleeping, her lack of physical and mental recreation all were important contributory factors. The therapy was directed toward getting the patient to live a more normal life, which included more time for physical recreation, more time for social recreation, more attention to her personal appearance so that she would receive more invitations and social attention, a regulation of

---

[1] *Vide* p. 291.

her diet and sleeping hours: in short an entire revamping of her mode of existence. Secondly, the patient was taught how to adjust to the irritating situation at home. She was taught not to be irritated by her nagging mother, to regard her mother sympathetically in the light of her mode of living, and of all the normal satisfactions which any woman would have wished and which her mother had not had. She was trained to listen to her mother "with the mind and not the heart" so that she could evaluate intellectually what was said and follow what she considered right, without permitting herself to be aroused emotionally.[1] It took fourteen visits to inculcate sufficient of these principles so that she could "carry on" on her own; and when she was seen three months later, she was as her brother remarked "a different person." Her menstrual periods at that time lasted five days and were normal in every respect.

Menstrual cramps, low back pains at menses, hyperirritability, and attacks of depression are common accompaniments of the menses. In most women, these symptoms when they are present, come on one or two days before the onset of menses, and disappear after several days of menses. However, there are extreme individual variations so that some patients have such symptoms almost a week or ten days before and do not get any relief until several days after menstruation has ceased. Some patients are worse during the menses, though as a rule the intensification of symptoms lasts only during the first day or two of heavy flow. Again, some patients suffer slightly at the period of ovulation, but this condition is more uncommon than common.

In many instances these symptoms result from pelvic pathology, or from endocrine dysfunction. Indeed the dysfunction which produces these symptoms may on occasion give rise to an actual "menstrual psychosis," in which the psychotic personality is more or less latent, but sufficiently precarious that it can be thrown into a manifest psychosis by the menstrual period.

Miss K. V., aged twenty-five years, was diagnosed as having a schizophrenic psychosis. However, the illness had begun first to evidence itself at about sixteen and had continued since then with exacerbations and remissions. These exacerbations occurred during the menstrual period, and lasted from ten to fifteen days. During this time, she was frightened, irritable, and had many fearful hallucinations. Men were trying to attack her, and she was annoyed by electrical vibrations, etc. In between her menses, these symptoms subsided so that she was relatively normal, though she still

[1] *Vide* p. 200 *ff.*

retained a quiet, withdrawn attitude which is commonly found in catatonic patients. In this case, the menses in themselves were the precipitating factor; and the nervous system was so unstable that the change in endocrine activity upset her.

The reverse situation, however, is also true; intense emotional activity can disturb the menstrual function, as indicated by the cases cited above. Moreover, mild physiologic sensations which ordinarily pass unnoticed may be seized upon and over-emphasized by the psychoneurotic patient. Stated in another way, the threshold to pain and irritability has been lowered so that slight disturbances are more keenly felt. This lowered threshold is generally part of a total irritability, and tends to occur in persons who are suffering from a general state of tension. Some patients may be able to wear a mask over their feelings during the month and give up their restraints over the menstrual pain which is so common as to be considered justifiable and expressible. During menses, just before and just after, there is in most normal women usually an increase in sex desire;[1] and where sex maladjustment is present, the sexual associations may be a prominent factor in the production of emotional symptoms, and hence in the production of increased irritability, etc.

In the therapy of these menstrual symptoms there are four procedures which are most effective when used in conjunction, although the emphasis may be placed on any one or group of these procedures. Thus the first step should be to *deal with the physical substrata*,[2] whether it be pelvic pathology or insufficient endocrine secretion. This technique, for example the widespread use of theelin or progestin has often been overdone, since any disorder involving irritability, insomnia, etc. occurring during the fifth decade in women is often assumed to be the result of an early menopause. (2) The *disturbing emotional elements* which are existent *should be analyzed, and psychotherapy instituted* as necessary;[3] indeed, emotional difficulty is often the major difficulty in that it is usually a primal cause in the menstrual distress and in that it requires much time and effort to treat. (3) The person's *threshold to pain must be raised*[4] so that what cramps there are can be borne with greater equanimity and less awareness. Continuation of physical activity and of any other activity will serve to keep the attention focused on something else. The patient must consciously make the effort to think of other things, and let her attention

[1] *Vide* p. 100.   [2] *Vide* p. 122.   [3] *Vide* Ch. VI.   [4] *Vide* p. 222.

wander as little as possible to her uterine peristalsis. It will be found that most women can become more resistent to pain sensations, provided their underlying emotional pathology is corrected. In nursing schools, for example, a general discussion of the pain mechanism with an emphasis on the ability to control it and to overcome the associated irritability is followed by a definite decrease in the number of nurses who become ill and go to bed once a month. (4) However, the cramps are often very severe, and it is well to alleviate them, using medication in gradually decreasing doses,[1] so that point number three can be carried out. A very effective compound is codeine sulphate $\frac{1}{4}$ grains and acidiacetylsalicylici 5 grains in capsule form, one to be taken every three hours as necessary. Generally two or three will enable the patient who formerly had to spend the first day or two in bed, to continue with her work; and in subsequent doses the amount of codeine is gradually reduced.

This general outline must of course be modified to fit each individual case, and there will be considerable variation in the amount of emphasis placed on the various methods used; nevertheless, the most successful therapy will concern itself with the emotional background as well as with pathophysiologic backgrounds.

Vaginal cramps, pains and "drawing sensations" are very commonly the result of emotional difficulties which are of a sexual nature.[2] On occasion one may find some irritating lesion or excretion, yet even in many of these conditions the sensation is out of all proportion to the physical basis. In many women, "drawing sensations" occur before or after intercourse; and in the extremely maladjusted persons, these sensations may come on when there is merely the thought of intercourse. The actual sensations are the result of contractions of the pelvic musculature as well as of vaginal irritation and paresthesias of "central" origin. These contractions and irritations are stimulated by intercourse and yet are also the result of the person's desire. If this desire becomes strong enough, it may play the important role in an actual psychosis.

Miss G. N., aged fifty years, had various abdominal complaints for which she was attended by the family physician. One day she called her brother and told him that she was in love with her physician and he with her, and that they would soon be married. In haste the brother called the physician, only to find that he knew nothing of the situation. The patient admitted that he had given no cause for her statement other than that he smiled "knowingly" when she was in the room with him and that when he came

---

[1] *Vide* p. 233 *ff.*   [2] *Vide* p. 92.

near her he exerted some sort of force "like mental telepathy" which caused her to have a drawing sensation in her vagina. Thereafter, whenever a man came near her, she experienced this sensation and elaborated on it either by rejection of the sensation and accusation that the particular man was after her, or by acceptance of the sensation as evidence that the man wished to marry her.

This woman, a single, chronically neurotic person, had been reared by a strong and domineering father whom she feared and yet whose attention she desired more than anything else. Her personality was such that she did not have any proposals except one, and the suitor in that case suddenly disappeared before the marriage. She envied all her married friends, and resented keenly the slurs on "old maids." In this setting the above symptoms developed, and the drawing sensation in the vagina was a real as well as symbolic expression of her desires. The therapy was two-fold: one, chemotherapy in the form of metrazol; and two, psychotherapy to reorient her attitudes toward "old maids" and to adjust her to a marriageless life.

Vomiting during pregnancy[1] may have its origin in various mechanisms not the least of which is the psychologic status. To most women, pregnancy is an exceedingly important experience not only in itself, but because of the increased attention which is expected and obtained. Moreover, neurotic as well as non-neurotic women become pregnant, and the emotionality where existent is continued into and exaggerated during pregnancy. As a consequence there is finnickiness about food, the desire to have certain attentions, vomiting at the slightest provocation, etc. This last mentioned may be aided also by the fact that there is some physiologic disturbance early in pregnancy to which the body has not become accustomed. Yet one not infrequently finds women with vomiting of pregnancy who believe they are pregnant but have not even missed the first menstrual period. The treatment of these conditions lies in the calm statement of the problem to the patient so that she understands the mechanism involved and the role of the emotions. Then the most disturbing problems are discussed and the patient is urged to handle them objectively and philosophically wherever possible. Finally, particularly if hypnosis is used in conjunction with the above treatment, most patients will lose their symptoms.

OTHER PSYCHONEUROTIC SYMPTOMS

Insomnia.—Insomnia is one of the most difficult of symptoms to treat, for the problem which confronts the physician is not only the inability to sleep but also the restless, dreaming sleep from

[1] *Vide* p. 92.

which one awakens tired. The actual mechanism of sleep is unknown, though there are many theories thereon. The disturbance of sleep, however, commonly falls into five etiologic categories: toxic states, inadequate habit training, overstimulation, neurosis, and depression.

Toxic states are frequently found after operations, in acute and chronic illnesses, and in drug poisoning. In these conditions, if the toxin is stimulating and irritating, sleeplessness will be produced; if the toxicity has gone beyond the irritative stage into the depressive stage there may be oversleep and comatose states. The therapy of these causative conditions is essential in order to produce sleep. While the toxic state continues, it is inadvisable to use drugs such as bromides, which in themselves may become toxic factors. Indeed the least objectional of all drugs during the toxic state is morphine without the hyoscine, for it has a valuable function in quieting fears and emotions as well as a hypnotic function; and the toxic state in general precludes the liability toward habit formation.

The *habit element*[1] is an important one in bringing on sleep. If one follows the same procedure and retires each night at the same time, sleep will tend to come on automatically. The more routinized one becomes in this matter, the more surely will sleep come on. The organism is given to automaticity; and one can make sleep come on just as one can train peristalsis of the intestine to come on at given intervals. In general, persons who are sleepless for long periods of time would do well to cultivate such a habit in addition to the other measures used. One frequently finds in many such patients a marked irregularity in retiring and, while many persons fall asleep quickly and well without the aid of regularity, one should use this as a help for therapeutic purposes.

Overstimulation, excitement, or an unsolved problem, particularly of a personal nature, may serve to keep the patient awake. The overstimulation may come about as the result of too much activity (a common cause of sleeplessness in children), of an intensely interesting play or discussion, or experience, or even from drugs, as caffeine. This central stimulation is sufficient to keep sleep from coming, particularly in tense, alert, or sensitive persons. These "stimulants" need to be removed, for they are the stress which precipitate the sleeplessness. It must be remembered, however, that if a person can lose sleep over such stimulations, it is an

[1] *Vide* pp. 42; 351.

indication that he is basically at a high level of irritability; and an examination of his reactions in waking life will show many indications of this fact. As a consequence, the *treatment of insomnia resulting from apparent overstimulation is not only the removal of this stress but also the reorganization of the daily life and attitudes.*

The normal person not infrequently has a night in which he cannot sleep, because of some such overstimulation. Every one has on occasion some worry, concern, or disturbance over a personal problem which will keep him awake. Such occasions are more frequent in some and less in others, and the average person has several sleepless nights a year. This experience falls within the normal range, and thus does not call for any special therapy, other than the use of a sedative should sleep not come after an hour or two in bed.

A chronic tendency toward sleeplessness, particularly if it lasts for many years (in contradistinction to the chronic insomnia of many months found in a manic-depressive depression) is usually the result of a *psychoneurotic state*, the most common variety of which is chronic tension.[1] In persons with this difficulty, the primary basis for the insomnia is conflict and emotional unrest over some difficult situation. The treatment of this insomnia to be permanently effective must be directed toward the cause. Medication, itself, will generally fail, and large doses result in a drugged sleep with "hangovers." When these persons go to bed they cannot sleep because they are extremely tense and carry with them the preoccupation of the day; and even when they deny "consciously" thinking of their conflict, the very existence of the unsolved emotional situation, indicates that they "unconsciously" are concerned over it.

These patients go to bed and toss for hours before they manage to get to sleep; and when sleep does come, it is interrupted by frequent waking moments, by fearful dreams, by a feeling of fatigue on awakening. It is difficult for them to get out of bed in the morning, and they are tired most of the day. This state of affairs exists with medication also, except that sleep is brought on more quickly; but this does not result in an amelioration of the restlessness, the disturbing dreams, the subsequent feeling of fatigue; and there is often additional sleepiness and sluggishness as a result of the drug.

There are many degrees, however, of psychoneurotic tension, and many degrees of sleep disturbance. In the milder forms, one may

[1] *Vide* p. 24.

simply find it difficult to fall asleep because of anxiety over some transient problem; in such a case a quick acting sedative is often efficacious. In the more extreme forms, very little in the way of symptomatic therapy is helpful, and a state of chronic exhaustion results. Insomnia is merely a symptom—an annoying, fatigue-producing symptom—yet merely the result of other causes. Above all the patient should understand that lack of sleep does not mean that insanity will occur or that he will be excessively weakened. To treat it in itself is to fail to recognize the need of the organism to be rid of the cause; and indeed on closer examination, one may often find that insomnia rarely exists in pure form; that there are many associated symptoms of the underlying cause.

Another major cause of insomnia is the *manic-depressive depression*. These depressions occur far more commonly than is generally recognized.[1] The insomnia of these patients is particularly intractable. Frequently, these patients can fall asleep quickly, but they then awaken at two or three in the morning and are unable to go to sleep again. Moreover, these patients tend to awaken with their jaws clenched and their fists tight, indications that even during sleep they were not relaxed. It is this *muscular tension which exists during sleep* which is in a large measure responsible for their tiredness on awakening. However, these patients often have several days of inability to go to sleep; and even with medication the sleep is a restless, tossing, irritable, nightmarish one. Various methods may be used; often a drug is successful for a while only to fail after a short period of use. Here again the maxim of treating the cause comes to the fore. As the depression spontaneously lifts, the sleep tends to become normal, indicating in another way that the insomnia is only a symptom. When these patients are treated with metrazol shock therapy, the depression and the sleep both improve together, and it is interesting to witness a protracted insomnia clear up after two or three shock treatments.

Hence the first principle of treatment of the insomnia which results from tension, from psychoneurotic phenomena is the treatment of the tension itself. This necessity is seen, for example, in the case of Mrs. O. N.,[2] whose concern over her alcoholic son, prevented the most powerful of sedatives from acting. From practical experience, one finds that long term ability to sleep (temporarily many drugs are very efficacious in producing a restful sleep, but they generally fail when the person returns to his normal environ-

[1] *Vide* p. 356.   [2] *Vide* p. 234.

ment and problems) is brought about in proportion to the ability with which one is able to remove the psychological tension.

One of the most valued adjuncts in producing sleep is hypnosis.[1] In hospitals it is far easier to use this method than it is on patients in their home, because of the limitations of the physician's time. Yet when it can be done sleep through hypnosis has advantages which far outweigh those of drug-induced sleep, for hypnosis functions not by physically toxifying the brain centers, to produce unconsciousness, but by relieving the psychologic tension which initially is at the bottom of the symptom. However, even in this situation, the hypnotic effect is temporary unless one removes the cause of insomnia.

Miss L. R. had suffered from chronic insomnia for many years. She would not go to sleep until late at night and then would toss about for many hours. She averaged two to three hours sleep a night; and although she worked every day, she fainted frequently. She went on "on her nerve."

When first seen, she was given pentobarbital grains $1\frac{1}{2}$ and told to take it every one-half hour until asleep. She took 7 capsules and slept for three hours. Several nights later, she was given some "white pills" which consisted of $\frac{1}{4}$ grain morphine sulphate, and told to take one pill every fifteen minutes until asleep. She took 3 grains of morphine and slept three and a half hours. Finally, in desperation, $7\frac{1}{2}$ grains of sodium amytal was given intravenously, and the patient went right to sleep but slept only three hours. Medication seemed to be of little avail in the treatment of her insomnia.

An effort was then made to hypnotize her. She succumbed quickly and went into the third stage. Under hypnosis, she was told not only that she would sleep long, but that her basic difficulties would be faced in another manner, and that she would no longer be tense over her particular problem. That night she slept nine and one-half hours without awakening.

The tremendous resistance that this patient had to the various drugs testifies not to their impotence, but to the potency of her emotional disturbance. Conversely, the effect of hypnosis, which was repeated frequently, testified to the emotional nature of her insomnia.

Further therapy may be in the nature of providing diverting interests just before retiring. Reading, for example, often puts one's trend of thoughts away from the self, and is succeeded by sleep. Even exciting and stimulating activities may be of value if, rather than keeping the patient awake, they provide sufficient relief from his own thoughts to be actually sedative instead of stimulating. Moreover, the alleviation of the neurosis itself requires the expenditure of effort in several non-personal directions.

[1] *Vide* p. 227 *ff.*

Medically there are several approaches to the production of sleep. The most commonly used principle is that of depressing cortical activity by some sleep producing drug. The purpose of these drugs is to quiet cortical activity (*i. e.*, in the ordinary case of insomnia) when the activity is the result of excessive psychologic stimulation. It is unfortunate that medical science has not as yet developed more efficient ways of diminishing cortical activity than by the use of depressing drugs. Nevertheless, many of the drugs used are invaluable in the absence of better methods. As a rule the quicker acting drugs which tend to wear off are better than those with long action, for the hang-over effect should be avoided where possible, and generally speaking in the neuroses, the difficulty lies in going to sleep; in contrast to the depression in which patients fall asleep quickly but awaken early in the morning and stay awake; and once sleep is produced it will continue on its own power. Sleep may also be "wooed" by decreasing cerebral circulation; by hot drinks or warm baths or massage before bed time, which have the effect of drawing the blood to the splanchnic area and to the periphery, away from the brain. A cold wet pack often accomplishes the same purpose by making use of the body's compensatory tendency. The patient is loosely wrapped in a bed sheet which has been wrung out in water about 60 to 70 degrees. This pack is distinctly chilly at first, but soon there develops a compensatory peripheral vasodilatation which permits the patient to drop off to sleep. Similarly it is easier, as a rule, to sleep under warm covers in a cold room; and conversely overheated rooms on very hot days are generally detrimental to sleep because the escape of heat from the organism is not so efficiently carried out.

Headaches.—Headaches[1] are one of the commonest of psychoneurotic symptoms. Here again, there is probably some vasomotor change; *e. g.*, in the meninges as in many other psychoneurotic phenomena, which is at the basis of the symptom. There are several types of headaches which are common. *Pressure on top of the head* is probably the most frequently described one. The patient feels as if there were a weight pushing down on his head, rather than a true ache. A second type of headache is *over the occipital region;* this headache probably is associated with tension of the trapezius and other muscles which insert on the skull in this region and the muscle tension is great enough to create an ache. The above two types are most common, but there are

[1] *Vide* p. 92.

22

many other varieties. The patient may complain of his head "being too full" or of a tight band about his head, of burning areas over localized "spots" which may be described "as big as a dollar" and the like, of pain over the eyes which the patient often spontaneously insists is the result of eye trouble, but which has no relation to eye fatigue. Frequently the site of headache shifts all over the head. The headache may be so intense as to cause the patient to stay in bed for days at a time or to submit himself to all sorts of harrowing procedures. The intensity is dependent upon two factors, the intensity of the underlying emotional difficulty, and the amount of "vasomotor" (it may be some other physiologic mechanism) resonance.

The treatment must be directed toward the cause. One cannot say enough about studying the physical constitution first. The case of the boy[1] who was said to have a psychoneurotic headache and finally turned out to have sinuses full of pus, is very much to the point. Yet when once it has been established that there is no organic etiology, as we think of disease today, then the psychotherapeutic procedure should always be employed. In such instances, in addition to relieving the emotional stress, it is important that the patient continue with his daily activities as much as is possible despite the pain in the head. Mrs. F. S. for example,[2] found that her intolerable headaches were greatly relieved not only by changed attitudes but also by forcing herself into social activity despite the feeling that she could not leave the house because of the intensity of the ache. In many instances, persistent intractable headaches are found in efficient, but driving and tense persons; and the therapy is directed toward relaxing these basic drives. Time and persistence are important elements in therapy.

---

[1] *Vide* p. 177.   [2] *Vide* p. 165.

CHAPTER XV

THE PSYCHOSES

THE psychoses differ from the neuroses;[1] but the distinction between the two is neither definite nor clear. Some men have termed the psychoses major, and the neuroses minor psychoses; but such verbal differentiations do not aid in an understanding of the illnesses. H. Douglas Singer believes that the neuroses are the result of psychogenic disturbances; whereas the psychoses have their origin in a physiologic disturbance, the pathology in schizophrenia[2] and manic-depressive psychoses[3] existing in the central autonomic system. Clinically, the psychotic patient tends to act or talk "queerly" while the psychoneurotic patient tends to appear as an average person who has some physical or emotional ailment. The phrase "tends to" is used advisedly, for in actual practice the distinction is often difficult to make. In a psychosis, the person's attitude toward reality is changed: the manic-depressive viewing all incidents either as hopeless or joyously probable; the schizophrenic withdrawing into phantasy, or projecting his thoughts so that they appear to be realities; and the psychoneurotic on the other hand reacting to life as do others in his community but in an overly tense or symbolic fashion. The psychotic patient as a rule must eventually be committed to an institution because he cannot get along in society; but the psychoneurotic patient rarely has to be. Because of the lack of clarity in distinction between these two groups, it is far better to speak in terms of the actual disease reaction patterns such as schizophrenia, senile dementia, or hysteria, than in terms of psychosis or neurosis.

The underlying personality plays an important role in medical as well as psychiatric disorders. When a person develops an illness, his reaction to that illness involves not only the particular part involved but also the entire personality in proportion to the extent to which it is influenced. Thus a patient with a chronic and painful condition such as gout will tend to be irritable and have explosive outbursts, while his perhaps more intense suffering from a fracture of the wrist may in no way influence his reaction. Persistent stimulation of the cerebral centers by painful impulses will, however,

---

[1] *Vide* p. 22. [2] *Vide* p. 378. [3] *Vide* p. 355.

sooner or later disturb the patient's personality. The same is true
in peptic ulcer, hypertension, spastic colitis, cardiac disturbances,
persistent headaches, muscular or neuritic pains, etc.: all of which
may in themselves result from emotional turmoil. Regardless of
their etiology, these symptom complexes tend to disturb the
personality reaction, and thus create a vicious cycle.

Not only does one person react in various ways to various pains;
but also different persons react to the same disturbance with different patterns of behavior. Some will become irritable, some will cry
and complain, some will be stoically silent and depressed, while
others may become philosophical and tolerant.[1] The type of response which comes to the fore under stress depends largely upon
the type of personality which existed before the illness. The type
of personality in turn depends, as we have seen in earlier chapters,
upon the type of heredity,[2] the type of constitution,[3] the molding
forces of the environment,[4] and so on. These personality factors
are modified by the degree of cortical control which we are able to
learn in our social and private lives. Indeed our entire social
structure is dependent upon the ability of man (by means of the
cortex) to modify his basic drives and desires so that he can exist
in the company of others.

In the psychoses, these basic personality features come to the
fore far more strikingly than in the usual medical ailments. In
some persons these basic personality features appear spontaneously
and without apparent cause: in those persons in whom there is
primarily an instability of mood, the psychosis will be of the manic-
depressive variety; in those in whom there is a marked inclination
toward phantasy formation[5] and inhibition formation,[6] the psychosis will be of the schizophrenic variety. If there are sufficient
balancing features, a neurosis may result. When the psychosis
springs sui generis, without demonstrable pathology, the physician
may be sure that prior to the onset of symptoms, the basic personality has been extremely susceptible.

If there is a disease such as general paresis[7] which involves the
cortex, the control over the basic personality traits will then be
diminished if not lost; or the control may be so disturbed as to
create excessive and ambivalent[8] actions. Such a disease process
would thus show symptoms both of the disease (in this instance of

---

[1] *Vide* p. 220.   [2] *Vide* p. 262.   [3] *Vide* p. 183.   [4] *Vide* p. 46.
[5] *Vide* p. 74.   [6] *Vide* p. 78.   [7] *Vide* p. 352.   [8] *Vide* p. 76.

syphilis) and also of the released[1] underlying personality. It is important to keep this phenomenon in mind when one is confronted with a schizophrenic psychosis, for the precipitating factor may be some organic illness of the cerebral cortex, and when this illness is removed, as it can be in general paresis, the psychosis will disappear.

To distinguish between the two forms of psychosis, the term "organic psychoses" is used to refer to personality disturbances resulting from organic changes in the cerebral cortex, and "functional psychoses" to refer to those without apparent organic bases, even though the symptoms of both of these groups may in many ways be identical. The functional psychoses include the manic-depressive variety,[2] and the schizophrenic reactions.[3]

The following outline is an example of the form commonly used to obtain information about the patient who is psychotic. Much of the material must be obtained from sources other than the patient.

PARTIAL LIST OF TOPICS OF PSYCHIATRIC WORKUP
(As Copied From an Outline Used in a Psychiatric Clinic.)

Name, age, sex, race, SMWD, occupation, address. Addresses: correspondents, doctor.

COMPLAINTS of patient and friends, and the problems these suggest.

PRESENT ILLNESS given by patient and friends; plus data on sleep, appetite, constipation, weight, sexual desire, menstruation, medication, drugs, alcohol, compensation, insurance; and topics of Mental Status.

SOMATIC HISTORY.—Especially accidents, operations, diseases (esp. lues, encephalitis) headaches, vision, diplopia, dizziness, specks, aphonia, gait, paralysis, anesthesia, tremor, convulsions, dyspnoea, palpitation, G. I., G. U. Endurance and fatigue. Concern about body functions.

PERSONAL HISTORY.—Previous attacks; hospitalization. Birth injuries. Time of onset of walking and talking; school record; enuresis; spoiled child tendencies; nightmares, stuttering; chorea; thumb-sucking; nail-biting; sleeping arrangements. Stealing or lying. Legal difficulties. Finances. Work record. Attitude toward parents, sibs, spouse, children, friends. Sex information, development, activities (masturbation, homosexuality, heterosexuality, marriage, contraception). Religion. Fads and physical culture notions. Deaths. Disappointments. Quarrels. Promotion and demotion. Medical contacts. Responsibilities. Assets; successes, accomplishments. Interests, hobbies, ambitions.

PERSONALITY TRAITS.—Actions and attitudes, indicating that patient was: *sensitive*, *shy*, seclusive, shut-in, day-dreamer, *sociable*, outgoing, active, friendly, affectionate, *rigid*, plastic, stubborn, obstinate, *suspicious*, jealous, frank, *moody*, restless, dissatisfied, irritable, impulsive, cheerful, anxious, apprehensive, worrisome, *conscientious*, neat, orderly, meticulous,

---

[1] *Vide* p. 347.   [2] *Vide* p. 355 *ff.*   [3] *Vide* p. 378 *ff.*

efficient, cruel, stingy, *nosophilic*, eager to have sympathy, martyr attitude, *aggressive*, submissive, a leader, a follower, self-confident, apt to feel inferior, *religious*, ethical, moral, interested in the abstract and in "right and wrong", self-imposed discipline.

FAMILY HISTORY.—Nervous and mental illness, epilepsy, alcoholism, drug addiction; personality traits of relatives. Moodiness; seclusiveness; successes; failures. Suicides. Hospitalization. Social and cultural setting and deviations.

MENTAL STATUS.—(*a*) *Appearance and Behavior.*—Rapport, facial and bodily expression, condition of hair and clothing; postures, gestures, tics, grimaces, negativism, stereotypy, gracefulness; amount, character and speed of activity. Fear; restless; agitated.

(*b*) *Stream of Talk.*—Amount, rhyming, distractible, punning, flight of ideas, retardation, relevant, coherent, concise, disconnected, scattered, circumstantial, neologisms, word-salad, blocking.

(*c*) *Mood and Special Preoccupations.*—Mood statement, mood shown by expression and behavior (*e. g.*, tearfulness), emotional discrepancy, morning-evening variation, worries, suicidal ideas, topics of concern, "change in attitude of others," how treated by others?, "imaginations," "peculiar experiences," "bad luck," "anything can't understand"? perplexity, hallucinations, delusions (persecution, power, body-changes, poverty, immorality, hopelessness, guilt), ideas of reference, passivity feelings, obsessions, compulsions, phobias, difficulty in concentration and thinking, unreality feelings. Dreams.

(*d*) *Orientation.*—For time, place, person, situation. Clearness in comprehension, grasp, active and passive attention.

(*e*) *Memory.*—Remote and recent events, (*e. g.*, Dates of birth, deaths, marriages, starting school, graduation; time came to hospital; items of recent meals, etc.). Immediate recall of words, digits, story.

(*f*) *Calculation.*—Simple and difficult problems, 100 − 7; 100 + 7.

(*g*) *Information.*—Presidents, cities, wars, rivers, capitals.

(*h*) *Judgment.*—On business, sports. Plans. Give difference between: dwarf and child; lie and mistake; tree and bush.

(*i*) *Insight.*—In what way sick? How explain condition?

PHYSICAL EXAMINATION.—Especially tremor, pupils, reflexes, gait, nerve tenderness, speech, test phrases, writing, body build. T.P.R., B.P., Ophthal. Endocrine.

SPECIAL EXAMINATION.—Urine, BWaR., blood counts, x-rays, GA., BMR., B.Chem., bromide, L.P., Binet, psychogalvanic, Jung, Rohrschach. Consultations.

ORGANIC PSYCHOSES[1]

The organic psychoses are characterized by pathologic processes involving the *cortex* of the brain in a *diffuse* fashion, and by symptoms of deterioration of such intellectual processes as memory, orientation, and ability to calculate.

[1] *Vide* p. 19.

The organic psychoses differ from the so-called functional psychoses such as schizophrenia or manic-depressive psychosis, in that the latter have no demonstrable pathology in the cortex (or elsewhere as far as we can prove now, though there may be lesions in the hypothalamus) and do not show real defects in the intellectual processes.

The etiology of the organic psychoses may be classified according to the usual pathologic categories: toxic, infectious, degenerative, and traumatic. The symptoms of all these etiologic agents are of three sorts: (1) those resulting from the disease process itself; (2) those resulting from involvement of the brain tissue itself (these symptoms may or may not be identical with (1); and (3) those resulting from the personality disturbance. Thus a patient who has pneumonia complicated by a delirium may have symptoms of (1) the pneumonia process itself with fever, pain in the chest, cough, etc.; of (2) intellectual defect such as poor memory, disorientation, and lack of comprehension, symptoms resulting from the malfunction of cerebral cortex; and of (3) the underlying personality disturbance such as delusions of persecution, and other schizophrenic features. These latter features are seen in the non-psychotic person as shyness, sensitivity, phantasy formation and so forth; but when these personality symptoms are pathologically intensified they become withdrawal into one's self,[1] suspiciousness,[2] and hallucinations.[3] Toxic factors may include such common ones as alcoholism, toxemia secondary to infectious processes, drug toxins, etc. Infectious processes include most commonly general paresis, and any other primary (e. g., meningococcus) or secondary (e. g., streptococcus from a middle ear infection) infection. Degenerative processes include such states as senile dementia,[4] presenile dementia, and arteriosclerotic dementia. Traumatic psychoses are not common and usually are associated with widespread damage of the cortex, as we shall see later; for simple trauma to the brain does not produce psychotic symptoms.

The pathology of the disease processes, *to produce a true organic psychosis, must involve the cortex of the brain, and must be relatively diffuse.*[5] Lesions which involve the subcortex such as Parkinson's disease, or subcortical hemorrhages do not produce a psychosis, unless there is sufficient destruction of the white matter so that the functioning of much of the cortex becomes impaired, as occurs late

---

[1] *Vide* p.68 .   [2] *Vide* p. 23.   [3] *Vide* p. 380.
[4] *Vide* p. 352.   [5] *Vide* p. 19.

in encephalomyelitis periaxialis diffusa.   Only when the cortex is involved directly as by infection or trauma, or indirectly as by toxins does an organic psychosis occur.   Similarly, the damage must be diffuse to produce a psychosis (probably less diffuse over Pierre Marie's quadrilateral space than elsewhere to produce the same amount of intellectual change) for local hemorrhages, trauma, and brain tumors do not of themselves produce mental symptoms unless the injury is diffuse or produces increased inter-cranial pressure.   This damage may be reversible as occurs in acute alcoholic psychoses, or irreversible as in senile dementia.   In addition to these etiologic factors, there are the predisposing ones of inheritable or constitutional nature,[1] or even of tense emotional stress.   Patients who suffer from senile dementia and arteriosclerotic dementia frequently have progenitors who developed similar conditions.   Many persons have nervous systems which are easily susceptible to toxins, and these patients manifest deliria with the slightest degree of fever or infection.   Some persons who are under intense emotional strain, need exercise all their effort to control their reactions and having lost their customary control under the influence of some cortical irritant, may express delirious symptoms.   As in other psychotic conditions, there are multiple factors which may influence the production of the organic psychoses.

   The symptoms which result directly from diffuse involvement of the cortex are those of intellectual defect.   The cortex itself is the seat of "intelligence."   As Pavlov has so well shown, practically all conditioned reflexes are learned by the cortex, and without the cortex, learning either cannot take place or does so at such a low level as to be negligible.   Conditioning reflexes are in themselves one of the important bases of learning, remembering, and therefore of social control; and these phenomena disappear as the cortex is involved. When formally tested, the patient manifests defects (in varying degrees) in orientation, memory, ability to calculate, general information, and judgment.   These qualities are technically classified as intellectual, and are essentially a function of the cortex.

   Emotion as such does not have its origin in the cortex.   Although emotion is apprehended by the cortex, and the significance of emotion may be modified by cortical content, *emotion itself is a feeling tone resulting from the state of the whole organism, probably having its integration in the thalamus.*   Emotion and moods are

   [1] *Vide* p. 262.

highly integrated sensations springing from the state of the viscera, the efficiency of the cardiovascular system, endocrine balance, the state of nutrition, etc., as well as from pleasant experiences. It is common experience to "feel good" after a cold shower, or to be mellow, or hilarious after a few drinks of alcohol, or to be depressed and pessimistic after much fatigue. Such changes in the state of emotion result not from a "decision" of the person that he *will feel better* but from the physiologic actions of the aforementioned agencies. On the other hand, ideas may be depressing or stimulating to the degree that the person "feels" that which he thinks. The death of a stranger, for example, is accepted with intellectual appreciation but without any "feeling"; whereas death in the immediate family not only affects consciousness, but permeates through consciousness to the physiologic organism so that a state of "feeling" is aroused. Even death in one's own family is "felt" in proportion to the amount of physiologic reverberations which have become conditioned to the idea; *i. e.*, the depth and intensity of feeling are not identical with all members of the same family. Simple *intellectual awareness is not necessarily associated with emotion*. This fact is well seen, for example, in psychotherapy; the patient may understand that which is wrong, and know what to do, yet be unconvinced emotionally and therefore unable to implement his wishes. In psychotherapy it is essential not only to discover the underlying difficulties, and point out the correct mental hygiene, but so to train the patient that he "feels" that which he should think.[1] To put it still another way, one may say that in training a person to be emotionally stable, one must in reality train the *physiologic* system to react and respond in a stable fashion.

The above statement, however, must not be taken to imply the unimportance of the cerebral cortex in the *control* of emotion. The cortex is to a large extent the means by which emotions can be stabilized; and the cortex can so direct the entire neuromuscular system of the body as to produce elevations of blood pressure, contractions of the stomach, rapid or skipped heart beats, and so on. How the cortex acts is still unknown, but it is likely that the thalamo-cortical and the cortico-thalamic relationship is such as strongly to modify the action of both the cortex and the thalamus. Destruction of the cortex itself may bring about no emotional changes other than that the emotions may no longer have adequate control or that inhibitions may be excessively lost, thus releasing

[1] *Vide* p. 129.

thalamic activity. This change is evident in many senile persons,[1] who may have such a marked dropping out of cortical cells that they can no longer recall the names of members of their family, and yet being relatively unimpaired emotionally, may be happy and content. Should these senile patients have a basically unstable emotional system before the dropping out of the cortical cells, then the control which they formerly exercised over their moods is impaired, and the basic emotions come to the fore.

Conversely, in diseases where the cortex is left relatively intact and the subcortex is involved, there may be tremendous outbursts of emotion, even though there is relatively good intelligence. This situation is best seen in post-encephalitic children, who are extremely unstable, and may be so disturbed in their behavior as to require institutionalization. In these children the disease involves primarily the subcortex, and although there is an affinity for the striate body, lesions occur throughout. The cortex is left relatively intact, so that though the child may be vicious, have temper tantrums, and be exceedingly destructive and combative, he may yet demonstrate an excellent intellectual ability. In such instances the emotional seat, the thalamus and the thalamo-cortical connections, has probably been impaired, so that emotional integration is interfered with. In adults this same reaction is not so common; but since many of the so-called psychopathic personalities have similar outbursts of emotion, it may be that there is a similar basis in thalamic lesions.

Clear cut instances of purely intellectual defect, or of purely emotional defect are uncommon because every person is such an admixture of emotions and intellect as to make rigid distinction impossible. Nevertheless the concept is of value in understanding the psychiatric illnesses.

In the organic psychoses, the cortex is primarily involved, and hence, the primary symptoms are those of intellectual damage. The formal mental status examination to test these functions is given on page 342.

It will be observed that the functions of intelligence revolve about memory and the integrations which utilize memory; and memory, of course, is essentially dependent upon the cortex. Frequently the intellectual changes involving memory are very fine and will not be brought out by such crude questions as those neces-

[1] *Vide* p. 352.

sitating no more than recognition of the date or place; the changes may be so fine that detailed tests, compatible with the person's background, are advisable. For the psychiatrist it is important to distinguish between a real defect in intellectual processes which is a characteristic indication of the organic psychoses, and a pseudo defect, the result of lack of cooperation or attention.[1] Often it is necessary to test the patient repeatedly in order to arrive at an evaluation of the extent of the degenerative process. It is also important to distinguish between the lack of knowledge due to feeblemindedness[2] which has existed since birth, and the memory defects which result from an active process which diminishes what knowledge already exists. The amount of memory defect tends to parallel the amount and severity of involvement of the cerebral cortex.

Because of the mutual interdependence of memory processes, which are at the basis of thinking, and of emotional capacities, which are at the basis of personality, one cannot draw a sharp distinction between intelligence and personality defects. Clinically, however, the extreme cases show this difference quite well, for of two patients suffering from, let us say, alcoholic toxicity, one may be defective only in that his memory is poor and his judgment inadequate, while his emotional status remains relatively stable; and the other may have a relatively mild involvement of memory and yet be very emotional and neurotic. The cortical involvement in one has been sufficient to produce simple intellectual changes, while in the other, it has served merely to release (in the sense of Hughlings Jackson) the real personality[3] which had hitherto been inhibited by the normal intact cortex. It is this underlying personality which when it comes to the fore in toxic psychoses, tends to produce many of the disturbances.

The symptoms of one case with organic psychosis (e. g., alcoholic) may be of a schizophrenic[4] nature with hallucinations, delusions of persecution, projection mechanisms, over symbolization, etc. In another, it may be a manic state,[5] with laughter, flight of ideas, exaltation, wittiness, and over-activity. In still another, it may take the form of a depression,[6] with crying spells, feelings of hopelessness and inadequacy, constant worry, and a drive toward suicide. In a fourth, the symptoms may be those of a psychoneurosis, with many

---

| [1] *Vide* p. 381. | [2] *Vide* p. 413. | [3] *Vide* p. 339. |
| [4] *Vide* p. 380. | [5] *Vide* p. 358. | [6] *Vide* p. 361. |

hypochondriacal complaints,[1] or anxiety states,[2] or hysterical phenomena,[3] etc. In still another, there may be practically no psychotic picture other than a marked deficiency of the intellect, associated with confused restlessness and irritability.

It can further be understood, how those subjects who may have a latent schizophrenic personality[4] will tend to develop schizophrenic symptoms once conscious and cortical control is diminished by toxins; similarly, manic states, depressive states, hypochondriacal states, hysterical conditions, etc., may come to the fore in these toxic patients, depending upon their underlying personality and emotional status.

The treatment of the organic psychoses (the terms "delirium" and "acute phase of organic psychosis" are synonymous) depends upon the specific etiology and upon the general disturbance consequent to the brain damage. The *acute delirium* itself should be treated by reducing the fever to 100° or 101°, both by drugs such as aspirin and by frequent sponge baths; (2) by increasing elimination of toxic processes by means of increasing elimination and by forcing nutrient fluids such as fruit juices; (3) by a diet high in calories yet liquid or semiliquid in character to facilitate easy swallowing, and (4) by a high vitamin intake, particularly of vitamin B. The drugs[5] used should be those least liable in themselves to produce toxicosis; for example, bromides, because of the toxic nature of the drug, often make the delirious patient even more delirious; if sufficient bromide is given to produce a sedative effect, the patient on awakening often has enough of the drug left in his system for the effect to be irritative instead of sedative.

The entire question of the value of drugs in delirium needs a thorough reviewing. Drugs are often given "to quiet the patient" when in actuality the patient would be far better without such medication. The word "drug" itself implies what happens to the patient; the unfortunate result of much drug administration is that the physical organism needs to combat another toxin in addition to those which it is already engaged in eliminating. Often more damage is done to the delirious patient by sedative medication than by permitting the patient to talk or shout. It is of problematic value to the patient that he be drugged to the point of quietness or to cessation of restlessness, in order to avoid the loss of energy expended in moving about or in shouting. As a rule, the

[1] *Vide* p. 24.   [2] *Vide* p. 27.   [3] *Vide* p. 30.   [4] *Vide* p. 378.   [5] *Vide* p. 377.

delirious patient should receive a minimum of medication or sedation. The hospital, however, usually requires that something be done to quiet acutely delirious patients in order that others be not too much disturbed; and there should be special rooms or wards where these patients may be placed so as not to disturb others. In addition to those already mentioned, the best methods of combating restlessness and delirium are nursing care, hydrotherapy, and sleep-producing methods[1] (not simply by use of drugs).

A tactful, quieting, sympathetic, and patient nurse is one of the most important elements in the management of a delirium. Delirious patients are usually fearful, irritable, suspicious, and subject to vague impulses. Although these emotional states are the result of a disturbed internal environment, they may be intensified, or they may be ameliorated by external stimuli. Impersonal or brusque attention given to the patient by members of the hospital staff confirms suspicions and makes the susceptible mind a prey to hostile and disturbing ideas. For example, a nurse's insistence that a patient eat when he is not hungry breeds an antagonism which may irradiate[2] to include all requests or requirements. These situations can be done away with by employing the proper type of nurse. A nurse who can listen to the expression of irrational ideas without expressing alarm or concern, who can talk soothingly and quietly to the patient, who can have great patience in coaxing, not forcing, the patient is often more effective in therapy than any or all other forms of sedation. Hospital supervisors are commonly aware that the sleeplessness and restlessness among ward patients when one type of nurse is in charge will disappear without medication when a pleasant sympathetic nurse manages the ward.

Restlessness to the point of trying to get out of bed is also a problem of nursing care. Restraints should be avoided wherever at all possible. A patient who is disturbed sufficiently to try to get out of bed, will continue to try to do so even if restrained; and the very existence of the restraint will produce added fear, irritation, and effort, so that the patient is more exhausted and awake than he would have been had no anklets or wristlets been used. Moreover, if the patient sits up in bed (unless he have an operative wound which may break open on movement) no attempt should be made to force him to lie down; for here again, *force breeds fear and resistance which will make the patient expend greater energy than he would expend in sitting up.* Usually the nurse can accomplish the

[1] *Vide* p. 335 *ff.*   [2] *Vide* p. 77.

desired goal simply by gentle perseverance; and if she remembers to be patient she can prevent the patient from getting out of bed or from sitting up. This quieting of the patient may be accomplished if the nurse will stand beside the bed in such a manner that the patient in order to get out will have to force her aside. If the patient does the forcing there is relatively little anger or violent movement aroused, except for mild vocal complaints which the nurse can answer. Delirious patients are weak in relation to their usual strength; and although they may be very strong in great excitement, this strength calls for their last reserve of energy and moreover, is quickly exhausted provided there is no arousal or excitement. The patient may push and shove to get the nurse aside; but if she stands rather firm and does not mind a little buffeting, the patient will soon desist, and because of his weakness lie quietly in bed. The nurse, however, should be not merely offer passive resistance; for she needs constantly to be persuading and reassuring the patient. There should not be any strenuous effort to keep the patient quiet for, as stated above, shouting or physical restlessness does not harm the patient sufficiently to require the use of medication, unless from the practical point of view it be that the quiet of the entire hospital need be considered as of greater importance than the good of the one patient.

Hydrotherapy is helpful. Frequent sponge baths to reduce the temperature and ice packs on the head are of great value. If the temperature is not high, a prolonged warm bath (with the temperature between 94° and 96°) may be relaxing and sedative; in hospitals properly equipped with continuous tubs, patients may be kept in a sedative bath for several hours. Every form of treatment should be tried to avoid adding any toxic products (drugs) to the patient's already toxic state. Cool wet packs are often sedative. The patient is placed on a sheet which has been wrung out in water of about 65°, and the sheet immediately wrapped about him. Over the sheet warm blankets should be placed. Initially the patient feels cold; but very quickly, a compensatory warmth sets in, and the patient becomes relaxed. The usual tight pack should not be used; that is, the patient should not be wrapped so firmly that he becomes frightened at being bound down. The author saw one patient whose temperature rose 3 degrees in one hour from being tightly restrained and struggling to escape. A loose cold wet pack is therapeutically just as effective and avoids creating restraint-fear.

Sleep is important to obtain; for sound sleep of eight to twelve hours a day will do much to improve the anabolic state of the organism. This sleep should be obtained wherever possible without the use of drugs;[1] but when drugs are needed, those which have the least toxic effect and are most quickly removed from the body are of value. The best drug for this purpose is morphine, though in alcoholism it often acts as an excitant and therefore should not be used. Morphine given hypodermically in $\frac{1}{8}$ grain doses should be used primarily to allay fears so that sleep may come of its own accord; and if sleep does not soon result a quick acting sedative such as sodium pentobarbital should be given within an hour. Hyoscine or scopolamine should not be used with morphine because of the tendency of the combination to produce delirium, (although such a combination in non-delirious patients is very effective). Paraldehyde (of especial value for alcoholic patients) given by rectum or orally is very effective and is quickly eliminated from the system; doses of 2 to 3 drams are usually required. Intravenous sodium amytal, injected at the rate of 1 grain per minute until the patient is asleep is sometimes necessary; but since the blood pressure drops suddenly with sodium amytal great care is required in its use. In giving sedative medication, one can avoid over dosage by repeating small doses of the drug every half hour or more frequently until the patient is asleep.

Cold wet packs are often capable of producing sleep and obviate the necessity for medication.[2] The room should be darkened and quiet; visitors should not be permitted, though on occasion the wife or husband if temperamentally qualified may be more reassuring than any hospital attendant. In the meantime every effort should be made to treat the etiologic factor and to increase the patient's resistance.

When the delirium is cleared, the patient may return to "normal" actions; yet it is always beneficial and sometimes essential therapy to discuss the patient's problems with him, recommend the adoption of healthier attitudes, and train him in their adoption. Many of these persons "do not appear nervous"[3] and may even deny the existence of any disturbance; for the disturbances generally exist as part of automatic reaction patterns which are so automatic as to be forgotten or unnoticed by the patient.

---

[1] *Vide* p. 336.   [2] *Vide* p. 337.   [3] *Vide* p. 273.

THE CHRONIC DELIRIA

The organic psychoses are most properly termed chronic deliria,[1] in that the symptoms are primarily those of intellectual disorganization. The most common disease processes which fall into this category are the senile and arteriosclerotic dementias, general paresis and the traumatic psychoses. There may be no acute onset but a gradual and less intense development of all the symptoms found in the acute deliria, so that the patient's memory is gradually impaired, mistakes are made in ordinary activities of living, and the judgment becomes poor. With this intellectual damage there is released the underlying personality;[2] so that a person with a relatively stable background may show no disturbance other than his dementia; while others may present a picture of whining, irritability, depressive feelings, persecutory ideas, etc. In infectious processes such as general paresis, these symptoms are of quicker onset than in senile dementia.

The treatment of these chronic deliria resolves itself into treating the etiologic factor as adequately as is possible, and managing the patient and his environment. The *specific therapies vary* of course *with the etiology:* in general paresis, tryparsamide and fever therapy are curative in roughly one-third the patients, arrest the illness and improve the patient in another third, and are ineffective in the last third.[3] In arteriosclerotic dementia, general hygienic and palliative care directed primarily toward the cardiovascular system is the only specific therapy. In senile dementia there is no specific therapy. In the traumatic psychoses, damaged brain tissue is irreparable, but tumors of blood or blood cysts can be removed. *The general management* of these patients *consists in reducing the amount of required activity* to a level compatible with their ability and in educating the family to understand that the patient's outbursts are not the result of ill temper, *per se,* but secondary to brain changes.[4] Understanding the situation enables the family not to take offense at what is said or done and helps them avoid irritating the patient. Many of these patients become unmanageable as deterioration increases, and institutionalization in a rest home, or state hospital is essential in order that the patient

---

[1] *Vide* p. 19.   [2] *Vide* p. 340.

[3] Excellent results are reported on the use of mepharsen injected at the height of the fever which is artificially produced.

[4] *Vide* p. 160 (Case L. M.).

be not perturbed, and that the family be alleviated from their strain. Where specific therapy is not available or is ineffective, these patients continue to deteriorate, but may live for many years after the first evident symptom of brain changes. Death usually occurs by an intercurrent infection.

Mrs. C. C., aged sixty-two years, was admitted to the Research Hospital in October, 1934. At the age of fifty-one, the patient complained that she was unable to remember where she placed things, but she did not forget the names of her friends or incidents which could be observed. Physical examination was negative except that her blood pressure was 170/100. When she was fifty-seven, she had noticed that her hands would tremble; and the children noticed that she appeared "dumb" and did things without reason. She talked about looking at the stars; she would take off her wedding ring, and look through it; she fell asleep frequently and would sleep most of the day. She would "go twenty times to the store and each time forget what she wanted." A year later while working in her husband's store she was "held up," but she did not appear to be frightened by the experience. The next year the patient's gait changed, and when she started to walk, the walking would increase in rapidity until she ran. A year before she came for treatment she would leave the house and get lost, so that a neighbor or a policeman would have to bring her home. She frequently would run through the house out of the back door and through the front door, continuing this circuit for some time. She became completely disoriented: thought her husband was her father, and spoke as if her mother (long dead) were alive. She finally was admitted to the hospital, where her behavior continued to deteriorate and she died September 13, 1936. The diagnosis was psychosis with cerebral arteriosclerosis.

Mr. O. T., aged thirty-six years, was a normal hardworking tailor with no particular problems until May of 1935. At that time the first change in his behavior became noticeable. He and his wife were entertaining a group of friends and the patient began to argue violently, shouting at her in the most abusive of language. The only reason for this outburst was that his wife had asked him to wash the dinner dishes. The quarrels became more frequent and the patient began to drink. His work became careless and slowed, and he refused to recognize his errors. When a garment was handed back to him for correction he replied, "Nothing is wrong with that, I know when it is right." He began to smoke many cigarettes, and since he would leave them on the work tables he had to be watched lest he start a fire. In January of 1936 he began to permit customers to take out coats without getting their names or receiving any money. He would buy five or six times the amount of groceries and household supplies that were needed. He rarely brought home the right change and seemed to know nothing of the money he had. He fell and fractured his ankle and was taken to a hospital but refused to believe that his foot was broken and became quarrelsome and noisy. He seemed almost normal for two or three days and then his irritability returned and he began to leave the house slyly in order to drink. It was then decided to commit him.

23

The following is a copy of the formal intellectual status of the patient:

Orientation.—Name: Nicholas S.   Date: March 23, 1936 (actually March 25).   Place: Blank Hospital (correct).

Remote Memory.—The patient stated that he was born September 2, 1900, in Greece. He was now thirty-six. School was started at the age of ten and high school was finished in Greece at the age of twenty. He took up dressmaking because he liked the work and came to the United States one year after he finished high school. He was in this country for fifteen years and has worked all this time in one shop located at Damen and Armitage. He had infantile paralysis in childhood and several other illnesses which he could not remember. He was asked when he got syphilis and he replied "a year ago." He remembered being in the G. hospital for a week. (This history was essentially correct.)

Recent Memory.—The patient remembered the routine of admission to the hospital and the food he had the last three meals. He was asked to remember "yellow, brown, white, New York, Detroit, Pittsburgh, numbers 120, 31, 7." Five minutes later he was asked to repeat the above and he returned: "New York, Pittsburgh, Detroit, brown, white, yellow, I don't remember the numbers."

Calculation.—3 plus 3 equals 6. 4 times 4 equals 16. 99 divided by 11 equals 9. If three oranges cost 10 cents, how many can one buy for 90 cents. Answer 30. When the patient was told this was not correct, he replied "It's close to thirty." He was then asked to subtract 7 from 100 and continue to deduct seven from the result; his answer was as follows: *100 minus 7 equals 97. Then, 93, 86, 65, 59, 79, 72, 65, 57, 58, 41, and the patient continued to make many errors in his subtractions.*

(Italics are mine.)

General Information.—

President was Delano Roosevelt.

Population of U. S. was 120 million.

King of Greece was King George.

Who was Stalin?   Someone in Russia, a cabinet member.

What was the biggest river in U. S.?   The Mississippi.

Stream of Speech.—The patient answers questions monosyllabically. All his conversation is in answer to questions.

The above excerpt is an indication of the relative intactness of mental processes except where the 100 minus 7 test was given. A lay person examining this man would probably have said that his intellect showed no damage. Often it is only by rather careful studies that the formal examination will reveal the damage that is apparent to his friends in daily life.

The essential findings of the neurologic examination were unequal pupils which reacted poorly to light and to accommodation. The knee jerk was absent. Otherwise there was no clinical pathology.

The blood and spinal fluid Wasserman and Kahn were four plus. The spinal fluid was clear, there were 16 lymphocytic cells, the Pandy was positive, the protein was .087 per cent, the sugar was 53, and the Lange gold curve was 5555555530.

In the hospital the patient was proud of the job of sweeping the floor and worked well at it. However, he stole property belonging to other patients and ate voraciously. He forged a letter from a doctor which requested that he be permitted to go home. Otherwise he was cooperative and manageable on the ward without any special precautions.

The treatment consisted of a course of tryparsamide consisting of 10 injections once weekly. This treatment was in preparation for the malarial treatment and he improved under it. Tertian malaria was injected into the patient (obtained from a malarial patient one-half hour after he had had a chill) and 13 typical chills occurred in the next month. Quinine was then given to control the malaria, and two weeks later a second course of tryparsamide was begun. At the end of that time the patient was clinically improved and permitted to go home. The spinal fluid Wassermann remained positive and the Lange gold curve dropped to 00001110000 on August 17, 1936. When the patient was seen a year later he was perfectly normal.

MANIC-DEPRESSIVE PSYCHOSIS

Manic-depressive psychoses are physiologic illnesses characterized by swings in mood, alteration in activity, and change in the tempo of thought and speech.[1] In the manic phase, these changes are accelerated and elevated; in the depressive state, these personality alterations are decreased and depressed. This illness has, however, several variations of the basic pattern.

Most of what is written about this condition is based on studies of patients who have become ill enough to be committed to an institution, and there is a dearth of information about the vast group who never need to enter a psychiatric institution. Any age group may be involved, the peak age being between thirty-five and forty. The type of physique often found is the pyknic;[2] that is, those persons who tend to have round faces, narrow shoulders but thorax sloping outward, a round abdomen, well padded limbs, little hair on top of the head (there may be much hair before thirty, but baldness comes early to these persons), heavy hair on the chin and chest, and a personality which is aggressive, persevering, and more inclined toward sociability than seclusiveness. The illness usually varies from the manic form to the depressive and *vice versa*. Attacks tend to recur; but more than one-half of these patients have only one attack, and one-quarter, two attacks. (Pollock reviewing the patients admitted to the New York State hospitals in ten years gives the following percentages for women: One attack, 57.8 per cent; two attacks, 23.8 per cent; three attacks, 9.7 per

[1] *Vide* p. 285.   [2] *Vide* p. 284.

cent; four attacks, 4.2 per cent; five attacks, 2.1 per cent; more than five attacks, 2.4 per cent. The males have approximately the same percentages.) Spontaneous recovery is common, the usual duration of the illness being from six months to eighteen months; but there are many variations and exceptions. The most common cause of death in these patients is disease of the cardio-vascular-renal system, in contrast to schizophrenia where the most common cause of death is tuberculosis. These facts, as well as others, indicate the constitutional predisposition.[1]

There are, however, many patients who suffer from mild manic-depressive swings and do not come to institutionalization. These persons may suffer from the intrinsic symptoms of the disease and are said to be temperamental; or quite commonly they suffer from what appears to be a neurosis,[2] but is primarily a mild depressive state associated with psychogenic or physical disturbance. These patients also are depressed, fatigued, cannot concentrate well, "feel inferior," etc. It is difficult in any particular case, to determine how much is true depression and how much is the result of psychologic influence. Moreover, in many "normal" persons, there is a definite tendency to moods which last over long periods of time, and which come on spontaneously.

The cause of manic-depressive swings is unknown. Some correlations to physique and temperament, have already been mentioned. There is a strong familial and hereditary influence, but exact figures are difficult to ascertain. The "exhaustion" states which follow shock, operative procedures, or long illnesses, simulate depressive swings; but rarely are they other than precipitating in character. Care must be taken not to confuse with the etiologic factors those physical complaints which are merely coincidental with the depression. Pregnancy is not infrequently followed by a depressive period in which anxiety is a prominent symptom, but any other type of psychosis may also occur.[3] Psychologic stress or strain may often be influential in facilitating a manic-depressive illness, but it is very rarely "causative." Environmental stresses may bring about temporary sadness, and irritability; but in themselves they cannot cause the patient to develop the symptoms so characteristic of this type of illness: the tremendous suicidal drive, the inability to think about subjects not involving self, the inability to forget their "troubles" for a while and laugh. Moreover, psychologic factors may continue in operation and the manic-depressive

[1] *Vide* p. 20.   [2] *Vide* p. 279.   [3] *Vide* p. 385.

patient may make a complete recovery in spite of their continued existence, a fact strongly indicative of the *relative* unimportance of the disturbing circumstance. In general it may be said that the depressive illness will develop and will disappear, in spite of the emotional strain in the environment; though the depression may be prolonged or initiated by outward irritations.

These personality changes and the "mental" attitude are not psychologically determined, but result from *physiologic* changes.[1] Ideas and moods may be inculcated by training and stimuli, but their direction, facility and tempo are overwhelmingly influenced by the activity of the physical organism. Just where the seat of the physical disturbance exists, is as yet unknown, but that it does exist and disturb "mental" reactions, is clinically unquestionable. In this illness, particularly, is it brought home to us that "mind" is but one aspect of "body."[2]

Mrs. K. H., aged twenty-nine years, complained, "I'm not able 'to make myself do things.'" She felt fatigued, discouraged, cried "for no reason at all," slept poorly, and could not concentrate. She insisted that she was "going crazy" and she had had many medicines, injections of all sorts, and had been to a sanitarium where the "head doctor called me a fool." Her illness began, she said, six months before when she moved to a new apartment and for the first time furnished her home with her own furniture. She noticed that the Venetian blinds were always dirty and she cleaned and cleaned them, but dirt kept accumulating. She began to cry because "she couldn't keep them clean" and "the last thing she thought of on going to bed and the first thing she thought of on arising was those dirty Venetian blinds." Her husband tried to persuade her that such a trivial defect meant nothing, and that worry over it was of little use, but to no avail. The patient became worse, more and more depressed, and finally attempted suicide.

The "dirty Venetian blinds" was given as a cause of the depression; yet obviously such an incidental factor could not cause a deep-seated depression which eventuated in an attempt at suicide. When her history was studied further, it was found that she had gradually been less and less active, that she had become increasingly fatigued, and that she did not enjoy the company of friends as she formerly had. There were many other incidents to substantiate the fact that her depression had been coming on for a few months before the furnishing of the apartment; and the dirtiness of the Venetian blinds merely served as a focal point of irritation through which she could express all her depressive tendencies.

[1] *Vide* p. 361.   [2] *Vide* p. 39.

Finally, in an effort to satisfy his wife, her husband sold all the furniture and moved to a new apartment; but she continued in her depression until metrazol therapy was instituted. She recovered almost completely in a month.

The manic phase may develop under similar circumstances, with or without apparent stress. Not infrequently the manic phase begins suddenly, yet on closer examination, the physician discovers a preliminary phase of depression and a period of overactivity which was not excessive and so passed unnoticed. In many patients, the manic phase does not reach the wild state of excitement, and so the patient is spoken of as being in the hypomanic phase. This condition, however, is but a milder degree of the other.

The hypomanic phase is characterized by a marked feeling of well being and increased activity. The patient awakens bright and cheerful, eats very well, sings, and in other ways manifests his subjective well being. He talks a great deal, jumps from idea to idea, and makes many clever and witty remarks. He is active and forceful, often accomplishing a great deal during the day. If the degree of hypomanic activity is not so excessive as to be self-defeating, these persons may become very successful in business because of the pressure of their ideas and their energy.

Miss V. V., aged twenty-seven years, was a quiet pleasant young woman who appeared to be a quite well integrated person. She lived in a small town, working as a stenographer and living a seemingly uneventful life. In March of 1936 she became restless and talked far more than she formerly had. She became interested in societies and did a great deal of committee work, so that from a shy and relatively unknown girl, she seemed overnight to blossom forth in the role of a leader. Her parents remarked that she had never looked better in her life. She did not go to sleep until late; yet somehow had such a boundless store of energy that she never seemed to tire out. She became somewhat argumentative, however, and left the family home to live in Chicago with a relative. In Chicago, she soon entered into the spirit of the community and was the "life of every party." She had excellent background and appearance; so she easily procured a position selling season tickets for the opera. Her sales record was phenomenal, for she sold more tickets than any other of the personnel, some of whom had had extensive selling experience. She talked rapidly, vivaciously, and was always laughing. She was witty and charming. In September of the same year she began to have conflicts with her fellow employees. She became too vivacious and her speech seemed almost nonsensical. She could never finish a story, but jumped from idea to idea with lightning rapidity. She began to call up prospective clients in the middle of the night, ran up large taxi bills, gave elaborate parties which were expensive far beyond her means. Her overactivity finally became so great that she had to be placed in an institution. She recovered some eight months later and was well enough to go home. At the time of discharge, she was quiet, pleasant, interesting, an entirely different person from the one she had been in the previous year.

This girl had a typical hypomanic attack, which began in March and culminated late that year in acute excitement. But it will be noted that early in the attack she appeared to the casual observer to be merely an active, vivacious girl; and in fact *she was hypomanic only in relation to her accustomed and usual behavior*.[1] There are many persons who are "normally" as constantly active as Miss V. V. was in her illness, although when their behavior becomes extreme, even these persons may be termed hypomanic personalities.

The manic phase is but an intensification of the symptoms described. The patient is bright and cheerful to the point of euphoria; everything seems possible to him and there are few if any things which he is not confident that he can accomplish. Far from feeling inferior, he has the extremely rare "superiority complex" (a term usually misused to describe a compensated inferiority state). His thoughts come so quickly that he may not be able to express all of them, and what he says often sounds confused ("flight of ideas"). His activity may be so great that he cannot be managed in ordinary surroundings. This manic state of constant acute excitement as a rule is self limiting, spontaneous remission occurring within from six months to a year. The remission may be a return to normal behavior or it may be the beginning of a typical depression. The frequently characteristic alternation between manic and depressive phases was the basis for the old term of "circular insanity."

The depressive state varies considerably, both in intensity and etiology. A person may be depressed as the result of two general forces, or a combination of these two. The first type of depression has its origin in purely psychologic factors and cannot properly be said to be of the manic-depressive group; the second, in physiologic mood swings.

The first type of depression (*i. e.*, one due primarily to psychologic stress) occurs in the setting of a normal level of mood. The stress may be an obvious and overt one[2] such as a sudden loss of

[1] *Vide* p. 283.   [2] *Vide* p. 155.

financial security, the death of a parent or child, an intense domestic disturbance, etc.; or it may be a chronic, obscure, constant even though not intense type of stress,[1] such as concern over possible loss of a position, brooding over some "wrong" committed or suffered, or any chronic emotional instability such as have been discussed in earlier chapters. As a result of these situational or psychologic factors, the person "feels" blue and depressed; he is constantly concerned over the situation which precipitated his depression; he manifests his irritability by a psychoneurosis, emotional outbursts, or weeping. He may sleep well or poorly, but the difficulty in sleep usually consists of a difficulty in falling to sleep, in contradistinction to the physiologic manic-depressive who usually awakens early but falls asleep quickly (not true if the depression is accompanied by psychoneurotic features). The psychologic depression is usually of short duration, lasting several days or weeks; and its intensity does not remove the possibility of the person's laughing, if the stimulus is strong enough to make him forget. There is little sense of personal inadequacy, but rather a feeling of sorrow or anxiety over any difficulty. This characteristic attitude is modified in persons who have had a psychoneurotic tendency; for in such persons, the occurrence of a depressive state, psychologic or physiologic, is associated with an intensification of their emotional symptoms. Moreover, in the depressions produced by a chronic and subtle stress, the symptoms have much more of a tendency to be associated with anxiety and apprehension[2] rather than simply the feeling of being "blue" or "low." The simple feeling of hopelessness is complicated and intensified by deep concern and agitation. Many such persons will feel guilty if they have momentary moods of detachment or pleasure, being convinced that they have no "right to happiness" and "ought to be sad." Psychotherapy and diversion is a good and relatively simple cure for such psychologic depressions.

Mrs. C. C., aged twenty-nine years, was eager to have a child. She had been married to a University instructor for eleven years and though her time was well and happily occupied, she longed for the time to come when they could afford to have children. Finally she became pregnant and she prepared for the child's coming with tremendous emotional enthusiasm. She told all her friends, talked constantly about what she would do, bought clothes enough to provide for two or three children, and was supremely happy. Everything progressed well until the time set for delivery, but the child was not born till three weeks later. It was a still birth. The patient

[1] *Vide* p. 142 (Case S. D.).   [2] *Vide* p. 244.

cried for several days. She did not sleep, ate very little, and remained in bed. She continued in this condition for about a month, and then decided to adopt a child. She did so two weeks later and was then content, happy, and interested in the new child, apparently having given up grieving over the death of her own child.

On the other hand, the *physiologic depression* occurs without apparent cause, or with a trivial and inconsequential cause. On many occasions the cause seems sufficient, yet is only incidental; for when the physician examines the past life of these patients he will find that there have been many stresses which though they were far worse than the immediate one were not attended by any depression. Occasionally, one finds the most recent stress to be "the straw that broke the camel's back," and the "final blow" not to be endured. There are always other and unmistakable signs in a true physiologic depression.

The signs and symptoms of this type of depression manifests themselves as a rule very gradually. At first there is a quietness of manner and the customary loquaciousness disappears. Fatigue sets in easily, and even after much sleeping and little work the person complains of being tired. The appearance of the person suffers, and the fastidiousness of which he may have been proud disappears. Although he may berate himself for this deficiency, he does nothing to overcome it. The expression changes, and instead of the usual alert look, there is the appearance of tiredness and disinterestedness. The facial muscles lose their mobility, becoming relaxed and smooth, except possibly for the frontal muscles which may be corrugated in apprehension. Various gastrointestinal complaints[1] come to the fore: there is no appetite, constipation is common, and the patient loses weight. Sexual desire diminishes gradually so that intercourse may not occur for months. Sleep becomes poor, and characterized by constant distressing dreams. Recognition, approval and achievements give the patient no satisfaction, and "all the kick seems to go out of life." Small problems suddenly loom large and there is constant worry over innumerable small details. Friends become uninteresting, and the patient visits others less and less, eventually finding it very uncomfortable to be in the presence of others.[2] The future is regarded very pessimistically as are also the present and the past. Concentration becomes difficult, and the person finds it arduous to read even the daily newspapers. The memory seems poorer, and the

---

[1] *Vide* p. 300.   [2] *Vide* p. 68.

patient forgets where he left items, and what he was supposed to do. When actually tested however, the patient on effort, demonstrates an excellent memory; so that it becomes apparent that the defect lies in the fact that the patient so concentrates on and remembers his problems and difficulties that insufficient attention is given to everyday incidents. In actuality, the problem is not one of memory but of attention, and it is extremely difficult to force concentration.

As the depression increases in intensity, suicidal thoughts appear. The patient says he cannot "feel" anything; that emotions do not have the same meaning for him as they do for others. For example, mothers complain sadly of their inability to take "proper" care of their children, insisting that they seem to have no "feeling" for their children, and that it seems to make no difference what happens to them. In the very moment of self rebuke for having "no feeling" such mothers express great concern over this inability. Often the state of disturbed sensation is so intense, that patients actually welcome a physically painful sensation because of its contrast to the more disturbing peculiar "mental" state they are in. They find it extremely difficult to describe their state of "feeling." There are rarely any disturbed physical sensations as we ordinarily think of them; occasionally there is a "tingling" in the arms and legs, or shooting pains and twitches, but these are not common. Thermal intolerance is frequently found, for some poorly understood reason. Many of these patients complain of having an intense unrest after entering a restaurant.

The gradual disappearance of this condition is comparable to its gradual appearance. From onset to end, the average physiologic depression lasts about a year and a half. Here again there are marked variations so that depressive attacks may last from three months to an indefinite number of years. Often too, the depression is measured by the patient only in terms of the period of intense depression, without cognizance of the less distressing prodromal and convalescent features. Moreover, during this period, it is almost impossible to "cheer the patient up." Indeed happy music, gay parties even brilliant sunshine are depressing to these patients in contrast to the psychologic depression.[1] These patients, depressed as they are, compare themselves to the stimulating environment and become increasingly depressed because they "know they should enjoy the situation" but cannot. The efforts

[1] *Vide* p. 250.

of friends to cheer up the patient are generally more detrimental than beneficial.

Many persons are driven to suicide, when they are nagged to "snap out of it," or to "use some will power." These patients, often incapable of doing what is asked of them, criticize themselves far more acutely than do others; and when the criticism of others is added to their own self criticism, they become desperate, feeling that they have no one to turn to for some moral support. It is therapeutically unwise to criticize these patients;[1] though, as we shall see when therapy is discussed, a certain amount of urging is of value. It is important to understand that this type of depression is beyond the "will" of the patient to control.

Mrs. K. H.,[2] mentioned above, wrote the following history of her illness after her recovery, and extended quotations are given from it because it describes quite well the usual emotional status of patients in depression. The incidents she refers to in Wyoming have not been quoted in full, but she and her husband experienced many severe hardships both because of his small salary, and the fact that he was stationed at a railroad terminal where the housing consisted of a small shack which could not be properly heated during the intense cold weather, where the toilet was an outhouse some distance from the shack, and where the water had to be pumped from a well that was frequently frozen. Her account of the illness is as follows:

"We were so happy buying the Hoover, the desk and various other things. Then I started to go "nuts." We had lived so long the other way that it was hard to change. We were on our own—had to pay the gas and light and furnish the laundry. I got tight with the linens and worried about the gas and light bills, even made Tom turn off all the lights in the living room when he came out to eat. It had been so very dirty at the Gothic, I didn't think it was going to be dirty over there but it was. The heat wasn't so good all the time and I nearly drove myself wild running the Hoover every day and dusting those Venetian blinds. They were ivory color and the glare from them hurt my eyes and I felt just like I was in a cage all the time. One thing that drove me wild was the fact that some of my old pieces of lace, dishes, pictures and odds and ends that I had cherished so much couldn't be used because they didn't fit in with the modernistic. I would hunt in the store for various things—I had ideas of what I wanted but the salespeople said it just couldn't be used. The curtain man came out and said my ideas were all wrong but I see some of them in the paper lately. Then I was so lonesome. There was no woman neighbor across and being there alone all day—sometimes several days at a time seemed to get on my nerves. Tom

[1] *Vide* p. 128.   [2] *Vide* p. 357.

had lint all over him all the time and my coat had lint on it—lint—lint—everyplace—from a new rug, the laundry, and the bedspread. I thought I would lose my mind and yet millions of others go through that same thing all the time. When I look back at it now I wonder what ever was wrong with me. We had some friends in and they raved about the place but the compliments didn't thrill me. All of our furniture was heavy—not as nice as the traditional modern is now but still I can't forget it. Early in December I had gone out to Wyoming to get our things that were in storage (odds and ends) and to repack them. I was disappointed for they had been stored free in the freight depot so we had no kick coming, but over half the dishes and kettles had been stolen, and the pack rats had gotten into other things—it was a mess. We had to throw away a lot of things even after they got here. I nearly lost my mind trying to find some modern dishes to go with the blue chairs and couldn't get the drapes I wanted for the dinette nor the tie backs for the bedroom. It was just everything like that that got on my nerves. One Saturday night I spent four hours scraping paint off the bathroom when we should have been out having a good time. Little specks of paint were splattered all over everything. The apartment hadn't been cleaned well, but decorated and I had so much to clean up after the other tenants. The transom was filthy and even then big hunks of soot would fall down in the kitchen. I had never had to worry about window washing but had to attend to that there. The high third floor nearly wore me out. I just worried about everything and picked on everything until I nearly had Tom a nervous wreck. We had fourteen months lease with a thirty day transfer (business clause). We had gotten friendly with the janitor and given him a couple of drinks but he was the kind that did things when and how he wanted to so we had to be careful with him. I didn't like the way the window sills were done so made the decorators come back and sand them and do them over. That was a mess. I didn't cook much, tried to save on the gas—tried to keep the laundry bills down and then when it did come back it had lint all over it. Then Tom's mother came and she is a darling soul and I love her—before that I was getting so I couldn't sleep and one morning either late in January or early in February I woke up with a snap in my head and my first thought was—I wonder if I can get the Venetian blind up and jump out of the window before Tom wakes up but instead I got up—it went on for at least a month or more—I only slept two hours a night, would get up at 5 A.M. pace the floor in the cold and smoke six or seven cigarettes before Tom would get up for breakfast. Then I got so I couldn't eat—I had that big lump in my throat. His mother came and was here about ten days I guess and she was company for me but I would sit around or lie on the sofa and cry and shake. I had needle points all over my body, especially my arms and legs. We went in the car with Tom on trips to Indiana, and I would crawl up in the back seat and shake the entire time and never talk, if I did it would be about how terrible I felt. I began to lose weight and have dysentery. My friends kept telling me to snap out of it—that housekeeping couldn't be that bad but I wanted to go back to the apartment hotel, where there were people that I knew, where I could be free with the lights and gas, visit with the maid and not have to worry about things so. Tom was so worried—we had to get out of that lease. I either went with him on trips, because he was afraid to leave me alone or I would go spend the day with friends, curled up in a chair raving about my tale of woe. I feel so cheap now it is hard to face those friends. I started going to Dr. D.—— up north and he gave me theelin shots. They helped some. I also took Progynon for hot flashes. After making a fool of myself and running every prospective renter to death, we finally rented the apartment and got out of the lease. Also sold the furniture for half price. Sold the blinds with the apartment. I packed up and I'll never forget the look on Tom's face when he came home and saw those packing boxes all set and ready to go. I was so mean and insistent. I found that the only apartment vacant over here was a large three room at too much rent but I wouldn't stay over there another day and so we "snuck" out over there without anyone seeing us (the janitor) because we were supposed to be transferred, so we moved three weeks before we should have and paid double rent for that time. Tom wanted to put the furniture in storage but I wouldn't hear of it. I wanted it sold and gone off my mind. We had to go over there every Sunday until the last for the people to look at the furniture and they took a few small things with them. The last Sunday they brought friends and went out and got beer and made a party out of it. That nearly killed me. By that time I was sick of my change but it was too late and I thought after all of it was gone that I would feel differently. Mary went with me in the morning for them to take the last of the furniture and I couldn't describe to you how I felt that day. My heart was breaking. I was crying and every nerve and muscle in my body seemed so tight and such a pull on them I thought they would snap. It was awful. Prior to that time I had made several trips with Tom and he took me to a little night club. Thought the change would do me good. The first time I rather enjoyed it and ate a pretty good dinner but I was a wreck the next day from the drinks and the second time it was a flop. I climbed up on the window sill and nearly jumped from the hotel window. By that time those ideas were forming for it all seemed so useless and hopeless. No one, nor I, could see why I had to give up like that when I went through so much those two winters in Wyoming.

"I knew the apartment we selected had nice possibilities for normal people but I was so afraid of myself and the future—afraid I couldn't swing it and be happy and contented again and feel like life was worth while. The days went much easier and I could stand my own company but I still didn't care about being with people but had to several times and got by pretty well. This new apartment had light, traditional modern furniture and I wondered how I would react to it. We could change any time we wanted but here I felt somewhat ashamed of the small place and of what I've done. We had to live some place and it was only a six month lease there. Sometimes I thought I'd wind up in an asylum—I didn't feel sure of myself and I got those wild ideas, but they weren't so hard to control. My face still felt a little tense and I had lots of internal nervousness at times although externally I didn't think it showed much. The sex was at a very low ebb—I couldn't get satisfaction but I was getting a little more feeling than I had had for months. My memory was bad. I cried quite a bit yet and had a tendency to do that more when my husband was around or when he got affectionate. I felt so sorry for him to think he had gotten such a rotten deal. I knew he took me for better or worse and he got the worse. I told him several times that if he wanted to get rid of me it would be okeh but that just hurt him.

"I did not cook much but he complimented me on my meals. I thought he just was trying to make me feel good and cheer me up. I did not do much around there—kept saying I'd shop more and do better when we get settled in the other place and yet I wondered if I was only alibiing to myself or if I really would. I was not making any plans very far ahead—I seemed to be afraid to. I thought I would never get through those weeks but I did and it wasn't so bad, however, I spent much time job hunting and apartment hunting. That at least gets me out and I talked to strangers. I could bluff my way through.

"I had no particular interest in anything, was not interested in Tom's work, nor clothes, nor movies—I just felt like I was here from day to day, not sure of tomorrow or the future. I used to plan ahead for trips, etc., and when I would buy clothes, how it should wear and what could be done with it to alter it the next season. I didn't need so very many clothes but it was a good thing I had a few things to wear or I don't know what I would have done, for I hadn't the desire nor energy to go out and buy them. I claimed that I didn't want any more junk to move than we had. And that another thing—I just felt that I couldn't make this move—I must get out of there. I felt so cheap and hated to go by the desk and see the maid and other help, yet I didn't feel equal to getting things organized like I'd always done before, so Tom and my brother promised to take charge of the moving and I could do anything I liked for the day or go over to the other place and be the "receiving" clerk. I wondered if I wouldn't be prone to worry if I weren't on the job. That was being lazy I guess but I just didn't feel capable. We had moved so much that year I didn't know what we had. I was going to have to get over being sentimental about old things that don't fit in with modern furniture.

"I got these weepy spells every once in awhile and got so blue. I thought that I had brought this all on myself—it was just because I was selfish, self-centered, and a coward, and I allowed myself to wallow in self-pity. I cut many articles out of the papers that upset me, yet thought of saving them for a scrap book but I wondered if that would be wise. Everything like that I took to heart and decided it was meant definitely for me.

"I knew I had to live—first because God put me on this earth for a reason and I had to stay until he took me, yet I had to feel like I was earning my way and making something of my life. Did I have a right to happiness after what I had done? Or was this a punishment for something I'd done that was wrong? Others had had far worse misfortunes than that and come through okeh—I felt that I brought all that on myself—I felt so guilty, so wrong, so unfair. Our Wyoming hardship hadn't been my fault, perhaps that was why I could take it. Why did I feel so cheap and ashamed to face my friends. I wouldn't see some that were very kind to me on 25th street. Was I a coward, was it jealousy, what was it? I wondered if I could walk back into that 25th Street apartment with just the same furniture, everything the same as we had it, take off my wraps—would I be able to pick up where I had left off and start on again? It was too big a gamble to take a chance.

"I felt as though I had no right to plan anything and I could give suggestions and state ideas and opinions before—now I felt I had no right to and didn't seem to know them. I couldn't remember how to cook certain things. I was not interested in new recipes or ideas or things for the apartment. I didn't read much—no magazines and just the daily papers because I couldn't concentrate and couldn't remember. So many things came up that had happened the past summer and before too, that I didn't remember a thing about. My main answer to questions was "I don't know" or "I don't remember." Casual little things didn't interest me like they used to, nor did people, clothes, just everything.

"After we got here at 9265 Woodward again, it wasn't like I thought it would be. I quit talking to anyone—wouldn't talk to the maids, especially Rose, nor the manager, wouldn't go back to any of the stores that had known me before and wouldn't see many of my friends. I went home late in April and was so depressed while there I couldn't talk to anyone—very little to my family and practically none to my friends. Whereas, I used to love to dress up and go up town and see the old friends, I wouldn't go up town and hated to go to the little church for fear someone would say something to me or notice the change. I wouldn't go to see Tom's brother and family who only lived 21 miles west and I had always enjoyed my day's visit there. I had always been one who liked to dress up, or rather clean up—made it a point to have a bath every day and have something besides an apron on when Tom came home for dinner but during that bad spell on 25th Street I went a week at a time without a bath—wore the same old dress until it nearly rotted off of me and now Margaret says I used to twitch but I don't remember that. I do know that then (and even yet) I often shake my head for it sort of seems to clear it. Another thing that worried me was that I fell out with Margaret and Joe in the Fall. Joe lost his job and I got mad at her (I don't know why now) and never called her until one day when I felt so bad and begged her to come over, which she did, and was very pleasant about it—she didn't know about our move—she has been very nice to me since.

"Dr. B. seemed to think it was OK for us to move back to the hotel, thought it might help me but yet thought I was very foolish. He said I had a premature menopause. He suggested that I go to Milwaukee and my doctor brother suggested that I see a competent neurologist, who was also a psychiatrist. Dr. B. said I would get all those things in Milwaukee. I could hardly keep alive on that trip to North Platte and while I was there Tom attended the Golden Spike Days in Omaha and they had a similar parade in North Platte. I cried my eyes out when I saw the old railroad couples for I knew Tom and I would never be like that. I had a sample of six sleeping capsules that the doctor had given me but I hadn't used them. I was eating a little better and sleeping a little better by that time but my jaws were so stiff and compressed I could hardly open them and a smile was a rare thing. My folks just couldn't understand what happened to me and why we sold our things. When I told my mother goodbye, I didn't think I would ever see her again.

"(Another thing, while Tom's mother was there on 25th Street, we had that terrible snow storm and nearly froze in the apartment, and they decided to take up the hall rugs and do the halls—that made dirt and cold air in the apartment and we had to use the dirty back way and she is so stiff she could hardly make the steep stairs—those things got on my nerves too.) (I was so afraid there would get a scratch on the furniture—had always been careful with other's things, and yet didn't worry about them.)

"Around Decoration Day, I entered the ———— Psychopathic Hospital in M—— they wouldn't take me at the other one without a special nurse day and night because they considered me dangerous with my ideas of self-destruction. I stayed there a month—the nurses were kind to me but I hated the doctors. One called me a boob and another continually asked me morning after morning "if it were raining inside or not." I had the packs twice daily and they quieted me some but I slept poorly and didn't eat so very much. It was there that I got so hard, bitter, and cynical and mean. Tom noticed it. I never went to sleep a night, nor in one of the packs without first having the sensation of having jumped out of the window. Then when Tom came on Sunday instead of going out for a nice time, we sat in the private parlor and I fought with him, cried and begged him to take me back to Chicago. They said I should stay at least six months and I believe that after three months they might have used metrazol. During the week I would lay awake nights planning how I would go out with Tom on Sunday and get to a drug store and buy some razor blades or sleeping powders or both and some night . . . . But when Sunday came I never got out of the place. I know he was very unhappy and had been for months. He seems happier now and says he doesn't care about the furniture but I don't know whether to believe him or not. I've cost him so much—the loss of the furniture, the doctor bills and hospital bills, but he says the money is the least thing.

"They wouldn't let me leave M—— alone so my mother came and was with me from the minute I left M—— until I left for————. That was about June 1st. June and July were months of hell on earth. Mom had been here in 1931 and during the Fair and enjoyed Chicago so much. She is quite a talker and nearly drove me mad at times. I used to love the radio and be so intensely interested in certain programs but I got so I couldn't listen to them and yet she wanted to hear her pets. That annoyed me. Even now I can't stand to hear those programs such as "Life Can Be Beautiful," "I Want a Divorce," "What's Wrong With Marriage," "The Right to Happiness," etc. I went swimming a few times with Mary over at the University this summer and each time had a notion to jump off the diving board (I've never dived) but did jump off the side in the deep end. I drove recklessly when alone and talked constantly of the uselessness of life and how I wasn't any good, and was going to do away with myself. I wouldn't buy any new clothes for I didn't have any need for them. I wouldn't let my mother help me do what little there was to do—I tried to get away from her but never could—just couldn't get out of her sight for a minute. Some-one was with me constantly day and night for nearly six months. We went over to the lagoon and I rowed a boat a couple of times alone—she wouldn't ride with me, and when I got around the trees I was tempted—yet something just kept me from doing anything. She had no plans for going home and I knew she wouldn't leave while I was like that. I did ship her off to Green Bay, Wis., to see her brother. She had been wanting to go and I kept the knowledge of my having the passes from her for three weeks because I didn't want to go. Finally, she had a chance to ride up and I forced her to go. I followed a few days later but could hardly talk up there and wouldn't sleep with her—instead I slept out on the porch on a hard old cot. There was a day or two then that I must have been alone unless I was with Tom. I had that tightness in my back and arms and felt like someone was holding me back when I wanted to walk across the room. I did get back to the routine of daily bathing and keeping myself clean but just cooked enough for us to eat, baked very little, shopped from day to day (always figuring that I wouldn't be here much longer and we wouldn't need it), mended just what I had to—wouldn't shorten many of my dresses. Wouldn't take my mother to see people or places. We went with Tom a lot in the car and I got so irked at them talking about the crops, etc. I was sleeping better, although I don't remember so much about this summer, Tom says I was very restless. I know many a night I crawled in his bed with him. I haven't slept during the day for months. I quit writing letters to friends or relatives. I had nothing to say. I did Tom's typing all along for him and people at the office who knew I was sick, couldn't understand how I could type for him. I refused to go with Tom to the Boss' annual office party at a lovely country club on the lake. I had always enjoyed those before. I had some half unpacked boxes setting in the apartment and refused to do anything about them because I didn't care. Since it was on the second floor we used the front stairway and I felt if I could just sneak in and out without anybody seeing me it would be better. I had called several people while on 25th Street, who lived in this building, and had spoken of getting their own furniture offering to sell ours to them. I bragged so before and then to come running back like "a whipped dog with its tail between its legs"; I don't think I could put into words all the feelings I've had and how I've hated myself for what I've done.

"Finally, I could stand it no longer, the people next door were having a big fight, I had put off a couple of dates until we couldn't put them off any longer and I felt like everything was crowding in on me so on Sunday morning I took the 6 sleeping capsules (Phenobarbitol or something like that) and then woke up Tom and told him what I had done. Dr.—— came and they say I called him everthing under the sun and cursed him and they took me to the hospital. I remember part of it and remember going past the manager's husband with Dr.—— on one side and Tom on the other. You know the rest. I had two special nurses and survived. I think a priest came to see me; I'm not sure. I told Dr.—— he was no good and in four days insisted on leaving the hospital, much against his wishes. For several weeks he kept me coming to his office for shots and pills and each time I told him he wasn't doing me any good and that he didn't know anything, was just trying to run up a bill and the same went for that guy they were trying to keep me alive to see. I didn't want to go down to see you that first night but now I'm glad I did."

The above account is an excellent description of a patient's feelings of confusion and self condemnation during a depression. Rarely do patients with physical pain suffer so much as do

24

depressed patients. Physical examinations and laboratory tests reveal no pathology; yet there can be little doubt that such depressed states result not from disturbed ideas, but from physiologic change.

This picture of the physiologic depression may be modified by, (1) agitation, and (2) psychoneurosis. The agitated depression differs from the simple physiologic depression by the presence of marked anxiety which leads to agitation and restlessness. The patient may pace the floor constantly, rub his scalp, pick at the skin, and wring his hands. The patient complains bitterly of the way he feels, and talks much of the futility of living. There is a constant pressure of thoughts which revolve about specific errors committed and which are insisted on as being inescapably ruinous. There is marked indecision,[1] and it seems impossible for the patient to declare quickly and specifically that which he wishes. On occasion it takes hours to dress, if there is a choice of clothes to be made; and one patient spent an hour each morning trying to decide whether to put on first the left shoe or the right one. Crying is frequent, often assuming a whining character. There are so many plans which the patient wishes to carry out and yet is unable, and no amount of persuading will enable him to do one thing at a time. Spastic constipation is common, and retention of feces may require manual removal because of impaction. The drive toward suicide becomes very intense; and the old adage that those who threaten suicide never carry it out, is again and again disproved by just such patients. Suicide is committed in moments of anxiety, and the greatest ingenuity is used to obtain lethal weapons or drugs. In hospitals, when everything possible is removed that could be used toward this end, patients will leap headlong down the stairs, or run the length of the room smashing their heads into the wall in their desperation. One of my patients, failing in all other methods, tore out his big toe nail, in an effort to obtain something with which he could cut his wrist.

Since the discovery of metrazol therapy, these intense suicidal drives are for the most part eliminated. Attempts at psychotherapy alone, or institutionalization alone can meet with little success, for this state of depression is physiologically based, and psychologic factors are of secondary importance. These patients cannot control their emotional states by an effort of will.

[1] *Vide* p. 131.

Psychoneurotic Depressions. — Psychoneurotic depressions form the basis for a large number of medical problems and result from the co-existence of the psychologic and physiologic depression. Patients with this type of illness also have "blue" spells, irritability, anorexia, constipation, loss of libido, loss of weight, and insomnia. This depressive period is physiologic in character just as described under the depressive psychosis. In addition to this depression there is superadded a psychoneurosis, and the complaints of the neurosis form a focal outlet for the depressive irritability in such a manner as to fix the neurotic symptom very firmly in the patient's consciousness. To complicate the picture still further, there are many evidences of spasticity particularly in the gastrointestinal tract, so that actual physical symptoms result. Should there be a predisposition toward any particular disease, this period of depression will furnish a sufficiently precipitating factor to bring that disease into being. Thus, for example, it is my clinical impression that many peptic ulcer attacks,[1] particularly the exacerbation of the symptoms, coincide with the psychoneurotic features present in these depressions. Further, in the therapy of many of the ailments present during such a depression, far better results will be obtained by dealing with the underlying depression than by treating the symptom alone.

Mrs. H. H., aged forty-three years, was referred from the medical dispensary. She complained of intense burning in the stomach, which was constant morning, noon, and night. There was no relation to meals, to types of food, although sweet foods made the pain worse. X-ray examinations and an Ewald meal revealed no pathology. She wanted something done for her gastric distress, and she complained bitterly that no medicine seemed to give her relief. On giving further history, she revealed the fact that the gastric pain had occurred every fall (the interview was in November) for the last five years, and that it had lasted from two to four weeks on previous occasions. Moreover, she brought out the point that she had been melancholy during these years and the melancholy spells seemed to last for several months. At the present time she admitted that she was depressed, and on recollection admitted that the depression had started early in September, and in the past had continued until the spring. During this time she had not slept well, had eaten poorly, was constipated, and in the middle of the depressive episode, had developed a gastrointestinal attack similar to the one she had now. The pain in the abdomen had disappeared spontaneously as did the melancholia; and moreover, in the spring of the year she felt very happy and the worries she had most of the year did not seem to trouble her then.

[1] *Vide* p. 302.

This patient had an obvious manic-depressive psychosis which alternated between depressive phases which occurred in the fall of the year and manic phases in the spring and summer. The attacks were not very acute, so that she was classified as a neurotic patient; and when they were intense, her attacks had a focal expression in the stomach. The treatment of this patient consisted of treatment directed toward the depression, and with psychotherapy, social therapy, and work therapy, in addition to benzedrine and barbital she improved rapidly. The phenomenon was explained to the patient, and she was made to understand why no therapy was directed toward her gastrointestinal complaint. She understood sufficiently so that she did not ask for specific treatment, but co-operated well in an effort to get at and cure the cause.

Other vicarious reactions occur during the depressive period. Alcoholism[1] as will be discussed later, increased domestic difficulties leading to divorce, etc., are difficulties which may be precipitated by this physiologic depression. These presenting symptoms hide and confuse the underlying symptom complex, but all abnormal personality reactions should be thoroughly investigated, in order to determine the presence or absence of these physiologic mood changes.

THE NATURE OF THE PHYSIOLOGIC DEPRESSION

The nature of the physiologic depression is not clearly understood. It has generally been regarded as a "mental" disease, yet as we have seen, the illness develops and recedes with no apparent psychologic stress. Experience proves that psychotherapy is only an adjunctive therapy during the illness, and that the personality reactions are merely the reflection of the underlying slowing down of all physiologic activities. In a manic phase, a sixty year old white-haired woman may have youthful pink cheeks, and vivacious sparkling eyes, while the twenty year old girl suffering from a depression appears haggard, old, and lifeless. These are physiologic changes; and yet most of our present studies can find no consistent changes in the basal rate, in the blood chemistry, or in any other bodily function. Clinically, one has the impression of increased efficiency of all functions in the manic phase and the reverse in the depressive phase. When patients ask for the site of the lesion, I must confess to them our general state of ignorance about it, yet give them an explanation which, while not scientifically accurate, does have the virtue of being diagrammatically clear and comprehensible.[2] The simple improvised explanation is that in

[1] *Vide* p. 402 *ff.*   [2] *Vide* p. 178.

manic states the circulation of blood through the brain is increased so that there is better oxidation within the brain cells and thus increased activity. Thus the wittiness and cheerfulness of outlook are dependent on the cellular activity; and the converse is true in depressive states. Patients can do much to modify this emotional state, but it is important to realize that the *"mental" symptoms are the result of physiologic changes*, and that no amount of effort of will can make them "feel" happy. It is difficult for the patient to utilize this information, although he may readily understand it psychologically, and although it is repeatedly proven to him as he swings up and down in his cycles of improvement.[1] Nevertheless, the understanding of the nature of the illness, relieves the patient somewhat of the too frequent self-accusations of inferiority and aids in removing the neurotic features which spontaneously tend to be associated with the depressive state.

One can only theorize as to the site of the lesion in the manic-depressive swings. The fact that many "normal" persons are subject to such swings although to a lesser degree makes for the impression that there is some general metabolic or cellular fluctuation which we have as yet not been able to measure. In severe depressions, however, the very inability to "feel" normally, and the welcoming even of painful sensations so that one may experience at least some kind of normal sensations, would indicate that the highest level of sensation is disturbed. This level is generally associated with the thalamus, and Head's patients who suffered from destruction of one side of the thalamus experienced differences in sensation which are analogous to the disturbance of subjective sensibility found in severely depressed patients, although actual appreciation of touch, pain, and temperature is unaffected. One patient on recovering from the depression stated that she was better able to feel pain than she had been in the depths of her depressive state, indicating by her statement the change of quality of her appreciation of pain.

TREATMENT

The treatment of these manic-depressive swings may be divided into four parts: shock therapy, psychotherapy, environmental therapy, and drug therapy. The first will be discussed under the treatment of schizophrenia. It may be stated here, however, that shock therapy is of preeminent importance in the treatment of depressions. Manic patients do not, as a rule, react so favorably. In

[1] *Vide* p. 283.

agitated depressions, or the so-called involutional melancholias, the metrazol shock therapy[1] works almost miraculous effects. The dangers of fractures of the spine, of other bones, of damage to the heart, etc., are found in actual practice to be at a minimum, and certainly far less dangerous to the individual patient or to the family than the prolonged grief and anxiety experienced by all concerned if the depression is left untreated. Moreover, the percentage of patients who remain chronically ill without treatment is far greater than those that suffer from the treatment.

Psychotherapy is of great importance, primarily as reassurance. During a depression, the patient is very liable to consider everything as hopeless and strongly to contemplate suicide.[2] Moral support on the part of the physician is of inestimable value. Encouragement, reassurance, and a sympathetic attitude toward the patient are of primary importance in helping him survive the period of acute depression.[3]

Psychotherapy directed toward the patient's past emotional life and his behavior patterns tends to fail during the acute phase of either the depression, or of the manic swing. During this phase, the patient cannot think logically from conclusion to conclusion, and cannot believe even that which he has been guided to reason out. *Stronger than all reason* is the prevailing tone either of exaltation in the manic phase, or of hopelessness in the depressed phase. During the acute period, therefore, most of psychotherapy should be directed toward maintaining the patient's morale. Furthermore during this acute phase, there should not be any urging of the patient to force himself into activity. If possible the usual routine should be maintained and some forcing is desirable toward this end; but more should not be required. The reason for this injunction is twofold: first, the patient is incapable physically and mentally of doing more; and secondly, on attempting to do more, the patient will become more deeply depressed by the failures which are bound to occur. Often the relatives will insist that if the patient is permitted to do nothing, he will become worse; but they do not understand that the illness is not a matter of a "mental" attitude, but a real and definite clinical physiologic illness. The only chronicity may come from the psychoneurotic features which may be associated with the depression; and since there will be a spontaneous improvement from the depressive state *per se*, the physician can reassure the relatives that they need not be concerned.

---

[1] *Vide* p. 385 *ff.*   [2] *Vide* p. 370.   [3] *Vide* p. 361.

As the patient begins to recover, however, from the depression, and this improvement may take many months in some patients, it is well to begin to discuss with him his reaction patterns, how they came into being, how they are ineffective or harmful, and how to change them.   The depressive state will interfere with the patient's complete comprehension and ability to adopt what he learns in such interviews, but constant reiteration will in time help make these new ideas automatic.   During this time if the patient asks how psychotherapy can help a physiologic ailment (although the patient is usually convinced of his own accord that he is lazy, "a crazy fool," or going insane), he must be told that the psychologic attitude can do much to retard or accelerate recovery from such a physiologic state, and that every effort must be made to remove all psychoneurotic obstacles.   There may have been many psychologic factors in his life previous to his "breakdown" which predisposed him to his illness; and removal of these predisposing factors will be of value in preventing any future breakdowns.   The psychotherapy of these factors is the same as discussed previously. Rigid personalities[1] are common among these breakdowns, the patients often working at a high level of efficiency objectively, but being tense, overly conscientious, and restless subjectively.   On the other hand unstable, emotional and psychoneurotic features may characterize the life of the patient before the depressive illness. The clearing up of these factors may not prevent the recurrence of another manic-depressive episode, but it can prevent a neurosis from being grafted upon and continuing after the depression, and it can so modify the person that should a depressive attack reoccur, he because of his helpful psychologic attitude will not become so deeply depressed.

Environmental therapy depends upon many factors.   The financial status of the family may permit certain helpful techniques, such as providing a pleasant home and non-depressing surroundings, an intelligent companion, such diverting activities as golf, motion pictures, etc.   Where these elements are not available, psychotherapy of the family may be beneficial to the patient.   Training the family in how to act, in what to say, in understanding that the illness is not the result of lack of "will power," that encouragement and reassurance will do far more to cure the patient than criticism and nagging, that protection from self harm is constantly necessary, etc., often does more for the patient than do many attempts

[1] *Vide* p. 212.

at the psychotherapy of his emotions, particularly in the acute phase. The family must learn that the physician will not permit chronic invalidism to occur; because as soon as the patient "comes out" of the depressive state he, by intense psychotherapy, will be urged into more integrated activity than ever before; but until the physician recognizes the time, urging the patient to do more than he can do, results only in harm.[1]

Social therapy is of vital importance;[2] yet here again, it will be observed, that when patients are improving they will need very little urging to mingle with others. During the acute depressive episode, there is an intense aversion to being in the company of others even though the patients may previously have been very sociable. When these patients are able to get out into groups, the first few visits are often associated with much irritation and boredom, but these feelings are soon overcome, and there is a partial relief of tension as they have to enter into conversation with others.

Work therapy is also of value.[3] It is well for men who are engaged in occupations to continue with their work, unless their slowness and depression are definitely interfering with their efficiency. In these cases even a short course of metrazol is of value in order to overcome the acute phase, but thereafter, the routine work should be carried on. The necessity of forcing one's thoughts toward some objective problem, even though it be routine, is of help; for loneliness and lack of activity give the patient more time to think of his unhappy subjective state. Yet it is important not to overdo this required activity, for should the patient fail to continue at his occupation, his depression will be accentuated, and he may be driven to desperate measures if he becomes convinced that he is an utter failure. As a rule, less activity than usual should be required, but the activity should permit a full day's work, even if it is not intensive. Also since the morning hours are the most difficult for the patient, the work, if possible, should be done toward the end of the morning and during the afternoon. The patient may complain of being unable to concentrate, and of doing his work poorly; but if such work does not seriously jeopardize his livelihood, he should be urged to continue to do it as best he can.

Institutional therapy may be needed by patients who become so depressed that a suicidal attempt is imminent. It must be remembered that many patients talk of suicide for some time before they actually make the attempt; and one should not dismiss lightly suicidal threats, particularly if they are made in the setting of a

[1] *Vide* p. 138.   [2] *Vide* p. 249.   [3] *Vide* p. 252.

depression. It is as if these patients have to work up courage before making the actual attempt; and it is fortunate if the patient merely takes an overdose of sedative which can be checked in time. Once the patient has leaned out the window too far, there is no recall. Therefore, in many situations, institutionalization is distinctly advisable; for in addition to the protective elements, there is opportunity for the use of shock therapy.

In the institution, there is opportunity for many corrective procedures: hydrotherapy in the form of continuous baths (temperature from 94 to 96°), or needle sprays or scotch douches which spray a heavy stream of water down the spine; occupational therapy, with work in carpentry, basket weaving, loom work, needle work, bookmaking, leather working, and a host of other minor occupations which take the patient out of himself; recreational therapy in the form of motion pictures, outdoor sports, dancing, games, theater projects, and so forth. Moreover, in an institution, the care of nutrition, of elimination, of sleep difficulties is all facilitated because it is under medical control.

Drug therapy, exclusive of metrazol, may be stimulating, quieting, and sleep producing. The stimulating drugs are few in number, caffeine in the form of hot coffee being a common drug. In the milder depressive states, benzedrine sulphate, mg. 10 early in the morning and three hours later is of value. As mentioned previously the dosage may have to be doubled or halved according to the patient. Often it produces only a state of irritability instead of an improvement in mood. Generally, after several weeks the effect of the drug wears off, and it may have to be discontinued for a while before it is used again. Sedative drugs are many, and their main purpose is to relieve some of the anxiety and irritability of the patient. For many patients powdered opium is most effective in $\frac{1}{4}$ grain doses, but every effort should be made to prevent the patient from knowing what medication he is getting. However, this opium compound should be used only in very tense persons, for there is a marked constipating effect in an already constipated person. Diet, oil, habit, and enemas may be required. Barbital, in $2\frac{1}{2}$ grain doses three times a day, is often of value in the milder cases, not only in relieving tension but in facilitating sleep. There are many idiosyncrasies, however, and there is a wide variety of drugs which can be used for many patients. It is very difficult to find sleep producing drugs[1] which will

[1] *Cf.* p. 335.

continue to work and which do not leave any after effects. The depressive patient is very resistant to drugs. As has been mentioned, most patients go to sleep rather easily, but awaken in the early hours of the morning and are not able to return to sleep. Many different hypnotics will have to be tried, for the patient tends to develop a tolerance. Sodium amytal, sodium pentobarbital, phenobarbital, and seconal are particularly effective.

SCHIZOPHRENIA

Schizophrenia (formerly called Dementia Praecox) is one of the psychoses without any as yet proved organic pathology. It occurs most commonly after adolescence, is of gradual onset, and emerges from a shy, sensitive moralistic personality, slowly developing symptoms characterized by suspiciousness, ideas of reference, paranoid tendencies, phantasy formation, withdrawal from reality, delusions, and hallucinations.

Two-thirds of all cases occur between the fifteenth and thirtieth year. It occurs about equally in men and women, but is three times more common in single than in married persons.

Little is known about inheritable tendencies in schizophrenia. Some 3 per cent of the siblings of schizophrenic patients have schizophrenia; 5 per cent of the twin siblings of di-zygotic patients have schizophrenia; while 44 per cent of the twin siblings of mono-zygotic schizophrenics have the disease. An actual history of psychosis in the family of the patient is uncommon, while on the other hand personality peculiarities in the family tree are much more frequent. Heredity is undoubtedly important but not entirely responsible, for some 56 per cent of twins developing from one fertilized ovum do not have the mental illness of their twin sibling.

There seems to be a definite constitutional factor in this disease. Kretschmer pointed out that most schizophrenic patients are asthenic-athletic in their physical build, while manic-depressive patients are mainly pyknic.[1] (Asthenic individuals tend to be thin, with an egg-shaped head, much hair on the head and little on the chin, a flat chest with narrow shoulders, an acute costal angle, a flat or gastroptotic abdomen, poorly developed musculature, and small joints. Athletic persons tend to be tall, with a five-cornered shield-like face, well developed secondary sex characteristics, broad

---

[1] *Vide* p. 284.

shoulders, tapering down to a small but powerfully developed abdomen, strong muscles, and large coarse joints. Pyknic persons are relatively short, heavy, with a round face, a tendency to baldness early in life, heavy chin hair, as well as heavy hair on the chest, narrow shoulders, sloping outward to form a wide based thorax and an obtuse costal angle, a well rounded abdomen, well padded extremities, and fine delicate joints.) It must be remembered that pure types are not common and that each person is usually an admixture of several types. So-called introverts are much more predisposed to schizophrenia than extroverts.[1]

The life history of most schizophrenic patients gives a picture of shyness (occasionally an over-compensatory aggressiveness), marked sensitiveness, with easily wounded feelings; a deficiency in initiative though excellent ability to study and make good grades in school; excessive moralism on the one hand, sufficient to prevent smoking and drinking, and frequently over-concern about masturbation and sex, on the other hand.

The predisposition to schizophrenia varies greatly from person to person. In some, the predisposition is so great that schizophrenia will develop shortly after the stress of puberty. Many develop this disease in early adolescence after eighteen or nineteen, the peak age being about twenty-nine, which is the age at which most persons have to be sent to institutions. Schizophrenic symptoms may develop after sixty and seventy, when the brain structure becomes weakened by arteriosclerosis and senility.[2]

The more constitutional predisposition there is, the fewer or the less intense need be the precipitating factors. These factors may be: (a) physiologic, such as puberty and pregnancy, or they may be (b) organogenic with toxins such as chronic infections, pernicious anemia, thyrotoxicosis, degenerations such as arteriosclerosis, etc., or they may be (c) psychologic, such as acute feelings of inferiority, of "being different," or marital disharmony, and others. All of the above put the organism under a strain, and in cases of susceptibility the organism breaks down and develops schizophrenia. The greatest number of cases seem to develop in the postadolescent stage with almost no discoverable precipitating factor, unless it be the effect of physiologic changes during this time. Many causes have been postulated (auto-intoxication, endocrinopathy, aplasia of the circulatory system, dysplastic physical

---

[1] *Vide* p. 271.   [2] *Vide* p. 352.

types, improper emotional attitude, etc.), but none is generally agreed upon.

There is no definitely established pathology in schizophrenia. Changes are said to occur in the third and fifth layers of the brain cortex, but this theory is not widely accepted. Various workers have attempted to find lesions in the basal ganglia, in the autonomic nervous system, in the endocrine system, but without avail. Chronic infection, auto-intoxication, and many other conditions have been said to be the basis for this disease.

Physiologically the schizophrenic patient tends to be thin, his blood pressure is usually low, and the basal metabolic rate is on the minus side. There are other evidences of physiologic sluggishness, but they tend to fall on the lesser side of normal rather than into the abnormal.

The onset of the symptoms is gradual and emerges imperceptibly from the patient's personality. There may be increased irritability, with outbursts of anger over minor incidents. Suspiciousness develops, at first directed toward strangers, and then toward members of one's family. Sensitiveness becomes acute, and the patient feels that people are looking at him constantly, and believes that remarks made by strangers are intended for him. At the same time the patient becomes preoccupied, sitting for hours, staring off into space, and not paying attention to what is said to him until it is repeated two or three times. Habits deteriorate, and a once cleanly and fastidious person becomes slovenly in appearance and eats wolfishly or not at all. Asocial tendencies develop, and the patient refuses to go out, or goes into another room when company visits the home. Laughing to one's self and talking to one's self are frequent, and the patients seem to "have something on their minds." Mannerisms or peculiar motions and actions are repeated constantly.[1] Sleep is disturbed and these patients may put the radio on full blast at 2 or 3 A.M. or disturb the household in some way during the night. Not infrequently masturbation will be practiced several times daily; rarely are attempts made to have normal sex relations. Paranoid ideas may involve the family, patients often accusing them of poisoning the food, wishing to harm them, making a plot to kill the patient, etc. Delusions and hallucinations are common: the patients hearing voices of strangers through the walls, smelling gas which was injected into the room to kill them, seeing strange men signaling at each other, refusing to go

[1] *Vide* p. 55 *ff.*

out for fear of being spied on and followed, feeling electricity go through their body from some infernal machine, doing things automatically because they feel hypnotized, etc. Violent temper outbursts are common with shouting, breaking of furniture, and often with physical violence toward a parent or mate.

Late symptoms come on with various degrees of rapidity in untreated cases. Our mental institutions used to be and still are (though less so since the event of shock therapy) full of patients who had developed some dementia. In this late stage the patients may sit around for weeks and months hardly moving. Usually they become incontinent of bowel and bladder, soiling themselves wherever they may be. Saliva accumulates in the mouth and drools from it. Peculiar motions are constantly made, and patients may bow or jump, or salute, or make various symbolical gestures for hours at a time. Catalepsy or waxy flexibility is common, and one can put these patients in any position where they will remain for hours. Generally these patients are mute. The appetite is poor, and occasionally tube feedings are necessary to sustain life. These patients show no interest and appear to be entirely vegetative; yet should something occur to stimulate them (*e. g.*, metrazol) they may speak of incidents which have occurred about them, thereby showing that their intellectual functions have remained intact. Often they are unresponsive to pain, and can be stuck with pins and show no sign of awareness. Similarly they may walk about on broken legs, or an acute appendicitis may be accidentally discovered, the patient having made no complaint. Death most often results from tuberculosis or cardiac disease. The patients may live in the above condition for over forty years.

There are four main varieties of schizophrenia, all of which have in common many of the symptoms mentioned above. These varieties are not sharp and distinct but merge into one another.

Simple Schizophrenia.—Simple schizophrenia (schiz: to split or divide, and phrenia: mind) is characterized mainly by a general let-down in interest and activity. Ambition is markedly lacking, and these patients are often called lazy. The person is a daydreamer, is unable to concentrate, is often moody, irritable, and asocial. Masturbation is marked, and normal sex contact rare. In the home of understanding parents, such a patient may remain for years doing no work, rarely going out with people yet never harming others. The illness begins in adolescence, and paranoid ideas develop much later.

Hebephrenic Schizophrenia.—Hebephrenic schizophrenia (hebe: puberty, phrenic: mind) is characterized by silly, childish behavior, with vivid hallucinations, marked incoherence in thinking, violent emotional outbursts, alternating periods of excitement and periods of tearfulness. Before the onset of the psychosis such persons are regarded as queer and are shallow in their emotional response. This group deteriorates rather quickly, and "late symptoms" occur early.

Catatonic Schizophrenia.—Catatonic schizophrenia (cata: down, and tonus: tone or tension) is characterized by stupor, the patients being mute, refusing to eat, and showing signs of waxy flexibility. There are alternating periods of depression, excitement, and stupor. The symptoms tend to come on more acutely than in the other schizophrenic syndromes, and are accompanied by intense negativism[1] (doing the opposite of what is wanted), sterotypy (performing the same actions over and over), echolalia (saying the same words repeatedly), retention of urine and feces, and apparently a complete disinterest in their surroundings.

Paranoid Schizophrenia.—Paranoid schizophrenia (paranoia: madness), is characterized by the tendency to develop the so-called persecution complex. The symptoms tend to develop later in life than they do in the former groups. Suspiciousness gradually hardens into delusions of persecution. These delusions at first may concern many different topics, but as time goes by the patient begins to connect them all into one system. These systematized delusions are often reasoned out paralogically (*i. e.*, by illogical analogies; *e. g.*, since all men are animals, therefore, all animals are men), and untrained persons such as juries will often insist that such a person is not psychotic. One patient, for example, said that gas was put into his room and that electricity was passed through his body, but he could give no reason for his accusation. Sometime later, however, he fitted all he had said into a story according to which he was being persecuted by a gang because he knew some secrets about them and they had the hospital surrounded by men whom he could see dodging behind trees. These patients may be gainfully employed and able to take care of their ordinary tasks without interference by these delusions until they become acute. It is persons of this group who may shoot a passer-by whom they believe to be a persecutor. Gradually these patients deteriorate, develop mannerisms and marked incoherence in their reasoning, although in a

[1] *Vide* p. 71.

mental institution they may be able to perform adequately many routine duties.

Before the advent of the newer methods of therapy, these patients would generally become more and more deteriorated. Remissions tended to occur spontaneously in some 10 to 20 per cent of cases; but these remissions were rarely cures, and the patient would be able to go back to society only on an inferior level, and "not quite right." Readmissions to hospitals were common. The average schizophrenic patient remained in the mental hospital for twelve to thirteen years and died at about fifty. Paranoid patients tended to die after sixty. Since the shock therapies, those patients who are treated but do not recover are often greatly improved and deterioration is less common. Some authors claim over 85 per cent cures in patients whose illness is of less than six months' duration and about 25 per cent when the illness is over two years. The treatment is too new, however, to give accurate figures.

THERAPY

Prophylactic therapy is difficult to suggest for we know so little about the hereditary and constitutional forces. Even the effect of the environment is not clearly understood. No disease process has been isolated that can be prevented.

Early recognition of schizophrenic symptoms is important. As in any medical situation, the earlier the diagnosis is made the better are the chances of recovery. Eccentric behavior or idiosyncrasies should be looked into; for whereas in many cases they may be within the limits of normalcy, in many they may be the first signs of a psychosis. Of importance to study is any change in personality which occurs without apparent reason. In many such cases simple psychotherapy may prevent the disease from going further.

Normal mental hygiene should be used by everyone, especially by those who have personality difficulties. Mental hygiene consists of a healthy attitude toward life and its problems. It means facing facts directly and courageously,[1] solving them without undue fear, hate, or insecurity; it means being human, flexible,[2] and relaxed.[3] It means self-discipline without repression,[4] avoidance of oversensitivity,[5] and tolerance of one's faults while continuing to

[1] *Vide* p. 205 *ff*.　[2] *Vide* p. 212.　[3] *Vide* p. 244.　[4] *Vide* p. 217.　[5] *Vide* p. 58.

strive for their correction. Rigid rules of thought and action are best avoided.

Active Therapy.—There are several forms of therapy which have been used, and these will be listed below. In general, it may be said that the percentage of cure is in proportion to the earliness of the treatment. Patients treated within six months of their breakdown can be expected to recover in from 70 to 80 per cent of instances, and these cures are apparently complete and permanent, though our experience with these treatments is still young. Moreover, (a) chemotherapy must be supported by (b) psychotherapy, which is another way of saying that in addition to changing the physical state of the patient his methods of thinking and living must also be changed.

When the diagnosis is made, the patient should be placed in a sanitarium or adequately equipped hospital. The windows should be protected because of the danger of suicide, but the room should be as pleasant as possible. A cheerful and intelligent nurse is of great help.[1] A general diet and ordinary routine are instituted. A careful physical examination and laboratory tests will rule out any organic pathology. If one of the shock therapies is decided on, the family must be told of the patient's distaste of the treatment and that it is necessary to complete a full course of treatment regardless of the patient's objections.

Insulin Shock Therapy.—The principle of this form of treatment is to produce some 15 to 25 insulin comas in the patient. This number is generally sufficient to cure most patients. The technique is as follows: The patient is given 20 units of insulin at 6 A.M. and no food is permitted until four hours later. The next day 30 units are given, and the same procedure followed. Each day the dosage of insulin is increased until the patient develops coma. Most patients develop coma with 100 to 150 units, though some have gone into coma with 20 units, and some have not developed coma with more than 450 units. The patients are allowed to remain in coma for about an hour, and then revived by sugar. Ordinary sugar, sucrose, is given by stomach tube, 2 grams of sugar being used for every unit of insulin. Care must be taken to get the tube into the stomach as the pharyngeal reflex is very weak, if not lost. Aspiration with subsequent pneumonia is not rare. Intravenously, glucose is used in 50 per cent solution, but this should not be given routinely, as the veins become sclerosed. Occasionally the patient

[1] *Vide* p. 226.

may develop a protracted coma and not come out with sugar. Adrenalin, heat, and intravenous salt solution should then be used. Obviously, careful observation must accompany the entire procedure, which is extremely dangerous though fatalities are rare when there is careful watching. The patient may gain some 10 to 30 pounds in weight and his mental state be vastly improved.

Metrazol Shock Therapy.—This is of less value in the treatment of schizophrenia, than in the treatment of manic-depressive psychosis, involutional melancholia, and certain post-operative and puerperal psychoses. Metrazol was first used by von Meduna who, noting the well known fact that epilepsy is rare among schizophrenic patients, determined to produce epileptic-like siezures as a therapeutic measure. The success of his experiment was startling. Although it is now generally agreed that the percentage of cures is not so great as was at first claimed by various clinics (sometimes the figure was as high as 90 per cent), there is no doubt that the method is of great value in the psychoses. Manic-depressive psychoses yield well to this therapy, and patients who would ordinarily have to be in a sanitarium for eight months to a year, recover in several weeks. The manic phase does not yield so rapidly to shock therapy as does the depressive phase. (Indeed my experience leads to the conclusion that in manic states often its primary value lies in quieting the patient without appreciably shortening the period of illness.) Patients with so-called involutional melancholia, or agitated depression respond rapidly to metrazol. Depressed or schizophrenic-like states which may occur as a form of delirium particularly after surgical procedures or after pregnancy, often clear up with just a few such treatments.

The complications of metrazol therapy are very few. Fear of the treatment is probably the outstanding difficulty. This fear is not the result of pain, or of conscious awareness of convulsions. As a rule, twenty seconds after the metrazol is injected into the vein, unconsciousness supervenes, and the patient is not aware of the convulsion that follows. It is during this twenty seconds (there are infrequent variations to this time, which may last up to ten minutes, or even several hours) that there is experienced what is usually described as an "awful feeling." It is difficult for patients more accurately to describe what they feel. The sensation most closely approximates a sense of dying. However, the physician can minimize this fear by giving a hypodermic of hyosine, grain 1/100th, a half hour before the metrazol medication.

25

Fractures and dislocations may occur as a result of the violent contraction of the muscles. If the patient is held during a convulsion, the violent muscle contractions are the more liable to produce such fractures as tearing off the greater tuberosity of the humerus, or to tear muscles. It should be a rule not to restrain the patient, but merely to see to it that there is no object which the patient can strike while in convulsion. If a pillow is placed under the patient's shoulders so that the spine is partly flexed, the subsequent opisthotonus will not be likely to cause any compression fracture of the spine. Dislocations may occur if the patient throws his arm sideways and out, but this movement is usually prevented if the patient's arms are folded across his chest immediately after the metrazol is injected. Dislocations of the jaw occur also, but these are easily reduced during the period of unconsciousness which follows the convulsions. However, if the technique is carefully followed, these complications rarely occur. Pain in the back, particularly at the level of the lower portion of the scapula may occur and often lasts for several months. Occasionally the hair becomes gray at the roots. The memory for recent events may also be faulty for several weeks, but this memory defect differs radically from the memory defect of which the depressive patient complains; for the latter difficulty is the result of lack of attention to detail because of excessive concentration on one's self; whereas the evidence seems to be that the former is the result of actual cortical changes, which are brought about by changes in oxidation, blood flow, stimulation from the hypothalmus, etc., and which are usually reversible and temporary. For example, patients who have had metrazol therapy occasionally complain of difficulty in seeing, although tests for visual acuity are negative. Their insistence that they do not see so well, even though they may be able to read the finest print indicates that mild temporary changes, which give the subjective impression of visual difficulty, have taken place in the visual cortex. This difficulty, however, tends to clear up quickly. In one patient I have seen an actual aphasic reaction, occurring a week after the tenth metrazol convulsion, and lasting about ten minutes. These cortical changes are temporary and reversible, but as has been shown experimentally can be made to become irreversible, if excessively large doses are used or the patient is particularly susceptible. Deaths following metrazol treatment have been reported, but these are extremely rare, and on pathologic examination, the person shows no pertinent disease process. Occasionally multiple hemorrhages are found in the brain. There does not seem to be any pathology found in the heart that can be demonstrated in the living by clinical or electrocardiographic examination, and pathologic examination is similarly negative. In State hospitals, many patients who in the past would have died of exhaustion have been saved as a result of the quieting effect of metrazol.

The metrazol in a 10 per cent solution is given in the morning, the patient having had no breakfast. A large bore needle is used and the medication is injected as rapidly as possible. The initial dose is 3 cc. for women, and 4 cc. for men. If no convulsion results, the dosage is increased by 1 cc. and repeated the next day. It is possible to repeat this increased dosage ten to fifteen minutes after the first dosage, but there is some evidence to the effect that this procedure is inadvisable because of the possibility of brain damage. Overdosage is dangerous. The convulsive dosage is repeated every other day until the patient recovers, or until 12 to 15 doses have been given. The subsequent effective doses may be the same, less, or greater. If there is no recovery, it is well to wait a month and then give the patient insulin shock therapy. Many patients will recover after this second therapy, even if the first fails.

Other convulsants have been used: picrotoxin, methyl guanidine, electric current, camphor, etc.; but of all, metrazol seems, at the present, to be most widely used. Electrical shock therapy, however, is rapidly gaining favor. When we learn more of just what happens to the organism when these convulsants are used, we shall be better able to understand our limitations and capacities in treatment. It is probable that the convulsant action is secondary and unnecessary; and that the primary element in the therapy is the cerebral anoxemia.

Fever Therapy.—Fever therapy is far less effective in the treatment of the psychoses and is usually given by means of intravenous typhoid fever bacilli. *Prolonged sleep treatment* is also of value occasionally and the patient is kept asleep for ten to fifteen days, being allowed to awaken only for food and elimination. Sodium amytal or phenobarbital or barbital is commonly used. Enough sedative is given by mouth to keep the patient near coma.

Psychotherapy.—Psychologic therapy is of utmost importance. Without it much of the beneficial effect of the chemical therapy will go to waste. It must be remembered that the patient is confronted by many psychologic emotional difficulties which in themselves can be cleared up only by psychotherapy. One cannot stress this fact too strongly. *Many patients fail to recover after shock therapy because of the lack of adequate psychotherapy.*

There are several principles to follow in schizophrenia as differentiated from neurosis. (1) Constant encouragement and not overly obvious praise must be given to the patient because of the self-accusations and self-condemnation present in so many of these patients. Reassurance must be frequent and strong. (2) It is unwise at first to force these patients to face their problems. Their peculiar ideas can be unraveled and straightened out only gradually, and only as the patient begins to develop some self-confidence. If one attempts to do too much in too short a period of time, these patients will often tend to harden and fix their delusions rather than soften and dissipate them. (3) The physician should never attempt to convince the patient that his delusions are false. The delusions themselves are the result of an underlying emotional turmoil. These delusions are peculiar thoughts but they exist because of the internal conflict. All the discussion in the world about the delusion will do very little to change the underlying conflict which is the source of the delusion. In actual practice, attempts to change and rationalize delusions will result in the patient's becoming more fixed and unyielding about them. (4) It is often wise to give these patients a psychologic or physiologic reason for some of their actions. Thus, for example, if a patient has peculiar pains in the body, it is well to explain; *e. g.,* that "under nervous tension muscles may contract and in so doing give rise to peculiar skin sensations"; and that these sensations will tend to disappear as the muscles relax. Reasoning of this sort gives the patient a feasible explanation and substitutes a more or less rational interpretation for the delusional theory he otherwise would advance.[1] (5) Most of these patients have conflicts, and it is well to generalize about the fact that conflicts are present in every person and that certain wishes, desires, or ideas are normal. For example: in many instances there is a great deal of sex conflict in these patients and one may tell them repeatedly that sex is a normal biologic drive; that it is present in every normal person; that whereas one may not be able to satisfy this drive except under conditions which society recognizes, it nevertheless is a normal tendency. In a similar vein, one must understand many of the

---

[1] *Vide* p. 178.

conflicts of the patient and repeatedly reassure him on the fundamental nature and humanness of his desires. (6) Social and work
activity should be encouraged as much as possible; but here again
the patient must be coaxed and led rather than driven.

Mr. A. L., aged twenty-nine years, was discharged from a psychiatric
hospital in the summer of 1935 as a deteriorated schizophrenic. He was
mute; refused to speak; was violent; and force had to be used to get him to
eat, to undress for bed or bath; he had catalepsy, and stood for hours without moving; he spoke as though he was answering someone, when no one
was about; he was incontinent of bowel and bladder, and even smeared his
feces over the wall. When first seen in August, 1935, he spoke hardly at all,
but told of voices which accused him of being a moron, and a criminal. The
voices accused him of all sorts of antisocial and immoral acts. He did not
know where they came from, but he felt that a certain doctor instigated
them.
    This patient was one of six sons, brought up by a devout and strict
father. The father was kind and loving to his children, thereby earning
their respect and admiration; but at the same time he demanded that they
all follow his own most literal interpretation of the Bible. Several of his
sons, including the patient, Arnold, went into the ministry. Arnold grew
up to think and feel that almost every action of the human being was sinful
and motivated by the devil. In his frame of mind, to go out with a girl was
tempting the devil to his utmost. He worked his way through theological
seminary, volunteered for the mission field, and was put in charge of a foreign
mission. His work went well, he was tireless and devoted in his efforts, but
the relative undress of the women natives disturbed him, and he felt with
horror that his mind was contemplating unholy ideas. He threw himself
feverishly into work, and slept little. He walked long distances, 20 miles
on occasion, to fatigue himself and forget. The tension increased, for he
could escape neither his tantalizing awareness of the women nor the excoriat-
ing accusations of his conscience. One afternoon in his cabin, he seized the
colored maid in a frenzy and raped her. He stripped naked and ran out into
the clearing, screaming with excitement. There followed other symptoms of
an acute catatonic excitement. This incident occurred in 1934, and soon
thereafter he developed mutism. All the voices he heard in his schizophrenic state, were those of persons whose opinion he cared for or feared;
and they all accused him of immorality and degeneracy. They were projections of his own conscience.

Psychotherapy was begun[1] by making every effort to establish
rapport with the patient.

When he was first seen in the sanitarium, no effort was made to analyze
or criticize his behavior patterns or suggest activities. Instead I talked
about many incidents and topics which had little relation to the patient,
attempting to make the time pass as if there were ordinary conversation,

[1] At this time little was known concerning the shock therapies.

even though the patient spoke hardly at all. After two weeks, he was permitted to return home, his family having been instructed in how to act. He was to be left entirely to his own devices, except for an occasional and not too persevering effort to have him enter into groups and activities about the house. No allusions were to be made to the past; and in every way the patient was to be treated as an ordinary member of the household and not as one to be looked after. Members of the family were seen as often as the patient, for the success of his treatment was dependent upon the family's intelligent cooperation.

When the patient came to the office, he was constantly encouraged as to his recovery from his illness and as to his future. The past, he was told, was to be regarded as a bad dream which he needed to forget. No effort was made, at first, to search out the underlying psychologic mechanisms; and every attempt was made to give the patient a sense of security and to remove feelings of guilt and remorse. As time went by, explanations were given to him, first in generalities, and then specifically, about the universality of the sex drive, and its normalcy. Emphasis was placed on the normal basic nature of the impulse, and dispassionate explanations were given as to why society has developed a code of morals in regard to sex. He was made to feel that his impulse was normal, and that his standards were high. It was a moment of weakness which had caused his digression from his standards, but he was reminded of his preachings about the humanness of errors. As psychotherapy progressed, his complaint about the accusing voices changed so that in November, 1935, he came to speak of "a scroll" which was in the back of his brain, and which kept constantly repeating to him the accusations formerly "heard." This scroll was like a phonograph record, with the difference that sometimes it was acute and irritating to distraction, and at other times it was a soft sibilant whisper. This bringing of the projection mechanism nearer to the self indicated a distinct improvement.

When the patient brought up various delusional ideas, they were not discussed, or were minimized as to their significance. No attempt was made to convince the patient that he was wrong. Where possible, some pseudo-scientific reason was given to form a rational excuse. For example, he complained of someone's shooting electricity down his legs. Although no pathology could be discerned, the patient was told that the malaria which he might have had in his foreign service could have affected the condition of his skin and that the condition would clear up in time. The patient accepted this explanation, and except for an occasional mention of it later, made no connection between his leg and "someone shooting electricity down it." In February, 1936, he remarked, "When I'm active, the scroll doesn't bother me, but when I'm quiet it keeps going. Much of the time the scroll seems to have disappeared but there is a constant ticking sound in its place, just as if there was a clock in my head. BESIDES I CAN'T FORGET MY PAST." This last sentence was particularly significant, for it indicated that the patient had removed his guilt feelings and ideas of sin, away from the projection mechanism of voices, or scrolls, and had brought himself to face these feelings and ideas directly. The process of recovery was slow, and just as important as the psychotherapy (the patient was seen once a week) was the factor of time. In June, 1936, the patient stated, "I don't hear the scroll, but my conscience always keeps bothering me about my past, and it becomes so intense at times, that the scroll sometimes takes over and keeps on saying what my conscience said." This spontaneous recognition of and the alteration between conscience and "scroll" indicated to the patient his tendency to dissociate and split off his ideas from himself. The patient was definitely on the road toward getting well. The general formulations of mental hygiene were constantly applied. General discussions of the driving forces in life, of different methods of meeting life situations, of the need for self tolerance while exercising self correction, were carefully but continually made. The attitude adopted was of giving the patient understanding, rather than that of urging correction; for understanding in itself is corrective. The patient was urged, and his family encouraged to have him form social contacts, and his brothers asked him to help in all sorts of chores, in an effort to keep him occupied. For a while he filched money from purses about the house but it was deemed wisest not to shame the patient by bringing his actions to his attention. Instead, his spending allowance was increased, and in a short time the stealing ceased.

In August, 1936, the patient came into the office with a red, non-itching maculo-papular rash over his entire body. A Wassermann test came back four plus. The patient admitted having had sexual contact with some prostitutes.

To a sensitive person as this patient was, such a shock was terrific. The "scroll" returned to its previous function. "It keeps on saying, 'It's all your own fault—it's your punishment for the terrible sins you committed in the past.'" Every effort was made to prevent the patient from becoming too remorseful, and although his sex contact was not condoned, he was taught to regard it as "a human error." By November, 1936, the scroll had again disappeared, and "I'm doing my best not to let the past bother my conscience." He continued to become more interested in work and persons, and by the spring of 1937 procured a temporary position. By the summer he was working steadily and at the time of the present writing (1941) was normal and had had no relapses.

GROUP PSYCHOTHERAPY

Such responses to individual psychotherapy are very encouraging; but the time requisite for such procedure makes it often an impractical technique. When one deals with large groups of patients, as in state hospitals or in clinics, such individual attention is limited to a few selected patients. To deal with this situation group psychotherapy has been evolved. Patients are gathered into small groups and therapy is given to all simultaneously. The results are very good. Group therapy aids the patient not only by: (1) giving him instruction in mental hygiene concepts, but also, (2) by demonstrating to him that he is not the only person with neurotic complaints and thus alleviating much of his needless self criticism.   Moreover, (3) the activity of the group as a social unit makes many of these patients less shy and more interested in activities external to themselves.

There are various techniques which can be used, one excellent method being to obtain a psychiatric history before permitting the patient to join the group.   Then the physician knowing the particular cases can in the group meetings, guide the discussions to deal with specific maladjustments; and the patients can be encouraged to talk about their own problems before the others.   Skillful handling of the topic can prevent embarrassment, and the fact that each person discusses his problem creates a community of feeling which makes general discussion easier.

As a rule the sexes are separated in the therapeutic groups and members are encouraged to participate in social activities.   Group psychotherapy for patients suffering from alcoholism is very helpful in preventing recurrences; each member's knowing of the susceptibilities and needs of himself exercises a prophylactic effect on the others who may be tempted to relapse.

CHAPTER XVI

OTHER PSYCHOPATHIC STATES INCLUDING PSY-CHOPATHIC PERSONALITY, DRUG ADDICTION, ALCOHOLISM, EPILEPSY, AND FEEBLE-MINDEDNESS

THERE are numerous methods other than those of the neuroses or psychoses by which the human being expresses maladjustment on his socio-psycho-biologic level. Some of these methods are socially acceptable, while others are frowned upon and may be severely dealt with by society.

In the following discussion of a few of the socially disapproved of and unhealthy reactions to life's difficulties, it will be apparent that the physician has no easy task in the differentiation of causes. Hereditary forces, congenital influences, early environmental training, existing stress whether it be internal unrest or social and economic pressure must all be carefully investigated as possible determinants.[1]

PSYCHOPATHIC PERSONALITY
(Constitutional Psychopathic Inferior)

This classification of "psychopathic personality" is vaguely defined. It is in reality hardly more than a "wastebasket" in which are cluttered various groups which do not represent any clearcut etiology, pathology, or symptomatology. Some of the various groups are: habitual criminals, swindlers, kleptomaniacs, pyromaniacs, sexual psychopaths, malingerers, paranoid personalities, pathologic liars, sadistic personalities, prostitutes, chronic vagrants, and so forth. The causes of these various conditions are many; yet there are indications of three types of symptoms present in most of these conditions: (1) defective emotional control, such as occurs in children following encephalitis; (2) vicarious reactions to deep-seated emotional conflicts such as are found in the psychoneuroses; and (3) psychotic manifestations which are only occasionally severe enough to require institutionalization, and which may be in the direction of excessive mood swings, or in the form of

---

[1] *Vide* p. 118 *ff.*

paranoid traits.   Not infrequently the heredity is poor.   The symptomatology in many of these psychopathic states seems to center about an intense feeling of unrest which can be satisfied by, or rather the tension of which can best be relieved by, some markedly disapproved action, or some anti-social action.   Accompanying this feeling of unrest are such traits as emotional instability with temper outbursts so severe as to result at times in murder; impulsive behavior, with the slightest impulse determining far reaching decisions; repeated unwise actions, overbalancing any calm or restraining impulses; a lack of consideration of others and an excessive concern over one's own desires; complete disregard for the conventional morals; and inability to persist in a sociably acceptable position, primarily because of basic instability.   The treatment of this group has been taken over by legal authorities with the consequence that there is no treatment, but only punishment.   These persons are ill, just as is the psychotic patient; and *the habitual criminal is a socially sick person who may have a recoverable or an incurable illness, the true nature of which can be determined only by proper investigation.*   These psychopathic persons are today treated by society just as unintelligently as were the definitely mentally ill in the middle ages.

Adequate therapy presupposes first, adequate investigation of causes.[1] If there is a primary defect in the constitution of the person, then the case is seemingly hopeless,[2] but is not actually so. These patients often can be made to adjust in a controlled environment, where little demand is made upon them, and where although required to perform useful work they do not have any real responsibility.   Moreover, if the personality of those in charge is understanding and firm, any emotional outbreaks can be quickly handled without the use of force or punishment.   Bond and Apfel have reported such an ideal environment for post-encephalitic children who present behavior problems and they have accomplished much in training children who could not get along in ordinary social contact.   Occasionally, children or young men will do well in farm work, or in such a disciplined state as the army.   Society, however, has as yet not advanced to the point where it realizes its responsibility for furnishing large semi-hospital units where persons with psychopathic traits can live a useful and constructive life, in a controlled and directed milieu.   Criminals often are intelligent persons who have a great deal of energy, and who could soon come to under-

---

[1] *Vide* p. 119.   [2] *Vide* p. 183.

stand and adjust themselves to such a type of home without feeling confined, or even without having to be strictly confined. In other words, these persons are children in the sense that they cannot avoid conflict with society; and society needs not only to care for them but also to give them opportunity to develop to their highest social and personal level.

It is difficult, however, to decide in any given case, whether the psychopathic trait is the result of a constitutional defect. There are many factors in the socio-economic sphere which act as determining factors.[1] Poverty and its accompaniments breed alcoholism, viciousness, prostitution, and other abnormal reaction patterns; yet these same psychopathic states may be based on a constitutional predisposition. Where financial stringency is great, it is most difficult to do any psychotherapeutic work.[2] Surprisingly enough, there are many psychopathic persons who can come to adjust to very low financial levels and develop mental hygiene concepts which will remove their emotional instability and the consequent psychopathic reactions. In many others of this group, the psychopathic traits are in reality but a form of neurotic reactions, and their therapy is of the same nature as in the neuroses. As has been discussed under the headings of alcoholism and drug addiction, the motivating factors in these patients are often detected by an adequate study of background and personality; and by adequate psychotherapy, many of these patients can be persuaded and trained to adjust so as to live without disturbance in society.[3]

When the psychopathic states approach the symptomatology of the psychoses, the patient may need to be treated as a psychotic person. If, for example, the patient is brutal, paranoid, with outbursts of dangerous rages, hospitalization is preferable to permitting such persons to be loose in society. There are many instances where such persons cause untold suffering at home, and yet when finally brought to the psychopathic hospital cannot be kept, because they do not present a definite psychosis. These patients when treated with metrazol, will often change considerably in their behavior, particularly when this therapy is followed by adequate retraining. Such a course of therapy is often difficult to carry out, for some of these patients are so able to control their actions when examined and when they know that they are under observation that the lay person passes them off as being adequate but "misunderstood."

[1] *Vide* p. 40.　　　[2] *Vide* p. 155.　　　[3] *Vide* p. 259.

Miss V. W., aged twenty-three years, had been sent twice to the psychopathic hospital and twice released as not psychotic. She lived with her mother, father, and elder sister. She flew into terrific rages, throwing dishes, coffee pots, and even knives at the family when in rage. She became enraged with seemingly no provocation, and screamed at the top of her voice so that the neighbors often called the police. Her father as well as her mother and sister were physically afraid of her. She scolded, was cross, and made life almost unbearable for her family. She had no friends and prevented any of the family's friends from coming into the house. She did not work, and in a few attempts at work, had left the position after a day or two. When strangers came to the home, however, she was polite, quiet, and self-restrained, until they became less strange, and she then released her pent-up emotions. This exercise of self control enabled her to persuade the psychopathic hospital physicians that she was not abnormal. The patient had always been a tempestuous child, who did not get along well with girls or boys of her own age, or with her family. However, at the age of eighteen, she became enamoured of a young man who did not reciprocate her affections, and who was engaged to another girl. The patient then pretended that she was wealthy and told the young man that she had a fortune coming to her; whereupon he began to pay a great deal of attention to her. (The mother stated that this young man continued to go with his first girl, and that later he was arrested for larceny.) In order to keep up appearances, the patient insisted that the family buy a fur coat for her, and give her a great deal of spending money; and since the father was a day laborer, and his income amounted to $27.50 per week, it was difficult to grant her demands. The patient developed violent outbursts of anger, and finally the family in desperation withdrew their savings to get the coat. Soon thereafter, however, the young man learned the true state of affairs, and immediately discontinued seeing the patient. It was then that the patient's violent behavior became so intense; and she sold the fur coat for a fraction of its cost a few weeks after she had received it. She would look at herself in the mirror and burst into fearful screams, she would tear her hair, and throw the furniture about.

When the patient was seen first at the office she sat and talked almost normally. She stated that she felt inferior, that life was not worth living, that she was born an imbecile and ugly, that she knew she did "crazy things" but she just couldn't help herself. She wished "to be smart" but knew it was no use studying and that she was doomed.

Attempts were made to treat the patient psychotherapeutically but she returned to the office only at irregular intervals, broke appointments, and continued her unbearable behavior at home. During the last visit she was persuaded to go to the sanitarium for treatment, and following an impulse of the moment did so. Twelve metrazol convulsions were given her, and she changed remarkably. She became very quiet and talked with her mother "just as a daughter should." She left the sanitarium, seemingly cured, but had a relapse to her former behavior after a week. This relapse lasted for several days and then she again became normal, and in the succeeding year remained "normal."

In this patient none of the overt evidences of psychosis in the usual classification sense could be found, but her actions were obviously those which would not permit her to live in society. In part, her reactions were the result of frustration in her love affair, but underlying all her behavior was the psychopathic personality. The metrazol apparently removed some of the psychotic nature of her illness, and she was then able to readjust to her "affair" in a healthier manner.

DRUG ADDICTION

Addiction to opium and its derivatives is present in an estimated one million or more persons in the United States. About a quarter of a million persons are under the care of physicians. The Opium Advisory Committee of the League of Nations in an analysis of all available facts estimated that the total world production each year is about 8,600 *tons* of raw opium, which would be equivalent to 70 grains for every living person on earth. Cocaine and cannabis (marihuana, hashish) are similarly widely used by addicts. Addiction to these drugs implies a physical as well as a psychic dependence on these drugs, and more or less characteristic signs and symptoms result when there is a sudden withdrawal of the drug.

Addiction to coffee or cigarettes (some authors use the term habituation in these instances to imply that there is no physical dependence on the caffeine or nicotine) does not result in harm to society; whereas addiction to the opiates or to alcohol often results in anti-social acts or such personal harm as to make the addict a social liability. It is for this reason that drug addiction is considered a major social problem.

The principal drugs of addiction are: opium and its derivatives, morphine and heroin; alcohol, cannabis, and cocaine. To this group may be added the barbiturates, paraldehyde, chloral, and other depressants, all of which in large dosage over a long period of time may in some persons, produce addiction. Of lesser power to cause addiction (or habituation) are such commonly used drugs as nicotine (tobacco), caffeine (coffee, tea, Cola drinks, etc.) aspirin, acetanilid, and bromides. There are, however, a host of compounds and mixtures, many of them proprietary which are used repeatedly and habitually.

"Broadly speaking, it might be said that the potential addict, if he so becomes by choice, probably selects his drug of addiction to suit his personality.[1] A nervous, irritable, worried, or grief-stricken person may find temporary solace in the apathetic and dreamy state produced by opium, morphine, heroin, or a barbiturate. Persons of this type may be addicted for long periods (provided they have access to the drug) without becoming a social problem. If they are deprived of the drug they usually become a burden on society. From this class come many petty criminals, thieves, shoplifters, etc. Occasionally, when in a suggestive state, these persons may at the instigation of another, commit crimes of passion. Usually, however, individual initiative is reduced to a minimum. There is no such entity as the "heroin" hero of the dime novel.

"The phlegmatic, egocentric individual with a subjective awareness of inferiority may temporarily inflate his personality to become the 'king of all he surveys' by the use of cocaine, hashish, or in many instances, alcohol. The inflation of personality produced by these drugs is responsible for the acts of aggression committed under their influence. Unrestrained crimes of passion are not uncommon. The potential bank robber finds in the white crystals of 'snow' (cocaine) the temporary but necessary courage to complete his drama, even though murder becomes an essential to its success.

"The foregoing statements are obviously generalities and it would be an error to leave the impression that all addicts are vicious or that they come from the lower strata of society. This would be far from the truth. The factors responsible for addiction are many; as examples may be cited, easy access to drugs (physicians, nurses, druggists); injudicious use by physicians (therapy) and vicious associates."[2]

It is quite possible under certain circumstances for most persons to become habituated to drugs which are used over a long period of time. However, the fact that a person becomes addicted to a drug after taking it several times, implies a serious defect within the personality. In most persons who are given morphine for long periods of time, for example in severe cardiac ailments where rest is essential, addiction to the drug infrequently occurs; and yet in a small number of these persons, drug addiction is liable, if they are emotionally irritable, and in the habit of seeking support from

---

[1] This statement applies to alcohol as well as opiates and other sedatives.

[2] Seevers, M. H.: Drug Addiction Problems, Sigma Xi Quarterly,, **27**, 91, June 1939.

others. Similarly those who are treated by physicians and claim thereafter that it was the morphine given during illness which initiated them as drug addicts are generally those types of persons in whom there were personality defects so great that they would have sooner or later developed some form of addiction (if not of opium, then alcohol, or barbiturates). In many manic-depressive depressions, for example, powdered opium is a favorite prescription to relieve the tension, and when the depression clears up, so that the normal personality of the patient reasserts itself, there is no need for the opiate though it has been given daily for several months. Laudanum and paregoric have been widely used for diarrheal states, and have rarely resulted in addiction. It is important to recognize that addiction occurs primarily in very susceptible persons; and should the physician feel that his patient is neurotic and unstable, it is well to use as little of the opiates as possible. There is no definite criterion by which one can say that a patient will or will not develop addiction; but the family physician, knowing a patient or a family over long periods of time is often far better qualified to advise on the use of drugs than is the specialist who may see only the controlled personality. If it is desirable to give morphine it is well in all instances, and particularly for those who are very unstable, to misinform the patient as to his medication.

Psychoses as such are not common in opium addicts. Users of the drug rarely "go insane" though they may in their effort to obtain the drug be driven to many asocial actions. The morphine addict finds most of his pleasure in the initial use of the drug. During this time his physical dysfunctions are less disturbing to him, and activity is easier to carry out. He lapses into a dreamlike state wherein the most pleasant air castles are formed, and wherein there is little worry or fear. There is a tendency to a mild euphoria which while subjectively felt is not noticeable objectively to a stranger. After this initial stage, the continued use of the drug results in sluggishness of associations, and impairment of attention resulting from pre-occupation with the vague dream-like state, although the addicts are completely oriented and lucid if one can gain their attention. They care little for the "cold outside world" and disregard social customs, conventions, and obligations. "Right" and "wrong" have little meaning as long as they can continue to be unaware of external irritations; and should thieving, cheating, or even violence seem the easiest manner to obtain that which they wish, "conscience" will neither inhibit nor rebuke. That which requires an effort of will is too disturbing and irritating, and day dreaming is much easier; so that many activities which are required under ordinary conditions are dispensed with. The addict simply becomes indifferent.

Physical changes may be at a minimum; and the characteristic feeble, debilitated, and emaciated person, with a sallow, greyish complexion is found primarily in those who have become social outcasts and are penniless so that they do not get the proper nourishment. Tuberculosis often carries these debilitated addicts away.

When the drug is withdrawn, the addict becomes very anxious, and may show signs of a panic. He can think of nothing but the drug and suffers torture until he can obtain "a hypo." Physical symptoms occur and the more confirmed the addict, the greater the withdrawal symptoms. In severe cases, in animals as well as men, death may result. The withdrawal symptoms present themselves in the form of extreme pallor of the face, acceleration and weakening of the pulse, general prostration, cold sweats, and spells of yawning. If abstinence continues, the condition may become alarming; and the circulatory collapse is apparently at the basis of the fatalities which occur. Yet no matter how grave the symptoms appear to be, an injection of morphine nearly always gives relief.

The physiologic changes during withdrawal consist of concentration of blood resulting from loss of fluid, increased fluid in the brain (similar to the alcoholic wet brain), decreased oxygen in the venous blood, and diminished ability to withstand oxygen deficiency.

This condition can be reproduced in the monkey. The known facts are these: The cells, or reflex centers of the central nervous system when repeatedly exposed to a drug of addiction become increasingly irritable. This fact is true whether the drug of addiction is primarily a depressant (morphine) or essentially a stimulant (cocaine). This new and elevated level of irritability results in an increased tolerance to depressant drugs and a decreased tolerance to stimulating drugs. In the case of the depressants, the new level of irritability manifests itself only when an insufficient dose is administered or when the drug is withdrawn; whereas with stimulants, it is apparent, to an appreciable extent, only during the excitation of the drug.

Tolerance develops to the continued use of these drugs of addiction, so that subsequent doses need be much greater than initial doses in order to produce the same effect. This tolerance is, however, present for only a relatively short period of time so that within seventy-two hours, a dose of morphine equal in size to the last one administered, may be fatal.

The treatment of addiction to these drugs is eminently unsatisfactory. The acute symptoms of abstinence may be treated by the use of small doses of morphine, the substitution of other sedative drugs, dehydration therapy to relieve brain edema, the use of oxygen tents in emergency, warm relaxing baths, large doses of insulin, and a high caloric, high vitamin diet. Because of their tendency to weaken and procure the opiate anyway, the patients are best treated while in an institution. Most of these patients are very convincing prevaricators, and their word cannot be believed as to their manner of or faithfulness in following the prescribed training. Many of these patients ingeniously manage to procure narcotics even while in a hospital (confederates for example inject doses of morphine into oranges or candy; conceal small amounts in magazines; and even saturate handerchiefs or sleeve cuffs with the solution (the patient chewing upon a corner thereof or cutting off a piece); boil it in a spoonful of water over a match and inject the solution with a medicine dropper, etc.). In a controlled situation the opiate is given in rapidly diminished doses, the amount depending not so much upon the patient's complaint as upon the physical signs of abstinence (some patients come to the hospital asking for the "withdrawal therapy" and give their usual dosage as several times what it actually is, in an effort to obtain, in the "reduced" dosage, the amount which they desire). Every effort should be made to interest the patient in activities, and wherever possible, efforts to remove emotional factors should be made. Since there is actual danger of collapse and death, care should be taken to watch the patient closely during the withdrawal of the drug.

After the withdrawal period, and when there are no more physical symptoms, an effort should be made to study the personality and remove what emotional maladjustments may be there. In confirmed addicts this task is almost hopeless, for in a moment of weakness they may begin the habit again. Moreover, many opium peddlers make strong efforts to reconvert the patient, offering a free dose, which a distraught person in a moment of weakness will take; and so the vicious cycle begins over again. However, those who have not used the drug long and whose conscience and moral sense are not too blunted may be reclaimed. Intense psychotherapy should be directed primarily toward decreasing their drives

26

and restlessness, and toward developing satisfactions with what they are doing so that there is less feeling of inadequacy and futility. If environmental changes can be made in a similar direction, particularly if these persons can obtain moral support from the physician, mother, husband or wife, there will be less of an inclination to return to addiction; since the drug is taken primarily because the satisfactions in life are not great enough to compensate for the difficulties, and there is not sufficient moral stamina to stand up under the strain.

Prophylactic therapy is primarily an international control of the production of the drugs, so that they can be used only under the strictest of medical control. The development of adequate sedatives and pain-suppressing medication will also do away with much addiction. However, all these suggestions represent a superficial attack, a procedure which society is forced to use until it can learn to breed stronger members of society. There are many persons who are so unstable as to become confirmed narcotic addicts should the opportunity present itself, but who are alcoholics, severe neurotics, and marked eccentrics instead. In other words, *the majority of persons who are addicted to narcotic drugs would be markedly disturbed members of society in some other field* if they never had an opportunity to obtain opium. To put it still another way, one may say that as long as there is marked emotional instability among members of society, so long will there be drug addicts of one sort or another.

ALCOHOLISM

A definition of alcoholism is extremely difficult to give. Some would define alcoholism as a condition existing in the person who must have his whiskey and soda before retiring; while others would regard the man who drinks half a pint daily as being "normal" unless "he sees snakes." Occasional drinking does not in itself constitute alcoholism. *Alcoholism is a form of drug addiction*, and has a similar basis; *i. e.*, both drugs and alcohol are taken because of internal emotional unrest, or because of habit. If one drinks liquor in any form, at social gatherings, or on particular occasions for festivity, he cannot be classified as an alcoholic; if on the other hand, he is so insecure internally that he uses alcohol as a means of moral support, or because the habit is so strong that he cannot break it, then he may be termed an alcoholic. In other words, *the addiction to alcoholism is determined by the internal drive and not by*

the simple taking of alcohol. In this concept lies the basis of the treat-
ment: that it is essential to remove the basic instability which requires
sedation, and not simply to remove the alcohol, or attempt to make
alcohol in itself distasteful.

Intoxication is an acute alcoholic state. However, one may become very intoxicated after drinking a small amount at one time,
and be unaffected by a much larger amount at another time. This
variability is dependent upon the psychologic state as well as the
physical state. Again, damage to the brain, such as follows trauma
to the skull, tends so to lower the tolerance to alcohol, that those
who were able to consume large amounts of whiskey before the
accident usually cannot tolerate more than a very small amount
after it. Tolerance to alcohol can be built up by repeated use of
the drug. On the one hand, if one is psychologically prepared,
for example, if he (or she) wishes to enter enthusiastically into the
spirit of the occasion in which he is but "cannot let himself go" then
intoxication may be quick and require little alcohol; on the other
hand, should the group be irritating or the person be concerned
over some problem which he is desirous of solving, then many more
drinks are required to produce intoxication. Similarly, when one
is in a depressive mood swing,[1] alcohol will have relatively little
effect.

The type of response to intoxication from alcohol varies greatly
with the person, and within each person. Some tend to become
drowsy; others become sad, mournful, and pour out their tales of
woe; still others become happy, and subjectively euphoric; and yet
again, some become pugnacious, or suspicious, or irritable. This
difference in response is dependent upon the basic constitution;
for alcohol, like any other cerebral toxin first irritates, then de-
presses cellular activity, thereby permitting one's latent tendencies
to be exaggeratedly manifest. It is my impression that knowing
the personality response to alcohol, the physician should be able to
predict the personality response of that person, should he suffer
from general paresis, or any other form of "organic psychosis."[2]

Similarly, the personality response to alcohol varies within each
person from time to time. Conscious control, such as may be
necessary in moments of emergency, can "clear the mind," if the
person can be aroused to a sense of danger, and if he is not too
intoxicated. The ability of inhibitions to prevent going beyond a
certain degree of drunkenness is evident when one observes young

---

[1] *Vide* p. 285.   [2] *Vide* p. 342.

women who, conscious of the need of not losing self control, can drink tremendous amounts of liquor and yet give few outward signs of being intoxicated.

The chronic alcoholic person is subject to these various modifications; but as in the case of opium addiction, there tends to be present a more constant pattern of reaction. In the first place, the persistent use of alcoholic beverages indicates the existence of a need for drugging one's self (barring those who develop the habit as a result of social pressure); and this need is often found among persons who, although they possess the manners dictated by society for conformity, lack the moral stamina necessary to face the multitude of responsibilities necessary for civilized existence.

Mr. K. M.[1] came from a family in which there were many alcoholic persons. His uncles drank heavily, two of them dying as a direct result of alcoholism. His father died at the age of thirty-seven from alcohol. His brother drank constantly, and one cousin had to go to the state hospital as a deteriorated alcoholic at the age of twenty-nine. These persons were pleasant, kind, and idealistic, but subject to frequent moods. Responsibility did not rest well on their shoulders, one uncle for example, refusing a profitable share in his employer's business and preferring to remain at a far lower salary level than to having the responsibilities of the organization. The patient, himself, was a quiet person, afraid of "sins" which he had not committed but might have, and yet living a relatively blameless and model life. He was intensely unhappy, and sought refuge in religion, but failed to find it there because he could not rid himself of his "immoral" ideas. He was subject to many phobias and fears, being certain, for example, that he had syphilis, that he was insane, that he would be branded as a coward, etc. Outwardly he "was a nice, intelligent boy" but this pleasant exterior hid a constant turmoil of emotional unrest.

He detested drink and vowed not to touch liquor until he was twenty-one. He did not do so until then, and afterwards drank only very occasionally and not enough to intoxicate. His feeling of guilt and his phobias continued and finally he decided to marry in the hopes that assuming the responsibility of marriage would aid him. As marriage approached, however, he became very apprehensive, and started to drink in order to forget. Thereafter he would drink in sprees, and these were continued until he came for treatment six years later. "I can tell when a drinking spell will come on, because I become bored. Nothing seems to interest me. Time passes so slowly and an hour seems half a day. I become nervous and get depressed. I start off by drinking 'just a few drinks' but once I start I cannot stop."

In the treatment of Mr. M., it was pointed out to him that his drinking was the result of his own feelings of inadequacy plus a periodic tendency toward depressive spells, and that the cure of his alcoholism did not lie in simply removing him from the drug, but in readjusting his personality so

[1] *Vide* p. 260 (Case K. M.)

that he would be free from his fears and obsessions, and better able to face and deal with life as it is, and specifically so that he learn how to deal with his depressive attacks when they recurred. He was seen twice a week for one month, and then twice a month for a year. A detailed history was obtained, and every incident of unhealthy reaction was discussed in detailed fashion so that the unhealthy nature of the response could be seen, and the healthy type of reaction pointed out, particularly as it applied to his present life. His almost fanatical religious zeal was discussed and he learned to understand "sins" in the light of the phrase "to err is human; to forgive, divine." In the discussion, care was taken not to destroy the patient's faith and belief in his religion, but it was demonstrated to him that he had overemphasized concepts of sin and had not adequately evaluated the constructive tenets of his faith. Psychologically, his phobias and obsessions were traced to their understandable sources (fear of sex, of sin, of cowardice, etc.) and he was trained to deal with each of these problems directly. When his depressive spells came on, he learned to do less in the morning, to increase his social activities in the evening, and to force himself into amusements and recreations, not so much to make him happy, since his condition tended to preclude enjoying himself, but in order to divert his attention as much as possible from himself. He had first been seen in February, and seemed to do well; but had a drinking spell for three days in March. Psychotherapy was intensified during this period. He was then well again until September, when he relapsed for two days, but again he came back to "normal" quickly; since then, in the subsequent two years, he has been perfectly normal, not only insofar as his drinking is concerned, but also as regards his attitudes toward life and toward himself. During this period he was working, except for the period of drink when he was in a hospital for two days, each time, although no treatment was given other than palliative therapy. During this entire time, very little discussion was directed toward alcoholism, practically all therapy pointing toward ways of dealing with the basic instability.

Commonly this need for alcohol is felt by persons who develop mild manic-depressive depressions, particularly in the ages from thirty-five to forty-five, but who otherwise are fairly well adjusted.

Mr. F. D., aged forty-seven years, drank for a period of four years. He had been a successful salesman, well known, jovial, aggressive, and well liked. Gradually he lost interest in his work, failed to make the calls he should make, tired more easily, and began to sleep much of the time. In contrast to his usual energetic self, he sat about, was depressed, and did not mix much in the company of others, and began to drink constantly. He borrowed money on all sorts of plausible excuses and spent it in taverns. He gave no money at home, neglected the finances of the house and could not be persuaded by friends, or shamed by relatives into going back to work. His drinking averaged about a pint of whiskey a day.

The history of this patient pointed definitely to a depression, of the manic-depressive variety. He was an energetic, extrovert personality of pyknic habitus, who had gradually changed into a silent and asocial type of person.

The only fact which differed from the typical depression was his ability to sleep, and this was probably occasioned by his drinking, his drinking being a method of escape from the depressive feelings.

The depression, however, should ordinarily have disappeared within two years, so that the existing drinking state was one of habit. During the psychotherapy this problem was discussed with him, and the facts presented as simply as possible. The patient was willing to cooperate. Three doses of metrazol were given to clear up any remaining depressive tendencies, and the patient persuaded to start back to his work. He developed a mild manic-phase after the metrazol and thus was able to work more easily and to feel better than formerly so that when psychotherapy was used he felt little need for alcohol. Within a few months the patient had reëstablished himself, had ceased drinking entirely, and was an active provider at home.

It was fortunate for the therapist in this instance that the patient came for treatment about the time when his depressive tendencies were disappearing of themselves and the habit of alcoholism was not too firmly established. With the disappearance of his depression (metrazol is of utmost value as an aid for this purpose) the need for alcohol disappeared. In the psychotherapy, moreover, there was no blame or criticism of him for his acts, for criticism tended to make the patient resentful and he would drink "out of spite." Instead, an attempt was made to have the patient understand the "whys" of his condition, and thereby his cooperation was enlisted in overcoming the basic difficulties.

In such cases, therapy will succeed, if one can remove the basic factors, if the alcoholism has not reached the point where the habit is so strong as to be difficult to break, and if there have been no actual brain changes so that the cooperation of the patient cannot be obtained. Moreover, it must be mentioned that metrazol in itself is insufficient, for in practice it fails if it is used alone and not in conjunction with removal of the psychologic attitudes which accompany the chronic alcoholic.

Once the use of alcohol has been established for some years, the habit factor provides for the continuation of the use of the drug, even though the original etiology may have been cleared up. As a result, the therapy of alcoholism is directed toward removing these basic factors; and it is not sufficient merely to deprive the person of his alcohol, for drink will, in most instances, be resumed unless the only factor is habit. In the instance where there is prolonged instability, the cure will come only by psychotherapeutic efforts, such as have been described in other chapters; where there is periodic drinking, and the basis of both the periodicity and the drinking is a depressive swing, this should be dealt with. This depressive swing may be cleared up by metrazol therapy, or by other methods as described in Chapter XV under manic-depressive psychosis. The habit formation is exceedingly difficult to break at times; and where the physician finds that the patient will continue to drink if he lives at home, the patient should be institutionalized until psychotherapy can take effect, and abstinence diminishes the habit. As a rule, "moral preaching" is valueless for these patients; for those who wish to be cured have already advanced to themselves all the arguments against drink that others can give, and the moral precepts as to the evils involved, serve only to make the patient feel inadequate. If the patient does not wish to be cured, then there is little that will be of permanent value.[1]

The psychoses accompanying alcohol, which include delirium tremens, Korsakow's syndrome (loss of memory, confabulation), acute and chronic hallucinosis, alcoholic paresis, etc., are to be treated as are the other organic psychoses.[2] In addition, vitamin B is very effective in relieving polyneurotic symptoms.

EPILEPSIES

Epilepsy is discussed in this book primarily from the point of view of the influence of psychogenic factors. Epilepsy is a neurologic disease characterized by convulsions; and since convulsions may result from many different causes, one needs to speak of *different types of epilepsy*. There is the epilepsy of gross brain disease such as syphilis, meningitis, brain tumor, traumatic injury; there is the epilepsy secondary to toxins such as alcohol, uremia, eclampsia; and there are the epilepsies which are without apparent cause, and which are termed idiopathic epilepsy. However, this last mentioned type is one without specific meaning, the term usually being employed to designate that type of epilepsy about which we know too little to be more specific as to etiology; and one may find many factors which will precipitate these attacks. In this idiopathic epilepsy, according to text books, the hereditary predisposition is presumably bad; yet in actual practice, and in the more recent statistical studies, one does not find a higher percentage of epilepsy in children of epileptics than one does in the children of "normal"

---

[1] *Vide* p. 274.   [2] *Vide* p. 350.

persons. The percentage of epilepsy in both the children of epileptics and in the general population is about one-third of 1 per cent. On the other hand, some recent electroencephalographic studies have shown that a relatively high per cent of relatives of epileptic patients have brain waves commonly seen in epileptic patients although the relatives themselves have no epilepsy. Although practically all the epilepsies are based upon disturbances of an organic nature, they, like the psychoneuroses, may be precipitated by any of a great variety of factors. It is not unlikely that brain trauma sustained during birth (many normal children have blood in the spinal fluid at birth) and toxic involvement of the brain after children's diseases (measles not infrequently leave a clinical encephalitis, and in many instances there is probably a subclinical involvement of the brain which is not observed, but which may leave residual damage that may predispose toward epilepsy) may form predisposing factors which facilitates the development of epilepsy. It is probable that most cases of idiopathic epilepsy result from brain damage early in life, but manifest themselves only as the organism approaches maturity.

Idiopathic epilepsy has its peak of onset shortly after puberty, and over three -fourths of all cases begin before the age of twenty. In most of these instances no physiologic or pathologic basis can be determined. The first attacks may occur at intervals of some months or even some years and then become more frequent, until they occur several times a day for many months. The attacks may occur at night or during the day; they may be regular or irregular; they may be preceded by an aura or premonition, or not; they may be of the grand mal or petit mal type; or they may occur in abortive forms or epileptic equivalent forms. The grand mal seizure usually consists of an aura or premonition of an attack either by a peculiar sensation somewhere in the body or, as is most common, a peculiar "feeling" which starts in the pit of the stomach and sweeps upward. This aura frequently occurs a few seconds to a few minutes before the actual attack. The patient then becomes unconscious, may fall to the floor, and give a cry resulting from spasm of the respiratory muscles. The whole body is in tonic spasm and rigid, and this rigidity with cessation of breathing lasts, as a rule, from ten to fifty seconds. This phase is followed by a clonic state with jerkings of all of the muscles of the body, including the churning motions of the jaw which produce salivary foam, and biting of the lips. This clonic phase lasts somewhat longer than the tonic phase, and the absence of respiration results in the patient's becoming cyanotic and livid. When the movements cease, a deep breath is taken in and the patient may lie quietly in a comatose state varying in length from a few minutes to several hours. After such an attack the patient is sleepy, and may have a headache; but after a few hours' sleep is normal except for the aching of the muscles. If the attacks occur at night during sleep, the patient may be unaware that he had an attack except for the aching muscles in the morning. Urination is not infrequent during such a seizure, but defecation, while it sometimes occurs in the more deteriorated patient, is rare.

In many patients, particularly those under treatment, there may be abortive or "equivalent" attacks in which there is an apparent loss of consciousness but no convulsion. During this stage, the patients may be quiet, standing or sitting without moving; or they may perform all sorts of queer acts; they may run, fight, scream, undress, or do anyone of a number of things, for which they have no memory, and which they cannot explain. These actions are termed the epileptic equivalent and are a form of acute delirium. Shaking the patient, talking to him, or any other procedure does not restore consciousness, until the attack passes of its own accord. After such an epileptic equivalent, the patient is usually amnestic, and cannot recall any of the things he did. An attack of this sort lasts from a few minutes to several hours.

A still less intense form is the petit mal attack, in which the patient momentarily loses consciousness, and may drop whatever he has in his hand, or cease speaking, but does not fall.

The attacks may be precipitated by many factors. Great excitement may be a precipitating factor; improper diet (see Therapy) is important; constipation is often present before an attack; and in many patients, changes in weather—particularly those occurring about the spring and the fall—result in the advent of an attack or a series of attacks. Alcohol, in moderation, smoking, and ordinary activity seem to have little if any influence on the course of the illness.

The element of habit[1] is an important one in epilepsy. Every attack facilitates the production of another, and it is important therefore, in therapy, to do what one can to break the cycle even with great doses of medication, in order to decrease the habitual lowering of the threshold to seizures.

[1] *Cf.* p. 281.

The importance of removing the cause where possible is obvious and paramount. Any person who has his first seizure after the age of thirty-five should be strongly suspected of and investigated for general paresis and brain tumor. These two conditions are the most common causes of seizures after this period in life, and curative therapy may often be instituted. Generally speaking one may say that every epileptic patient should be studied thoroughly from the neurologic point of view, in an effort to find some localizing signs which may indicate the site of the lesion in the brain. Electroencephalography where possible is advisable. General physiologic studies, particularly of the glucose tolerance curve, may reveal some general instability which can be corrected. Only after an intensive and extensive examination should the physician, and then reluctantly, classify the patient as an idiopathic epileptic.

The therapy of idiopathic epilepsy is two-fold: one of sedation and the other of adjusting the patient to his disease. The principle of medical therapy consists of depressing the excitability of the brain so that no excessive discharge can take place.

There is no curative therapy now known for idiopathic epilepsy. It is hoped (and not infrequently it does occur) that sufficient sedative can be given to the patient to prevent further seizures; but in studies of patients who had had no attacks for over five years while taking medication it was found that removal of the medication resulted in the prompt return of the attacks. Moreover, the medication commonly used seems to have no deteriorating effects, and so can be safely used for an indefinite number of years. The most commonly used medications are bromides and phenobarbital. The smallest dosage to bring about the cessation of the seizures and to avoid toxic effects should be given. In the initial treatments, bromides grains 10, three times a day should be given; and in the ensuing weeks this dosage should be increased or decreased as necessary. If the bromides do not appreciably alleviate the attacks (grains 15 three times a day is generally the maximum most patients can tolerate) phenobarbital can be added, beginning with $\frac{1}{2}$ grain three times a day and increasing to grains $1\frac{1}{2}$ t.i.d. Patients under this combined dosage may continue to have seizures and be so sleepy that it is necessary to reduce the medication. A newer drug, sodium diphenylhydantoinate (dilantin) has proved to be efficacious in a large number of patients insomuch as it reduces the number of attacks and does not have the hypnotic effects of the other drugs. Dilantin is given in $1\frac{1}{2}$ grain capsules, and the initial does of 1 capsule twice a day is increased up to 2 capsules three times a day. Toxic symptoms may occur with the use of almost any drug and these should be watched for, and the drug discontinued or reduced as is necessary. Where bromides bring about acne, it is often unnecessary to stop the drug, for the skin conditions can be cleared up by the use of Fowler's solution.

In addition to the above medication, many patients are helped by a ketogenic diet. Restriction of fluid intake has been advocated but is of questionable value. Magnesium sulphate in teaspoonful doses every morning serves to keep the intestinal tract open without creating diarrhea. Atropine 1/100 grain with phenobarbital is often of value; but a number of patients who had attacks immediately on taking atropine, benefited by the opposite acting drug, pilocarpine. Countless remedies have been tried with varying degree of success and many new remedies which are tried for the first time seem to be more effective at first than later. It must always be remembered that these patients are very susceptible to suggestion.

The psychologic attitude adopted by these patients is of utmost importance in their adjustment. The proverbial epileptic personality which is supposed to consist of irritability, meanness, temper outbursts, sadistic behavior, etc., is not necessarily part of the epileptic illness. Rather *these symptoms develop as a defense mechanism* because the patient is so ashamed of his illness, and is so handicapped thereby. These patients come to feel that they are outcasts and "queer", that their company is not desired, and that they cannot do what all their friends do. Often these patients are intelligent and ambitious, and yet are relegated to inferior levels of activity because of the distressing nature of their seizures. It is in reaction to these disturbing facts that the sadistic personality develops.

When patients are properly treated, such an attitude can be obviated. These patients should be encouraged to live as nearly normal an existence as possible. They should not drive automobiles, nor work near dangerous machinery; but they should go about town, to school, and to work; they should attend social gatherings, and mingle with friends; they should think and plan as if they had no illness; in other words, with relatively few exceptions *they should live a normal life.* Moreover, they should understand their illness in terms of organic pathology and remove from their attitude all traces of stigmata or ideas that they are insane. It is to be pointed out to them that many great men who have accomplished much have been subject to these attacks. Their self respect must be restored, and they should be given the necessary understanding so that they can function without being constantly irritated or depressed.

In actual practice, a large percentage of these patients can live a modified normal existence, and not develop any of the psychopathic personality patterns described above. Moreover, because of the lessening of tension the actual number of attacks is decreased. The patient is told to take an extra tablet of phenobarbital in moments of excitement, but *not to avoid excitement*. Often the attacks are more common just before or after the menstrual period; so the dosage of medication is increased at those times. Similarly when the physician carefully studies the record of the individual patient he may find a predisposition to attacks at certain times, and an increase in medication at such times is more helpful than an indiscriminate giving of medication throughout the day. Some patients, for example, have attacks only at night and are benefited by taking double doses before going to sleep; others have attacks just before getting up and medication on awakening often wards off such an attack.

For several patients who have been suffering from epilepsy which was associated with much tension and emotionalism, hypnosis[1] in addition to psychotherapy has yielded excellent results. In hypnosis an effort is made to teach the patient how to relax. Many patients are so apprehensive, that the fear acts to lower their threshold to precipitating stimuli, and psychotherapy plus the use of hypnosis often ameliorates the condition. Many such patients are able to work, and a much smaller percentage than usual require institutionalization when such therapeutic efforts are used.

Mr. K. L., aged twenty-four years, complained of having had "spells" since the age of fifteen. He was riding in a street car when he "fainted" and on recovering was told he had had a convulsive spell. Since that time he had several attacks each month. The number of attacks varied considerably however; some months there would be one or two attacks weekly, and some months there would be no attacks. There was no correlation observed between the number of attacks and food, weather, exercise, use of coffee, tobacco, alcohol, excellent sleep or poor sleep, or any other determinable factors. There seemed to be a few more attacks in the spring and in the fall, but even these showed no consistent relationships. The attacks were primarily in the nature of grand

[1] *Vide* p. 227 *ff*.

mal seizures, preceded by "a funny feeling in the pit of the stomach" and followed by a marked feeling of tiredness, sleepiness, and headache. No history of petit mal attacks could be elicited. There was no history of early trauma, birth and early development were "normal," and heredity showed no pathologic ancestry. He developed an irritability, had temper outbursts, was asocial, and suspicious. In addition he stammered a great deal. The patient was given phenobarbital grains $\frac{1}{2}$ three times a day; he was put on a ketogenic diet; he was advised to see to it that he had regular elimination; and from the psychotherapeutic point of view, he was advised to give up his seclusiveness, and go out as if he had no "spells." He was told to avoid driving a car, or engaging in any occupation in which he would be injured should he fall; but other than such restrictions, he should lead as "normal" a life as possible. If he were to go to a party, or some other affair in which he might become excited, he should double his medication. Above all, he was to prevent himself from becoming bitter, and angry first at his own incapacity, and secondly by irradiation, at the world. Hypnosis was used to teach the patient how to relax, and further to instill the above attitudes. The medication was insufficient at the outset to control his seizures completely, and the phenobarbital was increased to $1\frac{1}{2}$ grains morning and evening, and $\frac{3}{4}$ grain at noon. On this régime his attacks decreased to the point where they occurred two or three times a year, and the work that he procured as stock man and which required heavy physical labor gave him immense satisfaction as well as the feeling of independence. He was fortunate in that his several attacks always occurred away from work. His so-called epileptic personality disappeared, as did his stammering; and to all intents and purposes, the patient became a well adjusted person.

FEEBLEMINDEDNESS (AMENTIA)[1]

Feeblemindedness is a condition wherein the intellectual capacity of the person has been impaired since birth or since very early childhood. Such a person may be normal emotionally, and will tend to suffer from practically all the ills and experience all the desires of normal persons provided his capacities are not overtaxed. Feeblemindedness, as a rule, is not a progressive disease; there are no persistent pathologic processes which increase deterioration; the individual person remains intellectually at relatively the same stage after puberty as he was at puberty.

Feeblemindedness is a relative term, the "norm" of mental age for adults being fixed at about fourteen to sixteen. According to our present concepts, in all persons the actual intellectual ability or capacity increases from birth until shortly after puberty. Our increase in intelligence after that period is dependent upon knowledge and experience and not upon increase in capacity.

[1] *Vide* p. 19.

This intellectual capacity has been arbitrarily determined by giving many tests to children and setting as the mental age, the chronologic age of most of the children who have been able to pass the tests at one level but not at the next level. Thus for example, several thousand children, aged six years, were given tests of various degrees of difficulty, and those tests which 75 per cent could pass were considered as tests measuring the normal mental age of a six year old child. The seven year old child could pass a few more difficult tests, and when the grades in these tests were added to his score, he was said to have 100 per cent normal intelligence for his age. The tests given during the draft to the American Army in 1918 showed that the average male could pass only the tests of a thirteen and a half year old child; although these men were more efficient than children of that age, in that they had learned or memorized by experience how to act in certain situations. In actual life, a person whose mental age is about twelve (an intelligence quotient of 75 to 85, depending on the standard used) or less is considered decidedly stupid. Such a distinction is, however, a relative one. Two social workers were recently overheard speaking of a youngster who "couldn't quite make the grade in school" and "something would have to be done for his retarded state." This child had an intelligence quotient of 120; that is, he was mentally two years in advance of his chronologic age; but he attended an elementary school under university direction where the average child had an intelligence quotient over 130. Not infrequently the intelligence test is unsatisfactory for some reason and does not give a true picture of the child's mental ability. Moreover, our tests, as used today, are of far less value in judging the mental age of adults than of children. Further, it must be again emphasized that, as a rule, *intellectual ability is not related to emotional stability.*

When a person has a mental age of less than two years, he is classified as an idiot; when his mental age does not exceed that of seven years, he is termed an imbecile; when his mental age is between that of a seven and a twelve year old he is termed a moron (this word has been twisted by the newspapers to mean a sexual psychopath). The ratio of idiot to imbecile, to moron, is as 5:20:75; in other words, the distribution of mental ability follows a frequency curve. The number of feebleminded persons in the United States has been estimated to be over a million; but this figure is purely a guess, and the mental age where normalcy begins and feeblemindedness ends has not been sharply defined.

The causes of feeblemindedness are not always easy to determine. Undoubtedly one of the most important causes is poor inheritance, but this inheritance does not necessarily mean that the parents are themselves feebleminded; for it has been estimated that should all the feebleminded persons now existent be prevented from having children, the next generation coming from "normal" parents would have approximately 88 per cent as many feebleminded as there are now.   These feebleminded would spring from the recessive genes which are present among normally intelligent persons.   However, many persons become feebleminded.   Intrauterine disease, and disturbance in intrauterine circulation as well as birth trauma may play important roles in bringing about this condition.   Congenital syphilis, cerebral infections and toxins, certain neurologic diseases, head trauma, and endocrine disturbances are a few of the various factors which may play an important role in the bringing about of this intellectual defect.

The symptoms of feeblemindedness are of three general categories:[1] (1) those of the etiologic factor, for example birth trauma may leave the child both mentally deficient and with a spastic paraplegia (Little's disease); (2) signs of inability to cope intellectually with life's incidents as adequately as can other children of the same age; and (3) emotional outbursts and various neuroses which result from the resentment which grows out of recognition of inadequacy, or which result from being forced (by anxious parents *et al.*) to do more than he is capable of doing.[2]   These last mentioned symptoms may on occasion amount to intense psychopathic reactions, or even to psychotic symptoms.

The primary etiology of these conditions may at times yield to therapy.   Syphilis and cretinism may be treated; and in many instances the condition may be ameliorated, if the therapy is begun early enough.   However, in Mongolian idiocy (it more properly should be called imbecility since the mental age usually reaches about seven years), in birth injury cases, and in encephalitic illnesses, the damage has been done, and a cure is practically impossible to establish.   It is possible, however, to develop these children to a fairly high level of adjustment, with proper training, and in not too demanding an environment.   The symptoms of the original illness such as spastic paraplegia, epicantic folds of the Mongolian idiot, the small head of the microcephalic, etc., remain

---

[1] *Vide* p. 343.   [2] *Vide* p. 159.

unaltered as long as the patient lives; and these patients may live as long as do "normal" persons.

Many of these patients, however, are brought to the physician because of their retarded mental development. Many of these children do not sit up until they are ten or twelve months, do not walk until eighteen or twenty months, do not talk until three or four years, and do not play with other children of their own age. These ages vary from the normal according to the degree of feeble-mindedness. They seem dull of comprehension, and not so smart as others, although the mother will often vehemently deny that her child is below par and will give many evidences which she considers proof of normal or even superior intelligence. When the child is sent to school, he does not learn well; and often even the teacher will remark, "Charles is a nice boy, and I'm sure that he could do the work if he would only apply himself." At home the child does not play with children of his chronologic age but rather with children of his intellectual age. Indeed a crude estimation of the intellectual level of the child can often be made by determining the age of the children with whom he likes to associate. (Not all children, however, who play with those younger than themselves, are mentally deficient.) The intelligence quotient of these children tends to remain the same throughout their development. The intelligence quotient, written usually as I. Q., is determined by dividing the mental age of the child by his chronologic age. Thus if a child has a mental age of five and is seven years old, his I. Q. will be $\frac{5}{7}$ or 71 (really .71); when this same child is fourteen years old, his I. Q. will still be 71 (this ratio remaining constant) and his mental age will be ten years. In other words, the child will not "grow out of it" as is so often told the mother, and usually his mental age will fall behind his physical age in proportion to the ratio indicated by the I. Q. The main pitfall in such a prognostication is the accurate determination of the child's mental age, for there are many complicating factors which may make the child "appear stupid" without his actually being so. In addition to such difficulties as lack of proper cooperation from the child and imperfection of the test, there are such special difficulties as reading disability and mirror writing which may make the child appear to be less intelligent than he actually is.

The emotional outbursts of these patients is less the result of their lowered mental capacity, than of the pressure put upon them by anxious parents or a demanding environment. Frequently a mentally retarded child becomes mischievous, has temper outbursts, does not pay attention in class, will deliberately annoy the parents, etc., primarily because of an intellectual inability to do that which is demanded of him. Mothers and fathers will criticize such a child, urge him to study more, make fun of him in an effort to have him obtain better grades in school; and although the child is intellectually impaired so that he cannot perform the tasks, he is emotionally just as susceptible to criticism as is the normal child. Where this critical attitude of those about him becomes intense, or is constant, the child may develop sadistic or intensely vicious traits. If the pressure becomes too intense, the child or adult will develop acute neuroses or psychoses, characterized by fear or simple delusions. The case of the young man with the painful ear[1] is to the point.

The therapy of such children is directed not toward increasing their intelligence but toward modifying their environment[2] to their capacity, and training them to adjust happily in that environment. As has been discussed in Chapter VIII emotional difficulties result from environmental demand in excess of personal capacity; and it is of the utmost importance, therefore, to create and maintain emotional stability in these children. A simple environment, association with friends of the same intellectual level, or with intelligent supervisors, a full day of creative work which requires little mental and much physical activity, and finally a well planned social and recreational program, which is not on too high an intellectual plane: such a planned environment can make these children content and happy, and offers them adequate opportunity for the expression of their capacities. Moreover, little is as yet understood of the various natural abilities present in man; and some feebleminded children may have remarkable facilities in art, carpentry work, and other skills utilizing their hands and emotional capacity rather than their intellectual ability. When it is difficult to place a child in such an institution, the child may well be kept at home; girls may be taught to do excellent housework, and boys may become very useful in assisting around the house. There is, however, not only the danger of parents expecting too much from the child and thus producing emotional instability, but also there is the disturbing problem of sex. The actual sex desire is markedly diminished in these feebleminded persons even in adult life, and institutions which are properly regulated have very few sex problems in

---

[1] *Vide* p. 318 (Case Y. R.). [2] *Vide* p. 159.

27

men or women confined to the grounds for many years (these children may live until a very ripe old age). In an ordinary environment, however, the ordinary relationships between men and women, the awareness of marriage and its implications, the occasional company of some male who can take advantage of a feebleminded girl's lack of understanding, all tend to make sex a problem, a problem which may become serious and result in sadistic behavior. Again, many of these patients will never be able to earn their own livelihood; and when the parents have reached the end of their earning capacity, the problem of support becomes a difficult one. For these reasons, it is as a rule advisable for those markedly retarded to be placed in some public institution early in life, so that they can adjust while young to a routinized existence.

N. D., aged eleven years, was brought to the dispensary by the mother who considered her "nervous." On further elicitation of complaints, the physician discovered that the girl had not attended more than one year of school, had not learned to talk well, and could neither read nor write. Further, it was found that the patient had been delivered by forceps, that she had not walked until she was four years old, that she had never talked clearly, and that she was very awkward. Her mother spoke at length about training the child to overcome her "muscular incoordination." The child had had no serious illnesses. She was very emotional, and cried and laughed easily. She had no playmates and stayed in the home all day long, attempting to help the mother. The child's memory was poor and the mother was impatient with the child's "stubbornness" in not learning the ordinary routine of keeping house. The patient had two sisters, both of whom were normal. She enjoyed going to motion pictures and enjoyed seeing sporting events. There was no economic pressure. Physical examination revealed no abnormality. In conversing with the girl, one had to speak as if to a four or five year old because of her evident lack of comprehension. There were no evidences of delusions or hallucinations, and there were no fixed ideas. She was oriented, but she could not do arithmetic problems of the simplest sort, and could neither read nor write. On the Binet-Simon intelligence test, she obtained a score indicating a mental age of four years and two months. The diagnosis was feeblemindedness, subgrouping of imbecility. The prognosis for improvement was poor, there being practically no possibility of the child's developing into a normally intelligent person. The mother was informed of the diagnosis and prognosis; and when she asked for advice as to what to do, was told that she could keep the child at home and not expect too much from her. The mother was instructed not to urge the child beyond her capacities and to guard her from indiscriminate contact with young men, inasmuch as feebleminded girls are very easily influenced. However, if the mother was at all concerned about her future ability to support the child, it was advisable to institutionalize her in a state hospital at an early age so that she could adjust to such environment while young, and avoid some degree of unhappiness because the prolonged attachment to the parents would make later separation more difficult.

Mr. E. G., aged thirty-two years, was brought into the clinic by his wife. He complained of a pain in his neck and although no pathology could be found and his wife "knew" there was nothing wrong with his neck, she used his pain as an excuse to have him examined for his "mind." She stated that she had been married four years and that she was sure that he was "crazy." When he played with their two year old child, he would pull her hair, and make her cry "just like he was a kid teasing another kid."

A short conversation with the patient soon brought out the fact that he was mentally retarded. There were, however, no peculiar ideas, there was no evidence of delusion or of hallucination; he was not depressed or elated, and there were no signs of any psychopathic trends, other than his mental sluggishness. The patient was oriented as to time and place, but his memory was poor; his grasp of general information was very inadequate; his ability to do simple arithmetic problems was poor. A psychometric examination revealed that he had the mental ability of a child of eight and a half.

The social worker brought some very interesting facts to light. The patient had lived with his mother until his marriage four years ago. He had failed three times in fifth grade, and as a consequence had dropped out of school at the age of fourteen. He had never worked, could not write more than his name, and rarely read even the paper except for the comic strips. His mother took care of his every need, working while he stayed at home. Five years earlier in an effort to "settle" the boy, the mother cast about for a wife for him. The patient never went out with girls; and when his mother arranged a "date" nothing seemed to eventuate therefrom. Finally, she inserted an advertisement in one of the cheaper magazines under the general heading of "Lonely" and, writing as if her son wrote, stated that he desired marriage, that he was a six foot male of pleasing appearance who was lonely and in need of a good wife. The "wife" who lived in Tennessee, seized avidly at the opportunity and after an exchange of letters (the patient's letters all being written by the mother) and photographs, accepted the proposal by mail and came to Chicago to meet and marry the patient.

The patient never procured a position and was supported by private relief until the work relief projects were started and thereafter he worked as a day laborer. When questioned, the patient told of the "swell job" he had on W.P.A. and how he was content therewith. However, after working hours, the patient rarely came to his home but went to his mother's home, returning late in the evening to retire. The wife stated that he showed little interest in the child, and when he did play with his daughter, teased her and seemed to obtain a gleeful joy in making her cry. The wife stated that the patient had never showed any interest in sex, and that in their entire marriage, coitus had occurred only a dozen times, and then only on the urging of the wife. The wife was certain that "he must be crazy."

This case is illustrative of the tangled web which struggling, well-meaning, but ignorant mothers can weave. The boy had always been feebleminded, and he had no right ever to have married, let alone have children. He needed the sympathetic care and attention that a child should have, but he was woefully inadequate both for society and for himself.

CHAPTER XVII

PSYCHOANALYSIS AND RELATED SCHOOLS

MANY persons, without understanding the significance of the term, speak of a patient's being "psychoanalyzed." Psychoanalysis may not be psychiatry; and the study of a patient's personality or mental status is often not psychoanalysis. This term was first coined by Dr. Freud; and when some of his disciples (primarily Jung and Adler) broke away from him and used the same name for their respective schools, Freud insisted that the term "psychoanalysis" be restricted to mean solely his individual school of thought. By common consent, therefore, when one uses the term "psychoanalysis" by itself, he properly means the psychology of Freud.

Psychotherapy was used and formulated for many years before Freud; but he was the first to create a system of dynamics of mental life and to formulate a comprehensive theory on the laws of emotional expression in human beings. His formulation, although generally recognized to be the most important initiator in the study of psychologic dynamics, has nevertheless been the subject of bitter controversy. Many authors insist that Freud has over-evaluated the undoubtedly important role of the unconscious, that he has overemphasized the role of sex in the development of every human being, and that he has built a fantastic and scientifically unsupportable hypothesis on these exaggerations. On the other hand, his disciples insist that there is no other method of substantial value which understands and formulates the laws of mental activity.

Psychoanalysts are not required to be medical men. Any one who has fulfilled the requirements is eligible to be a practising psychoanalyst. Psychoanalytic societies have been formed, however, to which membership is rigidly restricted. To be properly qualified in America, for example, the candidate must have undergone a training analysis which lasts from one to three years; and then he must have analyzed three patients of his own under the supervision of an accepted analyst. An analysis consists of seeing the patient or the physician an hour a day, five or six days a week, for a year or more as may be considered necessary. Obviously, such an expensive and lengthy procedure, limits many persons from undergoing such treatment or such training.

(420)

A more specific outline of Freudian concepts will be given below. *In summary*, however, it is as follows: Every person (and not merely those who have symptoms) passes through several stages before the age of five. The first stage, occurring quite early, is the *oral* erotic phase in which the child centers his attention and derives most of his pleasures from sucking. If an adult becomes fixated at this level or regresses to it, he continues to get most of his pleasure out of oral eroticism. Quickly following this stage is the *anal* erotic phase, wherein the child centers his attention on the feces, and he may enjoy passing his stool or retaining his stool as an expression of this eroticism. Next comes the *phallic* stage in which interest is primarily in the genitalia. Having passed through these stages, or coincidental with them, the male child develops an *Oedipus complex* which is an incestuous desire to have sex relations with his mother. The girl develops an Electra complex with an incestuous desire for the father. This complex is strong; and, still under the age of five, the boy comes to realize that his desire for his mother is resented by his father; and that if he continues with the desire, his father will injure him. This injury will be a castration which to the young boy means cutting off the penis as well as the testes; and this fear results in the *castration complex* (which also may persist later in life). As a result of this castration complex the boy (still less than five years old) gives up his incestuous desire for his mother, and so solves the Oedipus situation. Should he fail to solve it, the Oedipus complex will remain strong and he will suffer from personality defects which may lead to neuroticism etc. The girl goes through a slightly different process, according to Freud. At an early age she develops a *penis-envy*, feels that she has been castrated, and blames the mother. She comes to desire to be given a child by her father, and develops hostility against her mother. This Oepidus situation is only slowly resolved because her wish for a child is never fulfilled and because of threats of loss of love in connection with her masturbation. All these phases occur before the age of five; after which there is a period of latency until puberty at which time there is a recrudescence of the Oedipus desire. Alexander believes that aggressive impulses are felt toward the parent of the same sex and rise out of the death instinct.

Psychoanalysis is based on understanding the operation of these forces which exist in the unconscious (preconscious and subconscious), where they serve to motivate most human actions. Further mental life is divided into three spheres of interest: the Id, which corresponds to the colloquially known "beast-like instincts"; the Superego, which struggles against the Id, and corresponds to "conscience"; and the Ego, which is more or less the conscious person and the resultant of the other two. The actions of the Id, Superego, and Ego determine the reactions of the personality. Psychologic dynamisms are built up on this basis.

The technique for determining these factors in the patient consists of: (a) free association,[1] and (b) dream analysis,[2] and (c) a certain amount of interpretation furnished by the physician at strategic points in the analysis, in order to overcome the patient's resistance. Transference enters into all analytic situations, positive transference being an intense love for the psychoanalyst, and occurring because the patient finds an opportunity to reënact the infantile child-father type of relationship, while negative transference is an intense hate of the analyst.

As previously stated, the patient who is being treated for a neurosis is analyzed an hour a day, five to six days a week, for a period varying from six months to three or four years. This time is spent in free association and in interpretation. Cures are not more commonly obtained by psychoanalysis than by eclectic psychiatrists, and what cures are achieved through the psychoanalytic technique of treatment occur because its therapeutic value lies not in its elaborate and questionable superstructure of concepts but rather in four very simple elements. In the first place, the patient finds in the analyst a sympathetic, non-critical listener.[3] In itself, being able to talk freely, without fear of condemnation, serves to release tension. In the second place, the patient discusses his disturbing and distressing attitudes at such length and in such detail that he becomes desensitized to them.[4] Third, through such discussion, moreover, he learns to view his problems objectively, to lose his sense of guilt or self-blame.[5] Finally, he comes to realize that his symptoms have little significance other than as the expression of underlying emotional problems;[6] the understanding of the fact of an emotional basis is helpful, even though theories about this fact may be erroneous.

These same goals can be achieved far more simply and directly by the therapy as advanced elsewhere in this book, and with the

---

[1] *Vide* p. 140.   [2] *Vide* p. 146.   [3] *Vide* p. 138.
[4] *Vide* p. 179.   [5] *Vide* p. 61.   [6] *Vide* p. 216 *ff.*

added advantage that not only is the patient taught thereby to understand and be tolerant of his various immature reaction patterns and "complexes," but also he is given a technique for actually meeting and solving problems as they arise.   Moreover, the mental hygiene concepts advanced in our previous chapters are so inculcated into the patient that they become automatic reaction patterns and not merely intellectually appreciated theories.

CONCERNING THE SO-CALLED OEDIPUS COMPLEX[1]

It appears to the author that in order to explain the emotional dependence of some children upon their parents there is no need to postulate an Oedipus complex and incestuous desires in childhood.

The emotional dependence of such a child upon his parents, upon which the psychoanalysts lay so much stress, may well be explained as follows: The child who has never learned emotional independence and has always avoided making any important decision unless he consulted the parent may similarly turn his thoughts to the parent when he thinks of sex.   Early in life, children come to identify themselves with parents of the same sex.   This identification is, however, not synonymous with feeling incestuous toward the opposite parent.   The boy learns that he is masculine, "just like father," and that marriage may occur only with the opposite sex, that is, with girls, "like mother."   The condensation of his subsequent train of thought is somewhat as follows: "Boys marry girls. I am a boy, and when I grow up I will marry a girl.   I will marry a girl just like mother, since she is the nicest, sweetest girl I know." When the attachment is overly great, so that the growing boy still is dominated by his mother and is emotionally dependent upon her, then the train of thought goes one step further: "If only I could marry mother."   Early in life such a train of thought is asexual merely symbolizing an imitative situation and an identification of himself with the father, and carrying out what is obviously expected of all people who "grow up."   Should he overly worship the mother, as occurs where parents are very subjective and demand strong emotional ties because of their own need for support, then he may be incapable of loving another woman.   Biologically, at the approach of puberty, he is forced to be aware of sex, and his thoughts may turn to the one he has loved the most until then. Rarely do incestuous desires develop consciously, but the entire

[1] *Vide* p. 421.

background of such an overly attached person will have vague, unconscious, incestuous wishes which will color his relations with other women. Such an attachment to his mother (or of the girl to the father) may demand that he choose a wife similar in most ways to his mother, and give rise to dissatisfactions with the wife, should she do or think in some different fashion. Sexual incompatibility in marriage often has such a basis.[1]

Such a formulation is entirely adequate for explaining the facts we have at our command without resorting to a complex and unproveable (*i. e.*, in any scientific fashion) theory.

Psychoanalysis may appear as fantastic nonsense and in an effort to give a fair and unbiased presentation of the subject, I have obtained permission of the publishers of one of the most comprehensive works in this field to reprint a rather full abstract of psychoanalysis, together with the opinions and beliefs of the associated schools of Jung and Adler. The careful, dispassionate, and illuminating text of Healy, Bronner, and Bower: "The Structure and Meaning of Psychoanalysis" should be read by all students of psychiatry, and the abstract that follows is condensed from this work.

THE STRUCTURE AND MEANING OF PSYCHOANALYSIS[2]

Cardinal Formulations.—*Libido*. That force by which the sexual instinct is represented in the mind, we call "libido." It is the energy of those instincts which have to do with all that may be comprised in the word "love." The nucleus of love has sexual union as its aim; but we do not separate from this, self-love, love for parents and children, love for humanity in general, and devotion to concrete objects and abstract ideas. All these tendencies are an expression of the same instinctive activities. "Sexuality" does not only refer to the genitals, but must be regarded as a more comprehensive bodily function having pleasure as its goal, and only secondarily coming to serve the ends of reproduction.

Jung applies the term "libido" to a more general energetic concept underlying the dynamics of mental life, representing the urge or push of life: for him this primary libido is utilized in the service

[1] *Vide* p. 68.

[2] Abstracted from The Structure and Meaning of Psychoanalysis, by Healy, Bronner and Bower, by permission and special arrangement with Alfred A. Knopf, Inc., authorized publisher.

of nutrition, of growth, of sexuality, and of all human activities and interests. He claims that Freud's theory is too one-sided and is correct only up to a certain point. Jung's idea of libido is identical with Bergson's "elan vital."

Adler regards the one great driving force not as sexual, but as an Ego urge, the urge to power.

According to Freud: the libido varies in intensity according to the different periods of physiologic development; it is present in early childhood; libidinal sensations do not belong to the sexual organs alone, but may become attached to various body areas; namely, the organs of nutrition, excretion, procreation; it is manifested in localized excitability which is relieved by appropriate stimulation; this localized process is completed by the fifth year. Finally, he maintained that the libidinal flow is constantly changing; it may be directed inwardly (narcism) or outwardly (object-love); it may be arrested and fixed; it may flow to levels representing earlier stages of development (regression); it may become dammed up (repression); or it may be deflected into other more socially acceptable channels (sublimation).

Cathexis is an accumulation or concentration of psychic energy in a particular place or channel, libidinal or non-libidinal. Libidinal energy is directed in three ways: towards self, towards objects, and towards inner mental creations or phantasies. (1) Ego-cathexis, or narcism, or libido directed towards self, predominates in the earlier stages of development, because the child discovers that the outside world is not his to command, and so has to discover interests within himself. Nacke used the term "Narcissism" to denote a perverse attitude of treating one's own body as one would a sexual partner. Psychoanalysis says it is a normal phase of development infused in a modified sense. Primary narcism is the original libidinal ego-cathexis, part of which exists in later life; while secondary narcism is that libido which has had an object cathexis, and then is withdrawn (because of some disappointment) and fixed on himself, a process known as secondary identification, and introjection. This narcism is gradually reduced in later stages, except for a period during puberty and adolescence. (2) Object-cathexis occurs when the libido is infused into an idea or an object in the outer world. Object love is essentially a motor striving towards the object, primarily as a source of somatic satisfaction. Adult object love is of two sorts: anaclitic, in which the object choice is one who has met his earliest demands, as mother or nurse, etc.; and narcissistic object choice in which the object cathexis is on one that resembles the self (either what the self was, is, or would like to be). The individual's first real love experience takes place early in childhood, and usually the parent of the opposite sex becomes the first object love.

The narcism may be so introverted that it is incapable of having an object-cathexis, and therefore no therapy is possible. Negative narcism is an exaggerated underestimation of self (melancholia). Homosexuals really love someone like themselves. Many "feminine" women are really in love with themselves, and love the man who loves them. Parental love is often really narcism, or love lavished on a part of the parent, himself.

Along with love there may coexist hate, this coexistence of opposite emotions being known as ambivalency. For every person there is a limit to the quantity of ego-libido that is compatible with health; and in the last resort, we must begin to love in order that we may not fall ill. The neurotic has more primary narcism than the normal, and therefore less object-cathexis, which he easily gives up. This is the result (Alexander) of the need of the neurotic for narcissistic libido to neutralize his self destructive tendencies. In the state of being in love, the lover tends to project his own narcism, and to idealize it, thus making the love object free from imperfection.

Phantasy-cathexis. In this state the libido is directed toward the inner world, instead of the world of reality, satisfaction being found in imagined response. It is normal, and follows the lines of the pleasure principle. One may seek refuge in phantasy, when there is pain in real life. Ordinarily introversion leads to the formation of wishes, which become ideals; but it may lead to earlier infantile wishes.

Non-libidinal cathexis is mainly that concerned with feeding the death or destructive instinct.

Polarities are certain aspects of mental life fundamentally characterized by being paired as opposites. In these polarities are activity-passivity, self-out side world, pleasure-pain, life-death, love-hate, masculine-feminine. Jung says that everything tends to go over to its opposite, sooner or later. The ego is passive in that it receives stimuli from the outside world, and active in that it reacts to it. Activity is fused with masculinity, and passivity with femininity, as a biologic fact.

Ambivalence was a word coined by Bleuler, who said that the same thing can have a positive and a negative feeling tone, and that strivings may be thus contradictory. It is found in the ucs., in children, in neurotics, and points to a poor integration of the personality. Hate is primary, is derived from the struggle of the Ego for self-maintenance; and is present before love appears. The earliest showing of love appears connected with what seems to be impulses of hate, the desire evidently being to incorporate the love object, equivalent to devouring or annihilating it. Later, hate may exist beside love, as an expression of these early impulses. The ambivalence may have its origin in the original universal constitutional bisexuality. Hug-Hellmuth maintains that the first cry of the infant shows opposition to the world. Graber maintains that in intrauterine life there is only the unity of pleasure; but that after birth there is the first experiencing of pain, and that is the basis of the pleasure-pain polarity. Jung says that all impulses in their "natural and unredeemed state" are ambivalent and therefore, besides the creative impulse there is the destructive impulse.

The Unconscious (ucs.) is that vast quantity of mental life which either never was in cs. or previously in cs. has been repressed. The elements of the ucs. are active constituents with a more important influence on the body and emotion than the cs. Its instinctual tendencies exist side by side, and are exempt from mutual contradiction. Its processes are not related to external reality. It is mainly infantile. The ucs. of one person can act upon the ucs. of another without cs. being implicated. Jones says that the splitting of the mind into ucs. and cs. occurs in the first year of life, because of the conflict between the uncivilized, non-moral elements, and the inhibiting forces. Freud says there is no complete split till puberty. The content of the ucs. is probably of phylogenetic origin. Jung has two levels: the personal ucs. with repressed painful memories, *et al.*, and the collective ucs. This personal ucs. results from the development of the potentialities of the individual which have been neglected by the cs. In the collective ucs. there is the transmission of primordial images from one generation to the next. It contains dominants which are phantasies of divinities, saviors, demons, etc. These inherited functional complexes exist as a special sphere of mental functioning.

The Preconscious (pcs.) or foreconscious, can be brought into cs. by an effort of will, or by some associated event.

The Conscious (*cs*) is that part of the mental life of which the individual is aware at any given time. It is infinitesimal, when compared with the ucs. It is the upper stratum of mental life, and developed to meet the demands of the external world.

The Ego, Id and Super-ego do not supplant, but are another point of view of the cs., the ucs., and the pcs.

The Id is characterized as follows: It contains all phylogenetic acquisitions; it is the source of instinctive energy for the individual; it forms the great reservoir of libido; the eros and death instincts struggle within it; it is the region of the passions, instincts, and habit tendencies; it is unconscious; the pleasure-principle reigns supreme in it; guided by the pleasure principle it guards itself against tensions and pain; it aims at gratification of libidinal urges; it is unmoral, illogical, and has no unity of purpose; the repressed merges into the id, and is then part of it. (Id is Latin for *it*; in German it is called Es.)

The Ego is derived from the Id by modifications put on it by the external world, and it is never entirely differentiated from the Id. It is characterized by a coherent organization of mental processes. Just as instincts play a great role in Id, so perceptions play a great part in the Ego. It is representative of the external world of reality; it represents what we call reason and sanity; it is a precipitate of abandoned object-cathexis; it is formed to a great extent of identifications taking the place of the abandoned cathexis; part of it is cs. and part of it is ucs. which produces powerful effects in becoming cs.; it regulates its own constituent processes; from it proceed the repressions; it has to hold in check the superior strength of the Id; sublimation may take place through the mediation of the Ego—in this way erotic libido is changed to Ego-libido; it goes to sleep, but exercises censorship in dreams; it strives to be moral; its processes are arranged in a temporal order and correspond to reality; it controls motility, and the approaches to the discharge of excitations; it owes service to three masters, the external world, the libido of the Id, and the severity of the Super-ego.

The Ego occupies a position between the world, and the Id, and tries to make the Id comply with the world's demands, and by means of muscular activity to make the world meet the Id's demands. After the Ego has repressed an idea it is shut off from the conscious Ego. It substitutes the reality principle for the pleasure principle. The Id is the driving power, and the Ego the steering wheel. If the Ego deals with an Id urge by repressing it, the Ego loses control of the urge which will express itself in various disguised forms: the neuroses.

The Super-ego is an outgrowth and a modification of the Ego. It is a ruler of the Ego. It is to a great extent ucs.; it is the heir of the Oedipus complex; it is a deposit of the earlier object-cathexis of the Id and represents the energetic reaction formation against those choices; it has many points in contact with the phylogenetic inheritance of the individual; it is borrowing by the child's Ego from the father to help in carrying out the repression of the Oedipus complex; its chief function is criticism, and it creates in the Ego and ucs. a sense of guilt; it acts in the form of a categorical imperative, and assumes a compulsive character; it is essentially the same as conscience; it may be hypermoral and tyrannical towards the Ego; it is always in close touch with the Id and can act as its representative in relation to the Ego; there is a very free communication between the Super-ego and ucs. instinctual trends; it is amenable to later influences, but it preserves throughout life the character given it by the parent complex; and it is a permanent expression of the influence of the parents; the injunctions of other authorities than the parents, also remain in the Super-ego. Alexander says it is the product of education, and also reflects certain phylogenetic echoes. Schilder points out that identifications with the parents will vary in the different stages of development so that there will be many different Super-egos. Rickman says that criminality has its origin in a defective Super-ego.

The Super-ego is related to secondary narcism; *i. e.*, libidinal satisfaction can be obtained by the Ego through the achievement of Ego ideals. The ideals are identifications with object-cathexis emanating from the Id. The Super-ego is more powerful in the neurotic. In women, the Super-ego is never so inexorable, so impersonal, so independent of its emotional origins as it is in men. The Super-ego has a ready-made reply for the Id. In the neurotic, the opposition of the Ego to the Super-ego is strong. Alexander defines the Super-ego as a "social faculty which guards the individual from satisfaction in reality of his social wishes, and even punishes him for his satisfaction of them in phantasy." Rank says there are three Super-egos: (1) a biologic Super-ego due to a libidinal missing of the breast, the resultant unsatisfied oral sadistic libido being abreacted either as rage toward the mother, or dammed up in the Ego, and leading to the construction of inhibitions;

(2) the moral Super-ego which arises in the anal stage as a result of sphincter training, the second privation; (3) the social Super-ego. He considers the strict mother (as conceived by the child) to be the nucleus of the Super-ego.

Principles.—*The pleasure principle* states that mental life and personality are shaped according to the pleasure-pain aspects of inner and outer stimuli. It is the basis of the ucs. reactions. This principle insists on immediate satisfaction, and thus comes in conflict with the reality principle which insists on the postponement of satisfaction. Alexander, citing dental work as an example, stresses the seeking out of pain in the interest of future pleasure.

The reality principle tends to shape mental life and personality according to external necessity. The reality principle supercedes the pleasure principle when the organism discovers that the former is useless and dangerous. Art is a reconciliation of the two principles.

The Nirvana principle is the tendency of mental life to maintain at as low a level as possible the quantities of excitation flowing into it, or to bring about a minimum of psychic tension. (Freud's original conception of pleasure was this.)

The repetition-compulsion principle is the tendency of waking life to redramatize, to relive, in different setting, some earlier emotional experience which has made a deep impression, or in dream life to reënact it with often much the same setting. In the transference neuroses the patient relives, in respect to the physician, one of the most deeply painful episodes of his life, the Oedipus situation.

General Instinct Directions.—*Instincts* (*Freud*) are primal trends which cannot be further resolved; and they connote a constant psychic force attacking from within the organism, having its source in important somatic processes, which forces are always seeking to create situations which will secure various specific forms of motor discharge, so as to release the tension. Complete instinct gratification can be achieved only through contact with the outer world. At first Freud spoke of these instincts as opposed to the libidinal instincts; but now he combines them for the self preservative instincts arising out of self-love. Herd instincts, according to Freud, are sexual, and arise from family relationships.

Eros or Life Instinct represents the fundamental tendency to maintain and increase organic life, and psychologically may be said to be composed of (1) uninhibited sexual or organ gratification impulses; (2) sublimated (aim-inhibited) impulses, derived from original organ satisfaction impulses; and (3) self-preservative impulses—that is, the impulses to protect and preserve not merely the body and physical life but primarily the personality and self ideal.

Death or Destruction Instinct results from the tendency to lead organic matter back to an inorganic state. Psychologically this instinct is composed of (1) regressive impulses—tendencies toward the reinstatement of an earlier level of personality adjustment; (2) self-immolating, self-injuring, self-destroying impulses; (3) aggressive impulses toward objects—through the turning outward of the instinct.

Fusion and defusion of the instincts may occur. Life is a compromise between these two tendencies. Ferenzi explains masochism by the death instinct. Alexander points out that many self injuries are the seeking of present injury to avoid future injury but that many cases can be explained only by the death instinct. The death instinct can be neutralized by being fused with the erotic components, and by being enlisted by the Eros. Alexander feels that the neuroses can be viewed as the result of the excessive turning inward of the death instinct.

Development Stages.—There are three periods of psychosexual development: (1) Infancy period, from birth to about five years of age; (2) latency period, from five to twelve years; and (3) adolescent period from about twelve to eighteen years. The sexual life of *early childhood* is far richer and more complex than is generally supposed. Every child is born with an organically determined sexual excitability, which during his early years demands various specific forms of motor discharge. Infantile sexuality is egocentric, primitive, and asocial. The child early senses the opposition between the crude desires and cultural standards, with the resulting conflicts. His early instincts are autoerotic; and therefore are satisfied in phantasy. He is polymorphous-perverse; *i. e.*, he is capable of many abnormal sex gratification acts.

Freud states that sexual excitation originates within the organism, as it were, as a by-product of a great number of processes as soon as they attain a certain intensity. Specifically, the sources are: (1) a gratification which is experienced in conjunction with other organic processes; (2) appropriate peripheral stimulation of erotogenic zones; (3) awakening in connection with other impulses, as looking, showing, cruelty; (4) rhythmic mechanical shaking of the body, hence the fondness of children for swimming, rocking, riding in railway trains, etc.; (5) muscular activities (Freud is not sure whether the pleasure derived from muscular movements is really sexual excitement or whether the former is the cause of sexual excitability); (6) intense affective processes—fear, anxiety associated with a touching of the genitals; (7) mental application on an intellectual accomplishment with result in a simultaneous sexual excitement.

The latency period is characterized by the dropping out of the crude infantile sexual interests, and the emerging of new interests, the energy for which is still believed to be derived from the influx of sexual excitation. Here the social feeling develops.

The pubertal period is characterized by a recrudescence of infantile sexual impulses. The influx of the old, together with the new, is a double threat to sexual development, and the child is at once plunged into a struggle between the standards built up by the Ego during the latency period, and the somatically reinforced infantile sexual desires. The final outcome should be fresh renunciations, and deflections of libidinal energy into new channels, together with a synthesis or a converging of somatic and sublimated sex currents into one stream.

Traces of every stage are always present, and may be termed fixations. If there is a hanging on to infantile wishes, and if large amounts of libido are involved in the fixations, neurotic tendencies develop.

In infantile sexuality, the libido is organically localized or centralized. First there is a diffuse body distribution of the libido, then it becomes localized: (1) in the oral region, lips, then teeth, and gums, then in the (2) anal region, first with pleasure at retention, and second with pleasure at expelling, and finally, (3) in the genitalia with a primary phallic stage with pleasure comparable to that gotten in the first two stages, and the secondary complete genital stage with a pleasure that is psychic and peculiar. This last mentioned stage is not reached until late in puberty, and may have secondary pleasure from the pregenital erotic zones, as preparatory to genital pleasure. Abraham states that the nipple is realized as being valuable, and in danger of being lost so the child develops the biting habit in an effort to get the nipple into himself. There is also muscle and skin erotism.

The sexual aim is the action towards which the sexual impulses strive, in an effort to bring about temporary relief of feelings of sensitivity in an erotic zone. Specific ways of sexual gratification of the infant are: sucking, biting, touching, rubbing, defecating, urinating, looking (voyeurism), showing (exhibitionism), rudimentary forms of fetishism, rhythmical muscular activities, and the aggressive and passive enjoyment of cruelty.

In the genital phase, the child is curious and compensates for his lack of knowledge by forming certain theories. Every child thinks of sex before puberty. The biting in the oral stage is the first sadistic tendency. The anal stage is also associated with sadistic tendencies, though both Freud and Alexander think it is caused by the death instinct. There is a conflict between love for self (feces) and love for the mother; between retaining and expelling feces.

Sexual Theories of the Child.—*The woman has a penis;* it is impossible for the child to imagine anyone without it, and the boy finds fancies to conceal the facts. If he is fixated on this idea, he will be a homosexual. The girl comes to discover her lack of penis through the excitability of the clitoris, and at first denies this fact, but later accepts it as a punishment for her masturbation.

The cloaca theory. Children do not know of a vagina, and conclude that the baby can be expelled only through the anus.

The sadistic conception of coitus is the result of witnessing coitus in the parents, where it appears to be an act of cruelty.

Being married according to the child's concept promises gratification.

In the normal development of the psychosexual life, the child's libido is without an object, then takes the Ego for an object, and not until after that stage does he turn toward external objects. The child compensates for the loss of the nipple by turning to the thumb, toe, etc. The three directions for the libido are: First the *Autoerotic* which utilizes the local erotic excitability without any accompanying libidinal relationship to the self or outer world, secondly, in *Narcism* in which there is a branching off of a part of the libidinal energy in the direction of self or Ego; in which there is a unification of all the zones of erotism so that the body is loved as such. This pleasure in the Ego, as differentiated from the uncontrollable outside world is called primary narcism. Yet objects do play a subsidiary role, and the reactions to them are expressions of the early object-love. So in the late oral stage, there is the strong sadism which makes the child gnaw, devour, incorporate, and destroy all libidinal cathected objects; while in the early anal stage, the predominating impulses are to expel, reject, throw away, lose

28

or destroy these objects; and in the late anal stage there is attempt to retain, master, and control the object. In the anal stage the child is believed to give as gifts to others the products of his own body, and this tendency is carried over into adult life where the person gives gifts instead of affection—anal love.

The progress from narcism to heterosexual object relations at puberty includes an intermediate homosexual adjustment with "chums and crushes"; for where narcism predominates, one prefers those most like one's self. The third stage *Alloerotism* occurs when the main libido is directed toward external love objects. This phase sets in at the phallic stage, and the child begins to transfer his sexual aims, till then achieved through his own body, to his parents of the opposite sex, and his masturbatory ideas are accompanied by phantasies connected with this parent. Feelings of affection develop for this parent with hostility toward the other one. Happy and care-free though they appear, all children become unconsciously aware of the incestuous nature of their object-love, and thus develop conflicts. Their play is symbolic of their sexual urges.

During the latency period, the incest barrier becomes stronger, and sexual aims are sublimated to affection, tenderness, devotion, and respect.

In the adolescent period there is sensuality which attaches itself to early incestuous objects of affection. Marked conflict should then take place between this libido and parental authority. A fresh wave of narcism aids this emancipation; and a short wave of homoerotic object-choice is said to follow and lead the way toward extra-familiar heterosexual adjustments. After the heterosexual choice, the homosexual tendencies are not done away with, but are deflected and are applied to fresh uses (comradeship, love of mankind).

Adult object-finding is frequently determined by fetishism; the love object must possess certain colored hair, wear certain clothing, etc., things that are traceable to early object loves. This tendency is pathologic when the fetish detaches itself from the person, and becomes in itself a sexual object.

The object is the most variable thing about an instinct, and is not originally connected with it—so that one object may serve many instincts.

The sex impulse does not need an object; it is a driving force in itself. According to Rickman, the libidinal impulses can change the object without altering the aim, so that anal interests may be displayed in feces, mud, sand, marbles, coins, negotiable securities, etc. Abraham points out that a passion for collection is frequently a direct surrogate for a sexual desire. Object-love is primarily derived from the Id, but is really much more the concern of the Ego, which modifies the reckless and rash desires of the Id.

DIAGRAM OF DEVELOPMENTAL STAGES

Libidinal Localization (erotogenic zones)	*Mode of Pleasure Finding*	*Libidinal Object-finding*		
INFANCY PERIOD				
Pregenital Period	Infantile sexuality	Auto-erotism	Narcism	Allo-erotism
1. Oral stage				
(*a*) early oral	Sucking, swallowing (incorporating)	At first objectless		Oral object
(*b*) late oral	Biting, devouring (destroying, annihilating)		Primary narcism	Oral sadistic object choice
2. Anal stage				
(*a*) early anal	Expelling (rejecting) (destroying) · Looking exhibiting handling inflicting pain			Anal and anal-sadistic object-choice
(*b*) late anal	Retaining (controlling) (possessing) · Submitting to pain			
Early Genital Period (phallic stage)	Touching, rubbing, exhibiting, and looking at the genitalia, investigating, comparing, questioning, phantasying, tender affection			Parent object-choice Oedipus phantasies
LATENCY PERIOD				
No new zone	Repression reaction formation sublimation affection trends	Further decline of auto-erotism	Diminished narcism	Development of social feelings
ADOLESCENT OR PUBERTAL PERIOD				
Late Genital Period Revival of zone sensitivity of infancy	Reactivation of modes of infancy period	Revival of auto-erotism	Fresh wave of narcism	Revival of Oedipus object-choice
Later, functioning of vaginal zone	Emergence of adult mode of pleasure finding			Homosexua then Hetersexual object-choice

I. THE EGO.
    A. From standpoint of adaptation to reality.
        (1) incorporation of the pleasant, that is, the Ego
            favors the urges of the Id:
        (2) negation of the unpleasant; *i. e.*, it acts after con-
            sideration instead of accepting Id urges at once.
        (3) the acceptance of unpleasant ideas, that is they are
            admitted to us, but are coupled with something else
            that modifies the pain.   Anxiety originates in the
            Ego, whence it arises when the Ego views some-
            thing that is dangerous to it.
    B. From standpoint of Ego development.
        (1) fear of loss of love, (2) fear of castration, (3) fear of
            the Super-ego.   Each of the above fears is normal
            unless there is a fixation.   Ferenczi suggests three
            stages of development.
        (1) introjection period when the child feels himself
            omnipotent and knows nothing of the outside
            world.
        (2) projection period when taught by experience he
            realizes he is not omnipotent, yet does not give up
            this idea, but transfers it to other powers who will
            do his bidding on the expression of his command.
            This attitude leads to placating the higher powers.
        (3) objective judgment period, when he realizes the
            truth of these ideas, and deals with the world in a
            real fashion.
II. THE SUPER-EGO.
    Freud places the origin of the Super-ego at the end of the
        phallic stage.   Ferenczi speaks of a physiologic forerunner
        of the Super-ego in the training for sphincter control *et al.*
        Alexander places its formation in the latency stage.   Klein
        thinks it begins to work in the second year.   The later
        Super-ego may be:
        (1) not too strict, and then the individual will later be
            normal;
        (2) as Freud thinks, most children pass through a child-
            hood neurosis with an overexacting Super-ego, which
            is later modified, either by successive identification,
            or through strengthening of a weak Ego.

Fixation and Regression.—*Fixation* may be defined as the halting of some part of the libido during its course of development at one or another of its somatic positions or zones. In other words, one of the infantile sexual aims has not been relinquished and often signifies that the person is clinging to an incestuous object choice.

Fixation depends on several factors: (1) some partial sexual impulse may develop in advance of the rest and through its pleasure-giving qualities may become very strong, and hard to relinquish; (2) the libido may be constitutionally adhesive; (3) a poorly developed Ego may allow a weak Id impulse to gain excessive strength; (4) the Ego may be too weak as in 3; (5) the Ego may be fearful of making new adaptations to reality and thus remain fixated on early traits; (6) some experience may awaken prematurely a sex component, and thus cause it to be so strong as to fix it; (7) the disappointments may lead to fixations at accepted pleasures though immature; (8) the environment may offer great opportunities for fixation. Each stage offers the possibility of a fixation, and thus a disposition to a neurosis later in life. The significance of a strong fixation lies in the following: the more the libido is tied up in a fixation, the less there remains to be directed toward the outer world and the more sensitive will he be to traumata; the fact of fixation means that the libido in general lacks plasticity, and so the unattached libido will meet reality in the same fashion. The need to keep up defenses, repression, reaction, formations, etc., on the part of the Ego means a constant drain on the energies, and the less able will it be to guide the unattached libido.

Jung has called attention to the peculiar "psychic inertia" of the neurotic. Freud feels that this is explained on the basis of fixation. The fixation points determine the type of neuroses or psychoses so that the paranoid is fixated between the narcissistic, and homoerotic level, while the dementia precox is at the autoerotic level. The melancholic has an oral sadistic attitude towards his object; the obsessional has an ambivalent attitude; the hysteric has a regression to the phallic stage or the Oedipus fixation.

Regression is the retreating of the freely moving libido to a lower level of development. The stronger the fixations, the more readily will external difficulties be evaded by regression to these fixations. Internal frustration means that the individual with a strongly fixated Ego has difficulty because the unfixated libido cannot so easily reach forth to mature development. The healthy individual will meet frustration either by holding the libidinal urge in suspension until a suitable substitute can be made, or by directing his energies toward wresting from the environment actual satisfaction.

In regression, the frustrated Ego takes refuge in phantasy, but has by no means broken off its erotic relation to persons and things which it still retains in phantasy, by substituting imaginary for actual objects. The cs. phantasies reactivate the ucs. infantile phantasies, and the libido begins to flow backward. These reanimated infantile wishes strive again for motor discharge, "the return of the repressed" and in the normal person show themselves in dreams and symptomatic acts, or in the neurotic by compromise-formations in the form of symptoms. If the pressure is strong, and the Ego tolerant, adult sex perversions will develop.

Oedipus Complex is a libidinal striving, taking the form of unconscious desire for sexual satisfaction with the parent of the opposite sex. In this connection it must be remembered that whole dramas and conflicts can be developed and lived out in the unconscious phantasies and can be handled by the ucs. Ego. To the Super-ego, a phantasy, ucs. or cs., has all the significance of an act and is thus capable of arousing a sense of guilt and a fear of punishment in the ucs. Ego. Thus the Oedipus situation may exist in the ucs., and be coped with completely without ever entering the conscious. It is a universal conflict, and rests on the usual taboo against incest, which is an inherited idea. Freud states that the ucs. psychic life of the child appears to recapitulate the evolution of the species. "Psychoanalysis is based on this concept." This conflict finds its cs. expression in the desire of the child to sleep with, caress, etc., the parent; while the ucs. strivings are those of direct incest. Out of this situation arises the sensing both cs. and ucs. of the parent of the same sex, as standing in the way of desired gratification; and hostile impulses are manifested more or less openly in such ways as the expressions of joy at the parent's absence, the lack of wish for his or her return, and the phantasy for the sole possession of the desired parent.

In the boy the simplest form of the Oedipus situation arises from the anaclitic origin. The early attachment of the boy to the mother (or mother imago) at the Phallic stage results in her becoming his love object; the boy identifies himself with his father in order to take his place in relation to the mother; and the father is felt to be an obstacle. However, not all cases are so simple. Many combine a father identification with a mother object love, and a mother identification with a father object love. This is partially a result of the constitutionally innate bi-sexuality. The amount of cathexis to the positive or negative situation depends upon the relative strength of the innate masculine and feminine dispositions. According to Freud's later theories this complex succumbs in the boy to castration fear; that is, his attention and interest become narcissistically centered upon the penis, and there develops in his ucs. fears of being robbed of it by his father; and this castration complex literally smashes to pieces the Oedipus complex. The result is a sublimated love or tender affection, a dropping of the hostility to the father, and an intensification of the primary identification with the father. Concurrently, there is a breaking up of the inverted (father object love) Oedipus, which consolidates the boy's masculinity. During the latency period, the sublimated love is extended to the father and then to others. It may be that the Id will cling to its incestuous aims, and the ucs. Ego may fail in its attempts at sublimation. In such cases fixations will occur, and will form the basis for later neurotic developments. If the inverted Oedipus is strengthened, then homosexual tendencies will occur. At puberty, even in the normal, there is a reënactment of the Oedipus situation so that later there should remain only tender affection for the parents. The rest of the libido should be directed to an exogamous love object, and emancipation from the parent established. Alexander states that the aggressive impulses felt toward the parent of the same sex arise out of the death instinct and their overcoming is by a process of fusion with the life instinct. He further points out that there is danger of the aggressive feeling against the father being turned back on the self, and in the neurotic showing itself in the form of conscience, and a need for punishment. Jung feels that the Oedipus is really a Possession Complex, and says that at an early stage of undifferentiated sex both the boy and the girl want the mother who is felt as a source of desire, and that both wish to be rid of the father. The element of erotism increases, and the girl begins to develop a typical affection for the father, and a corresponding attitude toward the mother of jealousy. Jung sees in Freud's incest desire only a symbolic expression on the infantile level of a return to the original source of life, to the arms of the mother for rest, and to the womb for rebirth. Thus the Oedipus is the struggle between the desire to be one with the mother, and to be an independent individual. Rank discusses the Oedipus situation from the point of view of his birth trauma-anxiety theory. The child senses the opportunity to transform the original source of pain to pleasure, but fails because of his immaturity, and because of the strong anxiety component. Freud feels that masturbation is attached to the Oedipus situation and serves as a discharge for the sexual excitement belonging to it. He feels that observations of parental coitus may act as a starting point for the child's whole sexual development.

In the case of the girl the Oedipus situation is far simpler. Tentatively Freud suggests the following pattern: her sex curiosity leads to the discovery of the anatomic differences between herself and her little brother and boy playmates; and penis envy develops. Normally then she comes to regard her lack of a penis as castration, and the Oedipus complex begins to develop. The girl who has taken the mother as a love object now takes the father as the object-love, either because of phylogenetic factors, or as a result of the loss of a penis. Penis has the same symbolic meaning as child, when the girl begins to have the desire to be given a child by the father. Hostility feelings then develop against the mother. The dissolution of the Oedipus takes place slowly, and comes about partly because the wish for the child is never fulfilled, and because of threats of loss of love in connection with her masturbation. However, the wishes for a penis and a child remain powerfully charged with libido in the ucs. H. Deutsch says that according to her experience, women pass through two phallic stages; in the first there is the clitoris pleasure and masturbatory activities which develop with a sense of guilt when she discovers her lack of penis and realizes the lack to be punishment for her masturbation; during the second stage there is a transference of the guilt feeling to the incestuous wishes which have developed with the father, and this transference brings about the dissolution of the Oedipus. The penis envy is seen in the envy which young girls have of their favorite brothers.

If the Oedipus complex is not fully dissolved and if it is only a repression so that it exists, in the Id, then it will show itself later pathogenically, as a neurosis. In these persons, Alexander feels that each new love relation will be treated as an incest wish. The Oedipus situation and the Super-ego are responsible for much cultural, creative, religious, moral activity as well as criminality and homosexuality. There are traces of the complex in many ways as can be seen by the choice of young men for older women; in the need for an injured third party love object, which means the choosing of a woman to whom some other man has a right of possession (brother, husband, or lover) as a reliving of the father's belonging to the mother, and the wanting of the mother (surrogate); the need for a prostitute type of object lover, in which he wishes to be jealous and doubtful of her fidelity toward him, even as he was jealous and doubtful of his mother's fidelity and her intimacy with his father. He wants to rescue this woman from her sins, even as he wished with his mother.

Rickman writes that the boy feels erotic desires toward his mother, but that these cannot come to expression because of interference by the father; he is unable to put up a fight because of (1) affectionate feelings toward his father; (2) because of physical weakness; and (3) because of danger to his genitals if he expresses any such desire. The solution of this conflict is to give up the direct sex desire for the mother. Klein believes that she has established a femininity phase in early sexual development which develops in the boy to a complex. He feels frustrated and covets his mother's vagina and breasts. He equates feces with children and desires to have children. His anal sadism and destructive tendencies are directed toward female organs, and he wishes to rob the womb of its contents which are the child and the penis of the father which he believes comes from the womb. As a result of these hostile impulses, he fears punishment from the mother (mutilation and dismemberment). The boy's desire for a child may lead to competition with the girl in other lines, as in intellectual rivalry. A tendency to excess of aggression has its basis in this femininity (inferiority) complex.

Castration Complex.—*For the Boy*, this term, castration complex, implies a network of ucs. strivings and thoughts in the center of which is the idea of having been deprived or the expectation of becoming deprived of the (male) genitals. The neurotics recollections always include threats of sexual injury. It is of universal occurrence, and is bound up with the Oedipus complex. It is part of the racial experiences which are passed on to the ucs. of every individual, and the sensitization to it is greatest during the phallic stage, so that the slightest hint of injury to the child is interpreted as a castration suggestion. During this period, *every* little boy is beset with fears of having his father rob him of his sex organs, and this fear shows itself in the general development of his character. Threats are given the child in connection with the boy's masturbatory activities. The discovery, usually accidental, that girls have no penis, forces him to believe the reality of the threat at which he may have laughed; and his first reaction is to deny the fact, or to take comfort in imagining that her penis is small and will grow. He comes gradually to the conclusion so fraught with emotion, that at least it had been there and had at some time been taken away. The absence of the penis is thought to be the result of castration, and then the boy is faced with the task of dealing with the thought of a castration in relation to himself. "This complex may cause the boy to have a horror at the mutilated creature, or a triumphant contempt of her." Even the misogynist and the homosexual are the result of this complex. The child's fear of the narcissistic wound leads him to borrow strength from the father in order to stamp out the unpermissible incest urge; and this is what Freud calls a "momentous loan." By thus identifying himself with the father, the boy builds up a Super-ego which consists of self imposed restrictions mainly on this incest urge.

Castration does not mean gonadal removal, but penis injury. Alexander feels that it is not necessary to invoke phylogenetic experiences, but that the same conclusions can be reached as follows: Birth entails a loss of the mother's body, and of the protecting fetal membranes, so that a pleasure giving organ is lost for the first time in life and is replaced by a painful condition. Then follows the loss of the pleasure giving nipple, and later the loss of the pleasure giving stool; finally there is the loss of the masturbatory pleasure through the fear of loss of the penis. Starke claims that the first ucs. castration occurs at weaning when a "penis-like part of the body is taken away from it," the child having come to regard the nipple as his own. Freud agrees that this sense of loss may occur, but insists that the use of the term be limited to the loss of the male organ. Feces handed out by children out of love for someone else are the prototype of the castration complex, for the child is giving away part of itself. Thus child, penis, feces form a unity—a concept of something that can be separated from the body. Freud points out that even if the mother threatens castration it always ends up with the child feeling that it is the father's threat; and that in man's pre-history it was the father who practiced castration only to tone it down to circumcision.

The child on discovery that females have no penis does not generalize and say that all women have no penis, but he assumes that the absence of a penis is the result of punishment for having the same forbidden impulses as he himself has.

For the Girl, the castration complex has a somewhat different meaning. The female child is extremely sensitive to the lack of a sex organ equal to that of the male, and she comes to consider herself as inferior to the male. This sense of inferiority is revealed in the wish of most women to be a male. Most girls discover the lack of a penis early, and penis envy sets in at once. Some little girls react by clinging to the hope that some day they will get a penis, or by denying that they were castrated. The mother is held responsible for this loss and so there is a loosening of the bonds of love, and the development of jealousy. She then takes her father as the love object. The girls have an intense feeling against masturbation, for the wound over the loss of the penis leads them to reflect that they had better not try to compete with the boys, and therefore it would be best to give up the idea of doing so. K. Horney says that the ucs. male psyche envies the ability of the woman to create children, and the male impulse to creation is simply overcompensation for a feeling of biologic inferiority. The girl fears vaginal injury just as the boy fears castration; and the deprivation of sexual enjoyment is just as real to her as it is to the boy. Sachs has found repeatedly in his analysis of normal women "passionate oral desires directed toward the father."

Development and Effects of Oedipus and Castration Complexes

In Boy

Narcism (primary) complete self love.
Early object relationships—object cathexes associated with primarily autoerotic infantile pleasure finding, narcissistic, and destructive tendencies.

Oedipus Complex—masturbatory impulses associated with phantasies of sexual relations with the mother. Four types: (1) Simple (positive) incest desire for mother and desires to get rid of father (castration and death wishes); (2) or complicated by minor elements of father object love and hostility to the mother. (3) Simple (negative) inverted Oedipus with father object love and mother hostility, or (4) complicated with minor elements of father hostility.

Castration complex
  Dissolution of the Oedipus
    Heterosexual normal
    Homosexual

Super-ego formation with the dropping out of the castration fear.

Neurotic solution with inadequate sublimation

Neurotic Super-ego formation with a weak Ego which develops sense of guilt and a need for punishment.

Later object choice
Normal revival at adolescence of Oedipus neurotic development.

Later super-ego alteration
Normally the Super-ego should become weaker and the Ego stronger.
Neurotic development.

Development and Effects of Oedipus and Castration Complexes

In Girl

Narcism: as in boy.
Early object relationships as in boy.

Castration complexes with lack of penis felt as punishment; denial of lack of penis and hope of obtaining one; castration accepted with giving up of masculinity and with compensatory desire for child.

Oedipus complex with turning away from mother who is held responsible for the lack of a penis; turning toward father as love object; desires child from him.

Dissolution of Oedipus complex occurs slowly and due to disappointment at not getting the child from the father.
Heterosexual normal solution.

Super-ego formation

Constitutional Patterns.—By virtue of a constitutionally inherited psychic plan, certain elements in the environment are reacted to and selected. The formation of the personality is mostly dependent on the reactions of this "plan" to the experiences during the infancy period. Characteristics of the structural plan of the young child are: (1) his erotic stimulability and his desires to secure libidinal gratification; (2) the effort to preserve his omnipotence or to compensate for inevitable feelings of psychic helplessness; (3) impulses of aggressiveness, destructiveness, and hostility forming a large part of his instinctual life, and directed mostly towards those persons whom he cares for, because they also happen to be the ones who are the frustrating parts of his environment; (4) through helplessness, craving to be loved rather than to give love; (5) accepting the frustrations of reality with difficulty and if they are too alien or hostile taking flight into phantasy; (6) as his Ego comes to recognize and side with the claims of reality (parental demands), and to set them up within itself (Super-ego formation) much of the child's behavior becomes motivated by an ucs. sense of guilt which becomes attached to his erotic and aggressive impulses; (7) if the unacceptable impulses are too strong to be relinquished or exchanged, the relatively weak Ego defends itself against them, repressing the ideas to which the impulses belong. It is this tendency of the Id to cling tenaciously, and of the Ego to repress, which lays the foundation for neurotic development.

Universal Experiences.—Typical early situations are: (1) marked dependence on objects due to its helplessness; (2) stimulation of the child's erotic life due to parental care and tendencies; (3) parental training and prohibitions, the child loving those who excite him libidinally, and later turning against them for not fulfilling his demands for pleasure.

Prenatal Experiences.—Freud stresses the birth experiences as a painful phenomenon which produces a sense of helplessness, especially after the intrauterine security. Birth establishes a physiologic anxiety pattern which the Ego makes use of in later danger situations.

Nursing pleasure and weaning trauma have been stressed above.

Defecation pleasures and sphincter training trauma. The passing of excretions gives pleasure because of the erotic stimulation and the relief of tension; training in control teaches the child the pleasure of retention and postponement of the act; the feces he considers part of himself and as related to castration.

Genital stimulation pleasure (Oedipus phantasies) and their prohibitions. The parents provide many sex pleasures, such as powdering, assistance in urinating by the father, etc., which prove to the child the love of the parent.

Discovery of Anatomic Sex Differences.—Various degrees of parental rebuff of sexual curiosity which lead to inferiority complexes and the setting up of his own theories.

Rank is a great believer in the physiologic as well as psychologic trauma at birth. He feels that the individual is always trying to get back to that stage of pleasure, which is symbolized by mother attachment. Reaction against sphincter training by the child is the earliest claim for freedom as *in utero*. Thumb sucking is an attempt to replace the mother's body by the child's own. Toe sucking is a reëstablishment of the intrauterine position. Masturbation is a sublimated sex union, or identification with the mother. Freud does not believe all these statements, but gives Rank credit for discovering the association between fear reaction to the birth danger, and later danger situations and their reactions. Kenworthy points out that security is the most important factor in intrauterine life, and that all later security patterns are based on this. She feels that the Caesarian section child is less sensitized.

Accidental Experiences.—The personality formation is influenced by: (1) premature arousal of some component sex impulse; (2) reawakening of some old fixation; (3) reënforcing of some constitutional trend; and (4) stimulating a greater tendency to repression. Some experiences are as follows:

1. Seduction experiences which include such sensations as may be brought about by cleansing of the child's genitalia, experimental activities of other children.

2. Observations of parental intercourse which is regarded as a beating of the mother.

3. Castration threats occur so frequently in analysis as to be regarded as universal in neurotics.

4. Coming of another child, which may revive earlier pleasure ideas as sucking and may arouse the Oedipus situation prematurely, and the mother may be regarded as faithless *et al.*

5. Excessive tenderness on the part of the parents due to unrequited love may lay the foundation for a neurosis in the child, by making it difficult for him to get rid of the Oedipus, or in the case of the girl leading to homosexual fixations.

6. Parental punishments can justify the hostile ucs. Oedipus complexes, or may be interpreted as a love overture; *i. e.,* the spanking is a rebuff.

7. Absence or death of a parent. When the father is away there is opportunity for the child's expression of Oedipus fancies, and return may increase the hostility felt. No father may hinder the working through of the castration complex: Death of a father may bring about excessive remorse for the hostile death wishes, and the need for punishment.

8. The presence or absence of siblings or playmates influence many factors such as the discovery of the penis or lack of it, etc., besides causing a fixation on the mother.

Ferenczi feels that some children are too well brought up, and that a little sexual traumatism promotes later normalcy.

Dynamics and Dynamisms.—The concepts of the Id, Ego, and Super-ego are necessary. The Id is a bundle of incoherent unorganized cravings predominantly sexual, and demanding various forms of motor discharge; they brook no delay and are bent upon immediate rash satisfaction. The Ego develops out of the Id, and at first is devoted to securing outlets for the Id. The Id and the Ego attempt to avoid the pain of frustration by various adaptive devices and disguises, all of which strive to bring about a discharge at the primitive organ pleasure level. The demands of reality and its own self preservative needs force upon the Ego a certain degree of separation from the Id, but there is essentially no opposition between the two, and the Ego's major task is to transform and desexualize some part of the libidinal energy which gives rise to tension within the Id. The Ego recognizes three typical danger situations which will cause it pain or render it helpless: (1) loss of love (which arises in the pregenital stages); (2) danger of castration (which arises in the phallic stage); and (3) danger of loss of Super-ego approval (which arises in latency). These fears are normally left behind, but the neurotic Ego acts as if they still existed. When the Ego is no longer in harmony with the Id or able to cope with it, then the Ego becomes panicky and employs certain defense dynamisms. These dynamisms are found normally; yet if they are excessive, then there is little psychic energy left to deal with the real world.

Dynamisms are various ucs. devices for the mastering of inner stimuli and thus relieving tension. Specifically they are:

Displacement is (1) a process by which one idea can surrender to another the whole volume of its cathexis, and is found in dreams and in the obsessional neuroses; *e. g.*, when a repressed sex experience becomes attached in cs. to a trivial dishonesty. It is seen in fetishism, and in dementia praecox. It (2) occurs when the Id uses one pathway of discharge instead of another if the first pathway is blocked; *e. g.*, if voyeurism is blocked, exhibitionism may occur.

Vorlegung von unten nach oben. (1) is a defense and (2) is a shifting.

Transference signifies the shifting of love from one object to another. It may occur many times, and is necessary for healthful mental life. Freud wishes to limit this term to the patient-physician relationship. It is really a form of displacement. In mourning, one is depressed over the lost love-object, but bit by bit the libido returns to reality; whereas in melancholia it never returns.

Symbolization is an ucs. process built up by association and similarity by means of which one object comes to stand for and represent another. The essence of symbolization is the displacement of emotional values from the one to the other. Jones points out that it is (1) ucs. and (2) the libidinal energy behind it has not proved capable of sublimation. Many symbols are of phylogenetic origin.

Unconscious Phantasy is composed of images or representations existing in the ucs. mental life, and free from the restraints of reality. Wishes are elaborated in the mind without the individual's being aware of them. It is of importance in infancy for the Oedipus situation is worked out in phantasy. Autoerotism makes possible the retention of phantasy instead of satisfaction with the sexual object. These phantasies differ from the cs. phantasies in that they are either always ucs., or were cs. and are repressed. The ucs. phantasies center also about the phenomena of birth, notions of procreation, assault or seduction, and about the bliss of intra-uterine existence; they are of phylogenetic origin. Varendonck says that hysteria is based not upon memories, but upon the phantasies built up on memories. Later ucs. phantasies arise on the basis of unrelinquished ideas or wishes. The wish to be ill is one of these phantasies. Deutsch says that the adolescent girl phantasies along lines of (1) parthogenesis; *i. e.*, having a child by herself (2) in prostitute phantasies, and in (3) rape phantasy.

Repression is the exclusion of painful and unpleasant stimuli from cs. and from motor expression. To suppress the development of affect is the true aim of repression. Repression keeps from cs. the material that never was cs. and also pushes cs. material into the ucs. The latter is repression proper. By repression the Ego protects itself by refusing to entertain in its own organization the pain-producing idea. Fear and anxiety are set up only in the Ego, and are motivated by the Ego's fear of the individual strivings of the Id. The repressed idea remains as an ucs. formation and may be very capable of action and makes renewed attempts to penetrate the cs.

Repression does not hinder the idea from further activities, and an attraction exists toward everything with which it can establish a connection. The fate of the repressed instinct impulse is much more important than the fate of the repressed idea, and the former may be completely repressed, or may appear in the guise of an affect of a particular quality tone, or may express itself in anxiety. Repression necessitates a persistent outlay of energy, and thus weakens the Ego still more.

Reaction formation is the development in the Ego of conscious socialized attitudes and interest which are the antithesis of certain infantile, unsocialized trends which continue to exist in the ucs. That is, there is only an apparent conformity with the reality principle. It is an auxiliary of repression, and is an erection of barriers. In ambivalence conflicts especially, the Ego is liable to resort to an intensification of cs. love in order to suppress the hatred. In moderation it is a social value; otherwise it is only a superficial hiding; *e. g.*, a hostile wish against a parent may show itself in excessive anxiety over him. Jones speaks of this as a correlative of sublimation. In compulsion neuroses the anal character is largely built up of shame and disgust arising on the basis of of intense anal interests—a reaction formation.

Orderliness is an anal character.

Projection is a defensive process under sway of the pleasure principle whereby the Ego thrusts forth on the external world ucs. wishes and ideas which, if allowed to penetrate the cs, would be painful to the Ego. It is explained by Freud as follows: External reality can be avoided or altered, while internal reality cannot thus be changed; therefore internal reality projects the disturbing ideas into the outside world. It is normal.

Isolation is a process by which memories of unpleasant impressions are deprived of their affective cathexis, so that what remains in cs. is a colorless idea. It is manifest in connection with a frustrating experience leading to a neurosis, wherein the experience is not forgotten but there is no affect connected with it or the neurotic symptom which has sprung out of it.

Undoing is the ucs. attempt through a symbolic act to abolish or will out of existence a past experience, the consequences of which have been painful to the Ego. It is more radical than repression which aims at annihilation of the impulse to repeat a pleasurable infantile experience; undoing aims at wiping out the past.

29

Conversion signifies the symbolic expression by means of physical manifestations of both repressed instinctual wishes and the defense set up against them. It is found in hysteria; and as Ferenczi says, the affective energy of what is repressed radiates into the bodily sphere. The symptom becomes localized in some organ because of a special tendency of the organ concerned to combine with the excitation masses liberated from repressed material.

Ferenczi says conversion hysteria is the genitalization of those parts of the body involved. The throat and bowels are manifest in these.

Introjection is the incorporation by the Ego of "objects presenting themselves insofar as they are sources of pleasure." Jones speaks of it as the ucs. tendency to incorporate the environment into one's own personality. It is almost the same as identification. It is a dynamism in dementia praecox where the environment is blended with the personality, with a consequent swelling and indefiniteness of the personality and the loss of reality which vary with the extent of the process. Projection is the paranoid type of reaction and there is a shrinking of the Ego. The introjection of a lost object occurs oftener than one suspects in melancholia; and this mechanism calls the object to life by setting it up within the Ego. In the latter there is a turning against one's self the hostility felt toward that object.

Identification is the ucs. molding of one's Ego after the fashion of one that has been taken as a model. There are two forms, primary and secondary. Primary identification is the earliest expression of an emotional tie with another person; it precedes later libidinal object choices and arises in the oral stage. It is what one would like to be (not what one would like to have). The little boy who wishes to be like the father identifies himself primarily and has no homosexual wish. This wish aids in the solution of the Oedipus. Secondary identification is the replacement of an object cathexis by a substitute object set up within the Ego itself. There is partial identification in hysteria, in sympathy. Identification is the basis of homosexuality, for "the boy does not actually abandon his tie with the mother, but transforms himself into her, and seeks for love-objects which resemble himself." Multiple personalities may be explained on the basis of several mutually incompatible identifications. Freud speaks of identification as "oral mastery of the object." A borrowed sense of guilt (identification) may be the sole remaining trace of an abandoned love object. . . .

In melancholia the abandoned love object has been loved with great ambivalence, and the Ego has attempted to solve this ambivalence by internalizing (or introjecting) the object. By this means one saves his erotic cathexis from annihilation by taking his own Ego as a substitute love object. At the same time he can find outlet for the hate element, and torment of the original external object through his illness. The actual symptoms are brought about by the criticism of the Super-ego. The concept of identification does away with the herd instinct theory. Group feeling arises from jealousy; for the child is jealous of his successors, but becomes conscious that his hostility cannot be maintained if he is to have the love of the parents, so he identifies himself with the successors, and gets the favors from the parents.

In the same way justice arises out of rivalry.

Sublimation is the exchange of infantile sexual aims for interests of pleasure finding which are no longer directly sexual, and which are on a higher social plane. Such sublimations are desexualized, and aim-inhibited. Sublimation is the basis of the choice of professions. However a certain amount of sexual satisfaction is necessary for most persons. Sublimation does not involve repression and is not a defense mechanism. Sensual love does not last so long as sublimated love, for sexual discharge is accompanied by a discharge of energy each time. Sublimation is possible only to a small extent. Jones points out that the primitive tendency that children have to eat dirt may be sublimated into painting, sculpture work, cooking, in opposition to reaction formation such as cleanliness, tidiness, etc.

Rationalization is a process which arises out of the need for accounting or justifying to the self for certain feelings, ideas, or behavior. It is the work of the ucs. Ego by which it evades the recognition of irrational behavior, and the Ego portends that the Id is showing obedience to the mandates of reality even when in fact it remains obdurate and immovable.

Idealization is a process possible both in the object libido and Ego libido. It shows itself in sexual over-estimation which Freud says "is the origin of the peculiar state of being in love." This idealized object is treated as one's Ego. This is not sublimation. The Ego ideal is a normal process of self love, which supplants the infantile Ego.

Dream Work is a special dream process by which there is a combining of dynamisms, so that latent dream thoughts are converted into the manifest content of the dream. Each dream has a double content, manifest and latent. The former is what is directly known and recalled by the dreamer; it often appears absurd and confused. The dynamisms entering into the dream work are: (1) displacement; (2) condensation; (3) symbolization; (4) dramatization, wherein the manifest dream depicts a situation or action in a theatrical manner (visual); and (5) secondary elaboration, the filling out of details as the dream becomes apprehended in consciousness.

Freud's censor is a function of the Ego, and though diminished still exists in sleep and represses ucs. impulses so as to cause much distortion. Dreams are compromises between the demands of a repressed impulse and the resistance of the censoring force of the Ego. The symbol cannot be known without the individual's interpretation thereof, though there are a few general symbols; e. g., water usually means rebirth though it can mean other things. Alexander speaks of paired dreams in the same night wherein the first dream expresses punishment and the second gratification of the same desire; i. e., the first expresses need for punishment.

Behavior. Personality Formation. Conduct. — *Phantasy formation* or day dreaming is freely wandering thought. It is free from reality testing, and is subject solely to the pleasure principle. Cs. phantasies are flight, and the Ego tolerates them when motor tendencies would not be tolerated. It is open in childhood and suppressed in adult life. The artist is concrete in his phantasy formation. Bleuler uses the term autistic thinking, but this is objected to by Freud. The two principal groups of phantasy are egocentric and erotic. The neurotic is a victim of his phantasies without being aware of it. Beating phantasies are common especially among girls who get sex pleasure out of the phantasy, for the beater is usually the father. Saving phantasies in which the individual imagines himself saving someone, is in the case of the male usually the identification with the father who is saving the mother. Freud points out a common girlish phantasy which occurs with nurses and governesses wherein the mistress is made to disappear and the dreamer takes her place. This type of phantasy is based on the Oedipus situation.

Dream Formation. The purpose of dreaming is to ward off external or internal stimuli which would waken the sleeper. The kernel of the dream is wish-fulfillment, and the ucs. wish makes use of the relaxation to push its way into cs. This entrance is pre-

vented by the censor. The interpretation of the dream is the interpretation of the latent contents. Explanation may be found for
every detail. The majority of dream symbols are related to sex.
The child's dream is identical for latent and manifest content.
The dream may show its influence in the mood of the next day.
Jung differs from Freud, and says that the dream may besides
being wish-fulfillment, throw light on the problems of the patient
at the time, and thus be of practical value to him. Dreams also
show the collective ucs.

Symptomatic acts formation. These are mannerisms, errors, forgetting, etc., of daily life which are within the normal, which are
temporary "errors," and which are either not recalled by the
individual, or if recalled are regarded as a mistake, or accident.
Examples are: (1) slips of the tongue or pen, as using the wrong
word; (2) ignorance, or omission or incorrect use of a name or fact
when this was previously well known; (3) holding beliefs which
were recognized before or afterward as false; (4) failure to carry out
instructions willingly undertaken; (5) making a promise, reluctantly and yet with intention to carry it out, and failing to do so;
(6) misplacing, losing or destroying some valued object; (7) awkward acts as injuring one's self, stumbling, etc., in an individual
who is well poised. These acts originate on the basis of the same
ucs. repressed material as do symptoms, and like them are compromise formations. There are two types of acts: (1) acts carried
out erroneously and intended to be done correctly, and (2) acts
which are manneristic and done automatically. All these acts
have an ucs. significance. The paranoiac interprets details in a
far reaching manner, but he often sees more clearly the hidden
meaning of most person's acts. In analysis every trifling disturbance of customary attire "means to express something that the
wearer of the apparel does not wish to say directly." Non-recalling
is a common method of shutting out pain evoking stimuli. There
are two forms of forgetting names, one in which substitute erroneous
names keep intruding themselves and these names stand in direct
relation to the forgotten name, and second the "screen memories"
which are accidental recollections, but are used to cover up the real
memories.

Personality Formation. The personality is built up partly under
the control of the Ego of the fundamental urges, and partly by
the Super-ego. Bad traits in childhood may evolve through reaction formation, into useful social traits. Alexander has outlined

four types of personality. (1) The normal personality in which there is a harmonious relation between the Id, Ego, and Super-ego. The original urges are not unhealthily inhibited, but are domesticated in the service of the individual and society. (2) The inhibited personality in which the influence of an over-strenuous, over-moral Super-ego produces a shy type of personality. It differs from the neurotic only quantitatively.

Disturbances occur as loss of pleasure in sex activity, in loss of appetite, in disinclination or weakness when walking, diminished desire for work, fatigue when working, etc. Inhibitions occur "in the service of self-punishment," for if an individual derives special pleasure from some work, he may also get some erotic gratification which is disapproved by the more severe Super-ego; and by developing a certain clumsiness or lack of satisfaction in this work, he satisfies his need for punishment and avoids a conflict with the Super-ego. Freud points out that inhibitions serve the same purpose as symptoms in withdrawing the Ego from danger situations. In some children there is a general inhibition of thought due to excessive repression on the part of the adults. There is a difference between symptoms and inhibitions: for the former are a disease process, while the latter have a special relationship to function. Jones points out that failure in school may be the result of inhibition of thought in relation to the subject because of some ucs. association. Walking inhibitions are often associated with fear that the erotic desire may run away with the person. Sexual inhibitions or frigidity in the woman is caused by the castration complex, the woman yielding to the sex act with the ucs. intent to arouse the man and then not satisfy him. General inhibition is found in melancholia. (3) The neurotic personality is one in which the person does not suffer from definite symptoms but whose behavior in life is in the highest degree impulsive, and even compulsive. Such persons are often regarded as weak willed, and suicide is common. Adventurers and swindlers are of this type. There are two types, the criminal and the over-sensitive who are driven to injure themselves. In these cases, the sense of guilt is present, but is not taken care of by symbolic over-compensation, but by a perpetual compulsion to self injury through the environment. Satisfaction is obtained by a specific way of living, living out his impulses, and at the same time managing to get himself punished, as it were, by the cruelty of fate. (4) The criminal character shows itself for the most part in defective powers of moral inhibition, and the anti-social tendencies which are inhibited in the normal person are cs. and given direct expression here. Education helps these. In *personality formation* the main traits of character are permanently determined for good or ill before the end of the fifth year of life.

Therapy.—In the beginning Freud used what is known as the cathartic method. He used hypnosis but abandoned it as unreliable. His aim was to aid the patient to recall forgotten memories of painful experiences, which when accompanied by a discharge of pent-up emotion was found to be followed by amelioration of neurotic symptoms, though often only temporary. He noted that different amounts of energy had to be used to accomplish this purpose and he conculed that the amount varied with the patient's repression and resistance. Freud also noted that a certain type of emotional relation arose regularly between the patient and physician, and he called this transference. He now employs three forms of technique: (1) Free association; (2) Dream analysis; (3) A certain amount of *interpretation* furnished by the physician at strategic points in the analysis, and serving to overcome resistance. Freud says that as little advice as possible should be given to the patient. The analyst does not listen with strained attention, but by suspended attention allows scope to his own ucs. Transference results from a readiness of emotion to be traced to the Oedipus complex; that is, in the analytic treatment, the person finds an opportunity for the reënactment of an infantile child-father type of relationship. Negative transference or hostility may also develop, which according to Glover is the result of a projection of the patient's guilt. Alexander distinguished three phases: (1) Primary transference; (2) negative transference, which is necessary for success; and (3) secondary positive transference. In the opening phase the patient finds himself in the old parental situation, but with a parent who does not reprove or correct. The analyst should watch for the direction of the pleasure principle and stimulate free association and allay anxiety. This stage merges into the transference neurosis which represents to the patient the reënactment of the whole Oedipus situation. This artificial neurosis must be controlled or broken up by proving to the patient that his feelings do not originate in the present situation, and then the patient becomes free. Jung defines the transference (psychologic rapport) as the intensified tie to the physician which is a compensation for the defective relationship to reality. Jung insists it is not a sexual tie, but a human relationship necessary to prove one's own individuality. Jung claims that when sex is the predominant thing in analysis, then it is the result of the physician's own attitude. Freud says that at the end of the transference the patient should not be allowed to react to his infantile Oedipus as he did when a child, but must be forced to react to it normally. Jung assumes that the neurotic has no goal or value in life, and that the analyst can communicate this goal or value to him. The transference neurosis has various uses; every detail of the patient's behavior can be used to illustrate ucs. phantasies and Ego resistances, so as to convince him of the existence of these reconstructed infantile attitudes; the element of dramatization makes the interpretation more convincing; it is a lever to recall forgotten experiences. Schilder thinks that toward the end of the transference, the physician assumes the role of the mother, and when rebirth phantasies set in (loss of protection) counter-transference may occur when the analyst feels like responding to the patient's emotions.

Resistance is anything which interferes with the course of analysis, and it is the work of the ucs. Ego. Such resistances may be: coming late, breaking free association rules, repudiation of the analyst's interpretation, falling asleep, inaudible speech, dearth of association, screen memories, new symptoms or exaggeration of old ones, extreme fluency of association (hiding words) or paucity of association.

The therapeutic aim of analysis is to replace the unconscious by the conscious.

INDEX

A

ABDOMINAL viscera, relation to diencephalon, 300
Aberrant energy expression, 254
Ability to control actions, 395
Abnormal personality changes, need for investigation, 372
Abnormality vs. normalcy, 314
Abortions, 326
Abraham, 432, 435
Absence of parent, 446
Abstinence symptoms, treatment of, 401
Accepting
  responsibility, 262
    inability (case), 318
  situations (case), 316
  unpleasant ideas by Ego, 436
Access (to drugs), 398
Accidental experiences, 446
Acetanilid, 397
Achieving the possible, failure, 205
Acid stomach (case), 302
Acne in epilepsy, 411
Action, control of, by psychopathic person, 396
  directed by emotional responses, 129
Active role (patient's) in direct suggestion, 224
  value of, 215
Activity, fluctuations of, 283
  in depressions, 376
  vs. passivity, 426
Actual
  facts, patient's right to know, 221
  problems, engrossing character of, 168
  want (case), 155
Acute illness, cause of insomnia, 333
Addiction. See Drugs.
  vs. habituation, 397
Adjustability, attitude essential for physician, 222
Adjustment to environment, Ch. VIII
    in therapy of feebleminded, 417
    of idiopathic epilepsy, 410
Adjuvant therapy, 132, 219 ff.
Adjuvants, use of, 126
Adler on Ego urge, 425
Adolescence
  arousal of sexual desire, 98
  cold hands, 314
  homoerotic object choice, 434
  homosexual tendencies deflected, 434

Adolescence
  menstrual irregularities during, 325
  recrudescence of Narcissism during, 434
Adrenal - sympathetic - vegetative system in orientation of organism, 237
Adrenalin, increased secretion of, 66
Adult
  object finding, 434
  love (kinds), 425
  sex difficulties (origin of), 101
Adventurers (neurotic) according to Alexander, 454
Advice, 193
  Freud's theory, 456
  relative value of, 202
  therapy of stress (case), 135
Age of onset of symptoms, prognostic significance of, 256, 265
Aggravation of symptoms, result of physician's manner, 219
Aggressiveness
  excess of, to be avoided, 205
  of child, 444
  of female, 100
  of male, 100
  over compensative, 172
  toward objects, 431
Agitated depression. See Depression.
Agitation in depression, 379
  in physiologic depression, 370
Ailments (involving smooth or striated muscles), habitual nature of, 281
Aim of psychoanalysis, 456
Aimless desires in psychoneuroses, 205
Alcohol, 395
  effect on cellular activity, 403
  on epileptics, 407, 409
  type of response, 403
  tolerance, 403
  withdrawal, 406
Alcoholic paresis, 407
Alcoholics, institutionalization of, 407
Alcoholism, 22, 395, 402
  basis for, 402
  cases, 258, 307, 404, 405
  cause of psychoses, 343
  definition, 402
  escape mechanism (case), 404
  form of drug addiction, 402
  habit factor in, 406
  in mild manic depressive depressions, 405
  in physiologic depressions, 372
  inability to face responsibility, 404

(457)

30

31

Q